CAPTAIN
REBEL

Frank Yerby

CAPTAIN
REBEL

THE DIAL PRESS　　NEW YORK

DESIGNED BY WILLIAM R. MEINHARDT

PRINTED IN THE UNITED STATES OF AMERICA

BY THE HADDON CRAFTSMEN, INC., SCRANTON, PA.

CAPTAIN
REBEL

CHAPTER ONE

IT WOULD NEVER BE THE SAME AGAIN. LOOKING DOWN THE black canyon of the street, edged by the thin columns supporting the galleries, to where the rain made a curtain of silver at the end, he knew that. It had, perhaps, been a mistake to come back at all.

He drew the collar of his greatcoat higher about his neck, though, where he was, on the banquette under the overhanging galleries, it was dry enough. The droplets clung to the ironwork balustrades, handwrought and fine, misting them over so that more than ever they had the illusion of lightness, of delicacy; their solidity gone, transformed into lace, into gossamer, airborne and soaring.

There was a wind slanting the rain, making a noise like crying.

A dirge, Tyler Meredith thought, for this, my city. A lament for New Orleans, and for all the South.

He started to move off, rejecting the idea, telling himself: It's all sentimental rot. Nothing's going to happen. Louisiana's too old, too stable, to follow those Carolina hotheads . . . But, even as he shaped the thought, he knew there was no hope. Before nightfall of this twenty sixth day of January, 1861, Louisiana would be out of the Union. Out, and perhaps at war. . . .

3

He saw the man coming toward him, moving through the mist-haze of the midwinter drizzle, muffled like himself in top hat and greatcoat, passing the alternations of grey-silver and blackness as he moved from gallery shadow into rain whisper; but the light was so poor that the man was upon him before Tyler saw who he was.

George Drake, he thought bitterly; the last man on earth I wanted to see. . . .

George Drake stopped short, and his round, peaceful face made a painful caricature of a smile.

"Ty!" he said. "Lord God, boy—never expected to see you here. . . ."

Know goddamned well you didn't, Tyler thought; but he smiled slowly and put out his hand.

"Didn't rightly expect to be here, George," he said. "But things rarely fall out on the line the way a body plans them. How are you, boy? And how's—the bride?"

George stood there, gripping his hand and looking at him. Tyler towered over him by half a head. But the advantage was more than physical.

"So," George said quietly, "you knew. . . ."

"Yes," Tyler said. "Sue wrote and told me. Mighty straight little girl. Congratulations, boy. . . ."

George dropped his hand. He shifted his weight from his left foot to his right.

"Reckon you think I took advantage," he said.

"No. My fault. Met a little filly from down Baltimore way, and went home with her for Thanksgiving dinner. Plumb unlucky. How was I to know she'n Sue were kissing kin? And that she was the kind that writes long letters?"

"It was more than that," George Drake said.

"I know. Last straw that broke the camel's back. This little filly on top of all the other little fillies. Reckon Sue figgered that the ring and the prayers weren't going to change things much—"

George looked at him.

"Would they have?" he said.

"No. I'm just plain ornery, I reckon. Sue's right. When you get into double harness, better be sure your partner's not going to kick over the traces. I'm glad, George. You'll make her happy. I would of made her plumb, downright miserable. . . ."

George searched his face. This time, when he smiled, his eyes were peaceful.

"Thanks, Ty," he said. "You've taken a load off my mind. Sure Lord would of hated to lose your friendship over this. Why don't you drop in on us today? 'Course, I won't be there for a while, but—"

"Can't. Haven't even seen the Captain yet."

"You just got in, then? How is he, Ty? I heard talk about his heart. . . ."

"Rot. The Captain's as healthy as a mule. Getting a mite old, that's all. According to a letter I had from my brother, seems he dined a mite too well a few weeks ago, and had some sort of a fit. Doctor Le Pierre thought his heart sounded funny. But those Creole sawbones are always excitable. Nothing to it. . . ."

"Glad to hear that. Everybody's mightily fond of the Captain. Lord, Ty, but a heap's happening! We're meeting at the Cabildo; going to organize a regiment. Planning to ask your brother to be Chaplain, after we're all set. Why don't you come along and—"

"Told you I haven't seen the Captain. Besides, George, I'd like to go slow on this thing. Feel about it just like I do about dueling: honest difference of opinion ain't rightly cause for killing a fellow. . . ."

"Won't come to that. The Yankees ain't fighters. Oh, they'll bluster about a bit; but then they'll give in. If it does come to shooting, I'll bet I could mop up all the blood spilt with my pocket handkerchief. . . ."

"George," Tyler said quietly, "you ever been North?"

"No," George said. "Why'd you ask me that, Ty?"

"No reason. Just trying to prove something to myself. Well, so long, George. . . ."

"Appears to me," George said, "that you're not going so slow yourself, Ty. I see you got out of the navy. You'd of finished up at Annapolis this June, wouldn't you?"

Tyler grinned.

"Didn't get," he said. "I was kicked. Just as well, though. Saved me the trouble of making up my mind."

There was a silence between them. But it was broken almost at once, to the relief of both of them, by the tapping of the blind beggar's cane against the banquette. Tyler dug into his pocket and came out with a coin. He tossed it into the blind man's cup. The man stopped dead.

"Would you mind looking at what you gave me, Sir?" he said. "That don't sound like money, somehow. . . ."

Tyler peered into the cup. Then he took the round piece of metal out again. It was of bronze and was about the size and weight of a silver dollar. But across the top of it was a bar to which a ribbon had been attached. The ribbon had been torn off, or worn away.

"Ain't you ashamed of yourself," George Drake grinned. "Cheating the blind. . . ."

"Didn't aim to cheat him," Tyler said. "Fact is, this is one of the few things I'm proud of. . . ."

He handed the medal to George and, taking a silver dollar out of his pocket, dropped it into the blind man's cup. Somehow, perhaps from the louder clatter it made, the man knew that this was more than the usual penny or two that passersby generally gave him. His face lighted up.

"Why, thank you, Sir!" he beamed. "Thank you mighty kindly!"

"Don't mention it," Tyler said and turned back to George Drake.

George was staring at the medal.

" 'Pistol shooting championship, Class of 1861,' " he read. "Knew you were might good with a handgun, Ty—even shooting from the saddle—but I'll be blessed if I thought you were that good."

"Other fellows had a bad day, I reckon," Tyler said. He stared at the retreating back of the blind man, a mocking smile lighting his eyes.

"Waste of money," he grinned. "Matt Pearson can see as well as I can. Still, I always give him something, if only to pay him for how good he is at play-acting."

"He's not acting," George said. "Doc Blumweiner, that Swiss eye doctor on Canal Street, says Matt hasn't got more than two per cent of his sight left. Sees forms and shadows, that's all. . . ."

"Well, boy," Tyler said, "reckon I'll mosey along. The Captain's expecting me."

"Don't you ever call him—Father?" George asked.

"Nope. He prefers being called Captain. Besides, since Joe's become a full-fledged Episcopal Rector, it would have been mighty confusing. 'Father, no, not you, Father—I mean His Saintliness, Father Joe—' That would get me all balled up. . . ."

"You didn't approve of Joe's becoming a parson, did you?" George said.

"I," Tyler said, "disapprove of parsons per se, and by the numbers. . . ."

"You're wrong," George said. "Joe's done mighty fine for such a young fellow. Assistant Rector of Christ Church, under Bishop Leonidas Polk—that's pretty high up the ladder, boy. Heard tell he's going to be Rector when the Bishop moves on. Many a young filly's setting her cap for him. Strange he hasn't married by now. . . ."

"Joe," Tyler laughed, "is twelve feet higher than High Church. Had his way, he'd introduce the confession and high mass into the Episcopal service. Reckon he's a mite sorry that the Captain came from the wrong part of Ireland. And, speaking of the Captain, I really had better get moving. Be seeing you, boy. . . ."

"When?" George said.

"Maybe tonight, if there's anything left of me when the Captain gets done. My love to Sue. . . ."

"I'll tell her. And Ruth. She lives with us, now. . . ."

"That brat? Lord God, but she sure used to give me a hard row to hoe. . . ."

"Maybe you'll be surprised," George said. "She's changed. So long, Ty—"

"So long," Tyler said. He moved off, through the rain, swearing a little under his breath.

"He waiting for you in the study, Mister Ty," Cato said.

Tyler looked at the Negro.

"How is he?" he said quietly.

"Like you'd expect: plumb fit to be tied. Lordy, Mister Ty, 'pears to me you'd learn to behave yourself by now. Always the same thing. Ain't you never going to get yourself married and leave other gentlemen's women-folks alone?"

"No," Tyler said. "Get along with it, Cato. Go tell the Captain that the Prodigal has returned—again. And I hope that fatted calf is already on the spit. I'm damned hungry. . . ."

Cato stood there, staring at his young master. Tyler Meredith was a shade under six feet but because of his thinness he looked taller. He was so lean that his fellow cadets at Annapolis had nicknamed him 'Rawbones.' His hands, feet, mouth and ears were all too big for the rest of him. When he was still, he gave people the impression of awkwardness, even of ugliness; but the moment he moved the impression was dispelled. Everything he did was controlled, certain, sure. His smallest gesture was graceful. His eyes were brown, and unremarkable, except that they were forever alight with laughter—a laughter directed in equal measure inwardly upon himself, and outwardly at the world.

"Lord God, Mister Ty," Cato breathed. "Ain't you scairt?"

"Of the Captain?" Tyler said. "Of course not. I got over being afraid of him before I was ten years old. Noise and bluster, that's all. Now quit stalling and tell him I'm here."

Again Cato hesitated.

"Father Joe in there, too," he said.

"Oh, hell," Tyler said. "Bell, book, and candle. Probing inspection of the state of my alleged soul. It's doing nicely, thank you. Why the devil doesn't my saintly brother take his precious religion elsewhere?"

"Mister Ty!" Cato said.

Tyler turned toward the window. "Oh, get along with you, Cato." He flung the words backward over his shoulder.

He stood there looking around the anteroom. From the outside, the house on Poydras Street was a typical New Orleans courtyard house, with iron balustrades, delicate and fine, around the galleries; shuttered against the world, turned inward upon its own green and flowering heart. But the inside was something else again: crystal chandeliers, ornate ceilings, plush and velvet, scrollsawed fretwork over the arches, every inch of it in such thunderous, crashing bad taste that Tyler, seeing it again for the first time in over a year, shuddered. Captain Patrick Meredith had tried his literal minded best to duplicate every feature of the passenger salons of the high stacked river packets which had gained him his fortune. He had succeeded notably. The interior of the graceful old house he had bought had been completely transformed. No one dared tell him he had created a monstrosity; dared not, or often was content;

for many Southerners thought the furnishings of the river boats of the fifties most elegant indeed.

Damned good thing he didn't build a new house, Tyler thought. I'll be blessed if it wouldn't have had twin stacks and a sternwheel. Well, I won't have to put up with it too long, what with the war. . . .

The door opened again.

"They says you's to come right in, Sir," Cato said.

Tyler walked serenely into the study. He was smiling that curious widelipped smile of his that somehow tied together his ill assorted collection of features into something, which, while it could not, by any extension of charity be called a handsome face, was nonetheless exciting and alive.

"Look at him!" Captain Meredith roared. "Grinning like a baboon! Is it that you have no shame in you, lad?"

"Not a drop," Tyler said, and put out his hand. "How are you, Captain?"

"How am I? How am I? At death's door! My heart, ye ken. And 'tis your own fault, you poltroon! I send you away to college; I badger Senator Devereux to get you appointed to the Naval Academy! And look at you —just look! Sent down—over a filly! Caught, sez the superintendent, in a most compromising position with the daughter of one of the instructors!"

"Hardly compromising," Captain," Tyler said, and turned toward his older brother. "Well, Padre—aren't you going to level a broadside?"

"No," Joseph Meredith said. His thick, red fingers riffled the pages of the New Testament that lay on the table. "I'd like to hear your side of it first, Ty—"

"His side!" Patrick Meredith spluttered. "His side! 'Tis clear upon the face of it, Joe! He was caught, I'll wager upon it, either abed with this filly, or running away with his trousers over his shoulders. Say that isn't so, you ungrateful blackguard that I, God forgive me, sired!"

The young Minister looked at his brother.

"Well, Ty?" he said.

"Guilty as charged," Tyler said. "Her father, who teaches gunnery, got a bit off course, and beat back to windward ahead of time. He wasn't alone, and was too mad to keep his mouth shut. There were witnesses—so: 'Conduct unbecoming to an officer and gentleman. . . .' "

Father Joseph stood there, staring at him.

"Ty—" he said at long last.

"Yes, Padre?"

"Under the circumstances, it seems to me you should have married the girl. . . ."

Tyler looked at his brother. He thought: He's half a saint. If there's one thing I can't abide, it's this saintliness of his. If it were based on anything real, maybe; but to conduct your life on a foundation of ancient superstition, involving quasi-cannibalism and blood sacrifice. . . .

He saw his brother's eyes, exact duplicates of his own, except that no mockery danced in them, ever, searching his face. They were very deep and sure, filled with—sorrow, Tyler guessed. Certainly not anger.

"Married her?" Captain Meredith snapped. "And brought me home a loose female for a daughter-in-law? Even if she were with child, he would have no guarantee 'twould be his own. No—he should have avoided her in the first place, and not have been fool enough to get caught in the second! I tell ye—"

"Captain," Joseph said, "your standards of morality are wonderfully uncomplicated, aren't they? Will you let me handle this? I'm not as old as you are; but I can plead some special training in these matters. Besides, Captain Pat, you're taking the wrong tack: you're concerned with family pride and Ty's disgrace, which really aren't very important—"

"Not important! Now hark ye, Joseph, Reverend or not, 'tis hard for me to see what could be more important! I've tried so hard to make gentlemen of you both; and you tell me that family pride and honor and the damnable fact that this whelp has disgraced us all are not important! If they aren't, I don't know what is!"

Joseph studied his father.

"Just one thing, Captain," he said quietly. "Your son's immortal soul."

The Captain took a backward step upon his short, bandy legs.

"I see," he muttered. "You're right, of course. 'Tis plagued hard for me to remember that my own son is a true Minister of the Gospel. Yes, yes—you talk to him, Joseph. I've given him up long ago. . . ."

"Ty," Joseph said. "Why wouldn't you marry the girl?"

"I'm not the marrying kind, I reckon," Tyler began; but his mockery failed him. It was always like that between him and Joseph. No matter how often he assailed his brother's faith, it proved unshakable, so that

all the bright, new-minted syllogisms of advanced free
thinking he launched against it fell blunted by the armor
of its surety. "No," he said. "That's not true, Padre. I
offered to marry her; but politics kind of got mixed up
in it. Her old man allowed he'd see her dead and in hell,
before he'd permit her to marry 'a trader in human flesh
—a man who gained his bread from the sweat of other
men's faces—' Can't say I see how the niggers got involved in it; but before he was done he'd accused me,
personally, of having murdered John Brown. . . ."

"New Englander?" Father Joseph asked.

"Massachusetts. Abolitionist and Black Republican.
Voted for Lincoln."

Joseph's face darkened in anger.

"They're fools!" he snapped. "Even Our Lord approved of the institution of slavery. 'Servants obey your
masters.' That was what He taught. Remember the
parable of the talents? 'Well done, thou good and faithful servant.' They'd fly in the face of even His words!"

He stopped suddenly, looking into his brother's face.
Try as he would, Tyler could not conceal the mockery
there.

"I see," Joseph said slowly. "I'd forgotten you're a
free thinker. That was in the superintendent's letter,
too: 'Open expression of blasphemous, even atheistical
opinions—denial of the existence of the Diety—' "

"Can't we," Tyler said, "forget that part of it, Padre?"

"No," Joseph said. "To me it's the most important
part. God can and will forgive a sinner who comes to
Him in contrition, but you must also come in faith. . . ."

Tyler smiled again.

"Afraid that's the hardest thing for me," he said. "You can't expect me to give over my reason altogether, Joe—"

"Intellectual pride," Father Joseph said, "is a sin, too, Ty. A decent amount of humility never hurt any man. And far keener minds than yours have found faith. . . ."

"Keen minds and no guts," Tyler grunted. "Look, Joe, let's drop it. Doesn't interest me a whit. My soul, if any, is my own concern. Right now, it's the future that bothers me. You know, the sordid things: like where my rations are coming from and how I'm going to keep myself in bourbon and cigars. . . ."

"And girls?" Joseph said sternly.

Tyler laughed.

"That—no," he said. "That's never been any problem, Joe. . . ."

"I'll pray for you," Father Joseph said. "I hope whatever it be that will bring you back into the fold won't be too terrible. Sometimes it is. Sometimes a man has to be broken before his soul can be free. . . ."

"Do that," Tyler said lightly and turned to his father. "Well, Captain?" he said.

The old man frowned.

"You can come to work in the office," he said slowly. "Or you can take second berth on a packet. Damme, I should throw you out to starve—still—"

"Still," Joseph said gently, "he's your own flesh and blood and the image of your own youth, eh Captain? Not to mention that you're fond of the boy. Why not admit it?"

The Captain permitted himself a hint of a smile.

"True enough," he said. "But I can be pushed a mite too far, mind you, Tyler. You will do the work, and take the pay of any other man in the same position. No shirking, no fancy hours. One complaint from your superiors, one more scandal, and out you go. Is that clear?"

"Yes, Captain," Tyler said, "and—thanks—"

"Don't thank me, thank Joseph. He pleaded for you. Well, lad, which is it to be: the office, or the river?"

Tyler didn't hesitate.

"The office, Captain," he said. "I'm a blue water man. I'd hate to try to take a packet past the snags and over the sandbars. . . ."

He could see Joseph looking at him, and realized his brother saw through his words as through so much window glass. To take second command aboard one of the Meredith steamboats would keep him out of New Orleans most of the time. Away from Hewlett's, the Saint Louis Hotel, the gambling halls, away from—Sue.

"By the way, Tyler," Joseph said, as though he had read his brother's thought. "Susan's name is no longer Forrester. She married the Drake boy two months ago. I performed the ceremony."

Tyler lifted a single brow.

"So?" he said. That was all, but it was enough. Joseph, whose knowledge of men was so deep as to almost constitute an invasion of their personal privacy, could supply the rest of it: "So—what difference does that make? That, or your hymns, or your sermons, or your mumbled prayers, or ring and vow and other relics of your barbarism? If I want Sue, I shall take her, despite husband, her sacred oath of fidelity or even your ancient,

angry God. And nothing will stop me. Not anything in
this world. . . ."

"Yes," Joseph said very quietly. "Yes, Tyler, I shall
pray for you. . . ."

The Drake's, Tyler found out by the simple expedient
of asking Cato, lived on Saint Charles Avenue in the
Garden District.

That means I'll have to ride, he thought; plagued
long way from here. Georgie-boy must have come up
in the world. That's the smartest district in town. . . .

He became aware, slowly, that Cato was still talking.

"Miss Ruth stay with 'em too, now. Mister Forrester
and the old Missus, they both upped and died the same
week—'bout a year ago—from the fever. Lots of good
folks died then. And, Mister Ty—"

"Yes," Tyler said. "Yes, Cato?"

"She sure done growed up into a mighty pretty young
lady. . . ."

"Pretty as Sue?" Tyler said.

"Plumb nigh. 'Course ain't nobody else that pretty;
but Miss Ruth look a mighty heap like Miz Sue, now. If
I was you—"

"But you aren't," Tyler laughed. "Don't worry, Cato.
I don't aim to get into any more hot water. I just want
to see Sue, that's all. As far as Ruth is concerned, she's
much too young. Lord what a pest she used to be! Always hanging around getting underfoot while I was
courting Sue. . . ."

"Reckon she kind of admired you herself, sir. 'Sides,

like I done said, she ain't no baby no more. Been a long time since you seen her, Mister Ty. Last few times you was home, she was off at that Female 'Cademy. 'Sides, the way I 'members it, ain't but three years difference 'twixt her and her sister. . . ."

"Good Lord!" Tyler said. "That would make her all of twenty. . . ."

"Going on that, leasewise. Her birthday's April the eleventh. . . ."

Tyler looked at the wizened little Negro. Then he started to laugh.

"Got it all figured, haven't you?" he said. "The exact date and all. Tell me, Cato, how long have you and Bessie been working on this matchmaking scheme?"

Cato grinned, sheepishly.

"You too smart, Mister Ty. All the same, it's a sure Lord fine idea. Everytime the Cap'n would get 'nother letter from that sailor school 'bout some tomfoolishness you done gone and got yourself mixed up in, Bess'd say to me: 'Cato, us got to find that boy a good gal to straighten him out.' We was sort of planning on Miz Susan, but when she ups and marries that Drake boy, we took a good look at Miss Ruth. Mighty pretty young lady, Mister Ty; yessir, mighty pretty—And good as gold, too. . . ."

"Thanks," Tyler said drily. "Only I'm not the marrying kind, Cato. Why should I confine all my charms to just one filly? I mean to make a lot of them happy, while I can. . . ."

"Mister Ty," Cato groaned. "You gonna be the death of your poor pa yet. You know what that doctor said about his heart. . . ."

"The Captain's as healthy as a horse," Tyler said. "Which reminds me—you'd better go tell Jeff to bring me around a nag. . . ."

"Yessir, Mister Ty," Cato said. "But I hopes that one of these days you'll pay some attention to what I'm trying to tell you. The Cap'n's an old man and his heart—"

"Get out of here, Cato," Tyler said.

It was not yet night, but the streetlamps were already lit. The lamplighter had come on schedule—that was all, though in fact the lamps could well have been lighted in the middle of the afternoon. It had been as dark then, as it was now. What had changed. Tyler saw, was the number of people in the streets. Before coming home to his painful interview with his father and his brother, the only living soul he had met between the docks and Poydras Street had been George Drake. But now, the streets were a sea of umbrellas and white, upturned faces, waiting.

The tension could almost be felt. Some few among the crowd talked to one another in low voices, barely louder than whispers; but, for the most part the crowd was silent, waiting in the rain.

There were an unusual number of uniforms among them. He recognized the State Militia's garb, but the others were strange. Then it came to him that these must be the political marching clubs: The Beckinridge-Lane, the Democratic-Douglas, and the Young Bell Ringers about which Father Joseph had written him. Strange they hadn't disbanded when the gangling, slang-wanging Illinois lawyer had won. But they hadn't; more, he saw now, they had become something else: a base, a nucleus for the military power of—

A new nation. Surely they really didn't believe that? The thing was madness. The South Carolinians were barbarians; but in old, cultured Louisiana, with her manifold contacts with the North, and with Europe, men must see—

He slowed his horse, and looked at them, his face frowning and intent. The time was fatally out of joint. Four states, South Carolina, Florida, Alabama, and Georgia, already out of the Union. The Yankee steamer, *Star of the West*, fired upon two weeks ago as she attempted to aid Fort Sumpter in Charleston Harbor; and at this very hour the Convention of the Sovereign State of Louisiana sitting at Baton Rouge, debating whether to join the secessionists or stay under the old flag.

Whether, he thought grimly, to live or to die.

They can't see it, he thought; they can't understand... I've been lucky—dozens of trips to the Northern States, twice to London to visit Cedric and Vivian. And I can't tell them. They wouldn't listen, anyhow. They're feeling, not thinking. Expect the Yankees to sell us guns and powder and ball to kill them with? We don't have a gunworks, hardly a decent foundry. Nitrates for explosives? A textile mill to make uniforms? Nothing but hard heads and plenty of guts. Not enough. Cotton to England and France for credits, then guns bought with the credits? Mighty pretty if they didn't have to bring the guns through the whole blamed Yankee Navy. I was in that Navy, and I know it's a first class piece of fighting

machinery. The guns they'll get through wouldn't arm
a platoon. . . .

He straightened up, smiling.

Easy, boy. It's not your problem. That's something
else again. A war turns things topsy turvy; and a man
with brains can come out of it richer than Midas. Going
to be touchy. Stay in good with both sides: trade. Get
that cotton to England and bring back the things people
are going to be hurting for. Take your pay in gold, not
shinplasters. Keep it hid 'til they've all gone smash, and
buy 'em up, lock, stock, and barrel. . . .

Friendly with the Yankees? Hell, yes! They're going
to win. With the Secesh? Likewise. They're going to be
hanging mad; and the idea's to stay alive 'til the pieces
are there for me to pick up. Nice pieces—even like Sue,
maybe. Never met a woman who wasn't for sale when
the going got rough. Long as I handle it delicately. Comfort is what I'll offer, not cash. It's only the money that
sticks that short, ugly word onto it. Straight barter is
plumb, downright respectable. . . .

Voices in the crowd came over to him as he rode.

"Both Fort St. Philips and Fort Jackson are in our
hands—that's something. They'll have to pass them to
get anywhere nigh New Orleans. . . ."

"And the Arsenal at Baton Rouge. Mighty fine lot of
muskets and ammunition there, I've heard tell. . . ."

"You should of seen that Yankee Cap'n's face when we
demanded the surrender of the cutter at Algiers! Wasn't
a damn thing he could do, though. The *Lewis Cass* was
plumb out of commission: engine half dismantled. Boy,
I sure admired the way he could cuss! But, in the end,

we marched them blue jackets off, meek as lambs. . . ."

Why, Tyler thought, it's war already . . . Time, boy, time . . . Got to be making a mighty heap of plans. . . .

"Ty!" a man called out to him. "Damn my mangy hide, it's good to see you! Reckon you'll be joining up, eh, boy?"

Tyler turned in the saddle. He recognized the huge, unkempt, unwashed, awkward man. Tennessee McGraw, he thought mockingly; Mister Tennessee McGraw— ward heeler, pimp, footpad, gambler, petty thief and blackguard par excellence. Joe and the Captain were right when they used to give me hell for hanging out with such riffraff. But what can you tell a fool smart alecky kid?

"Well, Tenn," he said, trying to keep the contempt he felt from showing in his face, "I reckon I'm going to give it a mite of thought, first. Can't do the fillies much good with a bullet through my head. . . ."

"You're right there, boy!" McGraw guffawed. "Say, Ty, could you spare me a dollar? Been nigh onto four days since I had a drink. . . ."

Tyler tossed him the coin at once, then clapped spurs to his horse without even waiting for McGraw's thanks. It was, he thought, as he rode off through the icy rain, worth a dollar to be rid of the man.

In the foyer of George Drake's home, the butler greeted him by name. Must be one of the Forrester Negroes, Tyler thought; none of George's would know me. . . But it was so dark in the foyer that he could not recognize the man.

"You wait right there, Marse Ty," the Negro said. "I'll get a lamp and tell Miz Sue and Miss Ruth. They going to be mightily surprised. . . ."

"I'll bet," Tyler mocked, and lounged there, trying to accustom his eyes to the darkness. Niggers, he thought, have eyes like cats. Damned if I know how he could see who I was.

The heavy clumping of the Negro's footsteps died away; but before they came back again he heard another sound: the whisper of a girl's slippers upon the carpeting, coming on very fast, actually running.

"Oh, Ty!" she breathed, standing there silhouetted against the doorway; and her voice was as he remembered it, low and husky and endlessly sweet. He wished that he could see her eyes, but it was much too dark. He shrugged. No need to worry about that; her voice had told him all he needed to know. Bye-bye, Georgie boy, he thought mockingly, and, stepping forward, took her in his arms.

Her back was rigid as a ramrod, frozen with pure surprise. And her lips were ice—for the first few seconds at least. Then, very slowly, they warmed under his, warmed and softened, parting a little so that her breath sighed through. He drew back a little, staring at her.

"Sue," he whispered. "Sue—"

Then the rigidity was back in her spine, and the hand that rested against his neck was death cold, suddenly.

"Not Sue," she said very quietly; "I'm Ruth, Ty—"

She made a gesture with her arms to break his embrace; but he held her, one instant too long, so that the Negro came into the foyer with the candlelabra, and Sue was at his side.

The silence could be felt. It had thickness and texture.

"You," Susan said at last, "run true to form, don't you, Ty? Now, if you'll be so kind as to release my baby sister. . . ."

Tyler stepped back. Then he leaned against the wall and loosed his laughter. It soared up, clear and mocking. But as he caught his breath, he saw Ruth's face. She turned then in a swirl of skirts and petticoats, and ran off down the hall; but not before he had seen the teardrops on her lashes trembling in the candlelight. His laughter jarred to a halt.

"Did you," Sue said, "have to do that, Ty? She's still a child—and very impressionable. It was shameful of you to kiss her—"

"I," he said, "found it downright nice, Sue. Well, aren't you going to ask me in?"

"I reckon I must," Sue said. "Yes, Ty, come in. It's mighty nice seeing you again—nicer than I thought it was going to be. You see, Mister Tyler Meredith, you just convinced me that I didn't make a mistake when I broke our engagement. . . ."

The house was Greek Revival and lovely. Tyler stood in the living room, looking about him.

"Can I git you a drink, Marse Ty?" the butler said.

"Yes—bourbon and water, Tim—light though. You, Sue?"

"A little sherry," Sue said.

He stood there, looking at her.

"Happy?" he growled. But before she could speak, he had his answer. The expression that crossed her face was fleeting; it was gone in half a heartbeat. But he had seen it, and he was sure.

"Of course, Ty," she said firmly, a shade too firmly, her voice rising and tightening, almost imperceptibly, so that the hesitation, the change, the heightening, would have escaped anyone else except Tyler; but he, hearing it, seeing it, felt in the core of his heart a surge of unholy joy.

Both of them, he thought. And little Ruth will provide me with an excuse to come here. . . .

"What are you doing home?" Sue said. "You were due to finish the Academy in June, weren't you? Don't tell me you came back to fight for Louisiana?"

"No," Tyler said. "I was pining for the sight of your bonny blue eyes, Sue. Got to be right pert bad. Used to wake up in the middle of the night and—"

"Tyler Meredith," Sue said wrathfully. "I'm a married woman remember!"

Tyler looked at her a long time and very steadily.

"Are you?" he said.

Sue's face whitened.

"Just what do you mean by that remark, Ty?" she said.

"You figure it out," Tyler said carelessly. "Do me a favor, Sue—go tell baby sister to come in here. I'm hankering to beg her pardon mighty handsome like. . . ."

Sue stood up. "I don't think she will," she said; "but I'll ask her. And Ty—"

"Yes, Sue? Yes, Babydoll?"

"Don't call me that! You've no right—"

"Haven't I?" Tyler said.

"Oh!" Sue got out. "That's just what I mean! That's the second time you've said something like that. Whatever on earth do you mean, Tyler Meredith?"

Tyler smiled at her, a long, slow time.

"Go get baby sister, Babydoll," he said.

To Tyler's surprise, Ruth came back into the living room with Sue. Tyler uncoiled his vast length from the great sofa and stood up, his brown eyes alight with mischief.

"Lord God!" he breathed. "Who'd have thought it?"

Ruth stood there beside Susan, looking at him. She was a little taller than her older sister; and she was going to be prettier. She wasn't yet; but she was going to be. They both had the same taffy blonde hair, and the same enormous, cornflower blue eyes, gold petalled with the sweep of lashes. But, despite their striking similarity in appearance, their beauty was somehow different. Tyler stared at them both, trying to decide what that difference was. Sue, he realized suddenly, is ever so much more delicate. She's like a flower, fragile and fragrant and sweet. Been like that ever since she was so sick the year I went to Annapolis. A man would have to take good care of her, keep her sheltered, kind of. . . .

But Ruth—heck, she's got that she-cat look. Nothing will ever lick her. Bet she's got teeth, and claws. Determined, too. What she wants, she'll go after. Now all I got to do is to make sure that what she wants is—me.

He smiled at her, gently.

"Sorry, Ruth," he said. "That was a fool trick. . . ."

"It's—all right," she said tonelessly. "After all, it was very dark and you'd just come in out of the light—"

"What," Sue said sharply, "had the darkness to do with it?"

Ruth stared at her sister.

"Didn't you know?" she said; "He thought I was—you."

"Oh!" Sue breathed; then: "Oh, my God!"

"Then I'm forgiven?" Tyler said.

"Yes, Ty—" Ruth murmured.

"Good. Reckon I'll be going now—"

"Wait," Sue's voice was edged. "Ty, I'd like to know what you meant by asking me, 'Are you married?' That bothers me. . . ."

"Yep, reckon it does," Tyler said flatly. "And that it does is answer enough. My respects, Ladies. . . ."

"I—I'll walk you to the door," Ruth said. "That is, if you don't mind, Sue—"

"Why should I mind?" Sue said. "You're almost twenty and you've every right—"

And again Tyler had the feeling that there was an edge to her voice, hard and sudden, like fine honed steel.

In the foyer, he took Ruth's arm.

"Well, Kitten," he said. "Now that I do know who you are, I've got a mighty hankering to repeat the offense. . . ."

Her hands came up, palms upward, resting against his chest.

"No, Ty," she said.

"No?" he grinned. "Why not, Kitten?"

"I don't like pity," she said quietly; "or even being kissed because it amuses you—"

"What do you like, Kitten? Had the feeling you didn't find it all that unpleasant—"

She stood there, staring at him.

"I'd like for you to mean it, Ty," she said. Then, very quietly, and with enormous dignity, she turned and walked back up the hall.

Well, damn me for a sinner! Tyler thought. Damn my no 'count soul to hell. . . .

He was about to mount when the man's hand came down hard upon his shoulder. He whirled and stared into George Drake's face.

"Thought I'd find you here," George said happily. "Come on, Ty—time's a wasting!"

"Now, what the hell?" Tyler said.

"We've done it!" George crowed. "Wire came in an hour ago! We're out of the Union, Ty! Louisiana is a republic, leasewise 'til we can get a Confederacy set up. Up with you, boy, we're going to celebrate!"

That, Tyler thought is the last thing on earth I want to celebrate; but he didn't say anything. Play it close to your chest, he told himself. Wouldn't do to come out too strongly against 'em. Can't rightly tell who's going to win this war. Likely the North; but whoever wins Ty Meredith is going to share the spoils.

"Right," he said. "I could do with a mite of celebrating, George. . . ."

"Come on, then," George Drake said.

Two hours later, the two of them and every other man present in the Eakins Club was completely drunk. At one time or another, every member of the club climbed upon the table amid the litter of smashed glasses, their heads half hidden by the clouds of cigar smoke, and made a speech. The speeches were masterpieces of rhetoric. The bourbon and branch water school of oratory, Tyler called it.

He sat there, the smoke from his cigar veiling his eyes, and listened. But listening increased his need for drink; sober, or even nearly sober, he could not have borne it.

On the table, the last speaker, young Caldwell Vickers, Banker Randolph Vickers' son, was whipping the Yankee Army in three weeks with a corporal's guard of old men and beardless boys. Caldwell, Tyler mused, should know better. He's Harvard trained and knows Yankees damn nigh as well as I do. . . .

He stood up. He was amazed to find that his legs were made of Indian rubber. He put his hands down upon the table to support himself.

"Speech!" the men roared. "Speech, Ty! Make way for Tyler! Speech!"

Tyler swayed there, blinking at them.

"Boys," he said solemnly. "Everybody else has told you how fierce we are, and how we're going to chase the Yankees back to Washington with an Army made up of twenty-five old maid schoolmarms armed with buggy whips. Now that's rightly a good idea; but I've got a better one: We'll just lay out a few barrels of this here bourbon across the Yankee's line of march. After they've consumed the contents we'll just drive along the lines, load 'em in wagons like cordwood, and deliver 'em to Mr. Lincoln's front door, with an ultimatum: 'Give up or we'll pour a couple o' barrels of the same into the Washington water supply—' "

"What if he won't give up then?" one of the men called. The others were already speechless with laughter.

"Oh he will," Tyler said easily. "First time he sees all the catfish crawling out of the Potomac awaving those lil' white flags, he'll—"

The rest of it was lost in the gleeful roar of his listeners. They pounded him on the back. They thrust brimming glasses at him.

"Boys," Tyler said thickly, "Let me out of here—I need air."

A group of them surged out on the gallery with him. And it was there that the Negro found him.

"Mister Ty," he said "You's gotta come home! The Cap'n—"

Ty peered at him. He couldn't place the man.

"Go 'way," he growled. "Leave me be. . . ."

"Mister Ty," the black man pleaded.

"Said go 'way, didn't I? Damn it, you burrheaded black bastard—get!"

The Negro plucked at his sleeve.

"But, Mister Ty," he pleaded, "the Cap'n, he's—"

Tyler put his bony hand in the middle of the Negro's chest. He straightened his arm in an explosive jerk. The Negro went over backwards—over the balustrade. The street was twenty feet below. The Negro lay in it, moaning. Presently he managed to turn himself over and crawl away into an alley. He had to crawl for the simple reason that his spine was fractured. Never in his life would he walk again.

On the gallery, they all laughed. A minute later they had forgotten all about the black man.

In the morning, when Tyler stumbled into the house, the sight of Cato's face shocked him into near sobriety. The wizened little Negro was crying too hard to speak. All he could do was to point toward the Captain's bedroom.

Tyler pushed the door open. Beside the bed, his brother knelt, his fingers telling the beads, his voice rumbling through the prayers. And on it—

"Good God!" Tyler got out; "He's not—?"

Slowly Joseph turned.

"Yes, Ty," he said quietly. "Heart attack. He and Morris Eakins got into a furious argument over secession. Doctor Le Pierre has been warning him for years that he mustn't get excited. But when Morris came here, sprouting his Unionist cant—"

"I—" Tyler whispered, "I didn't believe it. I thought he was imagining. . . ."

"There are," Joseph said, "an awful lot of things you don't believe, Ty—that are true."

"Not the Captain," Tyler said. "Not the Captain. . . ."

"What are you still standing there for?' Joseph roared at him. "Kneel! Kneel and pray for your father's soul!"

And Tyler Meredith knelt.

CHAPTER TWO

Somebody at the bank had talked. Tyler was sure of that now. For the first three days, he had been mystified by the sudden cessation of conversation when he entered a room, the level stares of men who had been friends—more, companions. He shrugged it off—all this and the women who drew their skirts aside as he passed, as if to avoid contamination. But it began to get to him.

"I'll drop in on Sue," he thought. "Maybe she's heard something."

But, at the Drake's, the butler greeted him with evident embarrassment.

"Nossir, Marse Ty," he said nervously. "Miss Ruth ain't in . . . Miz Sue neither. . . ."

"Not in?" Tyler said, "Or just not in to me?"

"Lawdy, Marse Ty," the Negro quavered. "I—"

"It's all right," Tyler said. "I'll just leave my card. . . ."

He mounted his horse, his face frowning and intent. He had a sudden, overwhelming craving for a drink. All this silence was getting on his nerves. He turned his horse toward Hewlett's. Mighty good bourbon at Hewlett's, he thought.

The fire-eaters were holding forth with such enthusiasm that his entrance went unnoticed. He walked straight toward the bar, looking neither to the right or the left. But he was still ten feet from it when he heard someone say his name.

"Ought to be tarred'n feathered," a man's voice growled. "And run out o' town on a rail!"

"Never would of thought it of ol' Ty. Damn' close to treason if you ask me. . . ."

"Now, boys," George Drake's voice came over to him, "the line was his—his to dispose of as he saw fit. Nothing treasonable in that. Probably figgered the risks were too great. . . ."

"It is treason!" young Devereux, the Senator's son snapped. "He sold those packets to a Yankee concern up Cincinnati way. Now they can use them to haul arms and ammunition and troops against us! If that's not aid and comfort to the enemy, I don't know what is."

"We weren't at war with them when he did it," George pointed out.

Good old George, Tyler thought wryly; his guilty conscience is whipping him on to stick up for me. . . ."

"Makes no difference," Titus Claiborne said. "Any fool knew by then what was going to happen. And that's not the worst of it: he sold them for gold, and shipped his money off to his cousins in England. Betrays an utter lack of faith in our cause. . . ."

Tyler, by then, was standing just behind him. He knew, as he opened his mouth that to speak at all was unintelligent, more, unwise. But he was consumed with icy anger. He had never been a man to suffer fools gladly. And Titus Claiborne was a fool. Besides, the fat was already in the fire. Whatever the cost to his plans, he wasn't going to knuckle under. Perhaps he would have to leave New Orleans because of this, get out of the South. But when it was over he could come back again. And not a manjack of these sprouters would be in a position then to gainsay him. He could feel himself trembling. But his voice, when he spoke, was cool and controlled.

"Any reason, justifiable or otherwise, why I should have faith in it, Titus?" he drawled.

They whirled as one man, staring at him. Devereux recovered first.

"It's your section. You were born here," he said.

"A biological accident. Didn't ask for it. Give me a better one. . . ."

"I'll give you one," Titus Claiborne said. "The South represents the highest peak of civilization. We are the only true chivalry left in the world. The only people remaining with the leisure to acquire culture, the only true leaders. We cannot permit a superior civilization to be destroyed by an inferior one! A nation of traders must take back seat to a country of knightly, courtly, landed gentlemen, descended from the old world's best, and—"

"Poppycock," Tyler said. "When was the last time you read a book, Titus?"

"Well—" Titus floundered, "Let me see— It was—"

"Exactly. We're the highest peak of civilization. Likewise of culture. Only, if we want our boys to get really educated we send them to Harvard and Princeton, because we haven't a college or university worthy of the name from one end of the South to the other. I can produce a dozen New England schoolboys, sons of friends of mine, who for pure book-learning can take every manjack here—including me. Read some mighty fine romances while I was in New York and Boston. All written by Yankees. Tell me, Titus, you ever hear tell of a Southerner who wrote a book? Painted a picture? Composed some decent music?"

"Now see here, Tyler Meredith—"

"That's the trouble. I really do see. The rest of you don't. I like facts, Titus. Take our aristocracy. I've spent three summers in England with my cousins. Read a right smart bit of history while I was there. All right—say you're an aristocrat now, Titus. You are, I grant you that. Would you leave Fairview and that imposing house of yours, to go shiver in a log cabin chinked with mud, or sometimes just a plain leanto? Afraid to sleep because you didn't know what night the redskins were going to come whooping down on you, scalping knives out? Not knowing if your powder and ball were going to hold out 'til planting season, and deer getting mighty damn' scarce? Would you?"

"Of course not! I don't see what the hell—"

"I'm getting at? Simple. Aristocrats don't pioneer. They stay put. They love their comfort. Pioneers, boys, are three parts good, hungry poor folks, and the rest scum. For my money, I'll bet on the scum; they're tougher. Debtor prison scourings, escaped convicts, correction girls—"

Titus Claiborne's face was white.

"You'll accept my card," he said icily. "Or do I have to slap you?"

Tyler smiled at him, lazily.

"Neither," he said. "I'm not a gentleman. I don't aim to get shot because I'm impolite enough to mention out loud in correct society that a goodly portion of our better families are the descendants of a boatload of Parisian whores. Nope. No cards. And if you slap me I'll beat you to a pulp with my fists here and now. Thank God, I'm not a gentleman. I'm under no obligation to make a fool of myself. . . ."

"Tyler," George Drake said. "Go easy, boy. These are troubled times. People rile easily. Seems to me you've got some good points, only this just ain't the time to make 'em. This, I think, is the time to—pray. . . ."

"Maybe even too late for that," Tyler said soberly. "Look, Titus, I'll apologize for opening my mouth too wide. Didn't mean to be nasty. Reckon the real trouble is, I love this stupid, puffed up, wrongheaded land of ours as much as any of the rest of you. I don't want to see it killed. I know—and I'm sorry that it's so—that the South is inferior to the North in every important aspect: agriculture, manufacturing, shipping, learning, money, population. I know we're going to get our front teeth kicked in; and after they've knocked us down, they're going to stomp us flat. So I took my money out. I aim to bring it back after it's all over; when folks are going to need jobs to feed their hungry families. Somebody's got to stay solvent, or the South's dead forever. Maybe that's not your idea of patriotism; but it's sure Lord mighty damn practical. . . ."

"But to sell those fast packets to the Yankees—" Devereux said.

Tyler looked him up and down, coolly, insolently.

"Why not?" he said. "They've got gold. . . ."

Then he turned very quietly and sauntered up to the bar.

"Bourbon, Joe," he said, "with just a touch of creek water. . . ."

His voice, speaking, was both cool and serene, despite the sadness inside of him, pressing down like a weight. I've done it now, he thought. Burnt my bridges behind me. But I won't run like a rat. I'll leave when I have to —with dignity, at a walk. Damn them anyhow! And damn me for not playing it smarter. He sat there, holding the glass of bourbon between his hands. Then, very slowly, he raised it to his lips. . . .

"Ruth," Susan Drake said. "I want to talk to you. . . ."

Ruth looked up from her journal. She had been writing—a thing she did religiously every evening—an account of the day's events. She put down her pen, and closed the diary slowly, keeping one finger between the pages so that the still wet phrases would not blot, thinking with some annoyance of how she could word the rest of the sentence that her sister had interrupted: "Perhaps, by our showing a certain amount of severity towards him, Tyler can be shocked into—"

Into what? She had started to write: "—into enough sober reflection to make him mend his outrageously unpatriotic ways—"; but even as she had chosen these words, she had the baffled feeling that Tyler's behavior was based upon exactly the kind of sober reflection she was trying to force him into. It was not Tyler Meredith who was acting upon emotion; rather it was his cold-blooded calculation that set him apart from the rest

of the world. But he was wrong! He had to be. Nobody
in his right mind could seriously believe that a nation
of traders and shopkeepers had either the courage or
the will to defeat the flower of Southern Chivalry. . . .

"Ruth," Sue said, raising her voice.

"I heard you," Ruth said. "Go on, talk—"

"Was it you," Sue said, "who told Timothy that
Tyler was not to be received?"

Ruth looked at her sister. Then, very slowly, she
smiled.

"Yes," she said. "Why?"

"That's what I want to know. Why in the name of
God, did you do such a thing? Tyler and George are
the best of friends, and—"

"And you," Ruth said flatly, "are in love with him."

Sue stiffened.

"You," she got out at long last, "will apologize for
that remark, Ruth. Sister or not, there are limits. . . ."

"Are there? Appears to me, it's you who should consider what they are, Susie-dear. To have your cake and
eat it, too, is going to be mighty difficult under the
circumstances. You married George out of pique, because that Maryland girl wrote you a letter that set you
wild with jealousy. Too bad. Turned out to be a bad
bargain, eh? George is a rightly nice and gentle creature;
but anybody with any brains can see he's not half the
man Tyler is. . . ."

"Ruth Forrester!"

"Sorry. I've got a mighty hankering to let truth out,
Sue. A little light and air hereabouts wouldn't hurt matters to my way of thinking. . . ."

"Does," Sue said quietly, "your sudden passion for the

truth go deep enough to let you admit that all this is silly schoolgirl vaporings—a childish scheme on your part to attract his attention? You accuse me of being in love with Tyler. What about you? Ever since the first time he came to call, you were always underfoot, making sheep's eyes at him. . . ."

"Never denied it. I love Ty. I mean to marry him—which is the one thing you're forgetting, Susie-dear. . . ."

"Don't call me Susie-dear! Good heavens, Ruth, I—"

"All right. Mrs. Drake. Mrs. George Anthony Drake, the Second. I'll be plumb, downright happy to call you that, because it's what I'm trying to remind you of; and Lord knows you need reminding. You've got yourself a husband, Susie-dear, such as he is—which we both know isn't much. . . ."

"Oh!" Sue breathed. "To have the nerve to talk like that about the man whose hospitality you're enjoying is pretty lowdown, Ruth."

"You're right, there," Ruth said slowly. "That wasn't nice of me, was it? But then the truth is so seldom nice. What I'm driving at, Sue, is seeing as how you've got your man safely hooked, it appears to me you ought to allow me some freedom in handling mine. And I didn't have Ty put off because I wanted to attract attention. Every girl child is born knowing how to do that—"

"Then why did you?" Sue demanded.

"Because I love New Orleans. I want to live here. And I sure Lord don't want to be a social outcast. People are already beginning to criticize Ty a right smart bit because of his stand in this secession business. After we've whipped the Yankees it'll be worse. So I've got to cure Ty before I marry him. Else it'll be likely we'll have to live in one of those filthy old Northern cities and—"

"You're mighty sure you're going to marry him, aren't you?"

"Yes, I am. The only person who ever was seriously in the way of that was you. And you took care of that stumbling block mighty nicely. So right now there isn't a thing on earth that can prevent it. . . ."

"Except," Sue said quietly, "Ty himself. And even perhaps the hand of God. . . ."

"That's a funny thing to say," Ruth began, but Timothy, the butler came into the study. He was excited. That Sue saw at once.

"Miss Ruth," he said. "He here. Marse George done brought him home. Wasn't a thing I could do. . . ."

"It's all right, Tim," Sue said. "Tell the gentlemen we'll join them in a minute."

"Yes'm, Miz Sue," the butler said.

"Come, Ruth," Sue said. "I'd like another display of feminine wiles from the young expert. But remember one thing, little sister: This is still George's home and mine. And we choose whom we want to invite—understand?"

"Yes, Ma'am," Ruth said mockingly. "The poor relation will remember her place, Ma'am, and will always be most humbly grateful for crumbs and castoffs. Shall we go now?"

"You—you witch!" Sue said.

Tyler was standing with his back to the fireplace in which a low fire burned against the April dampness.

George Drake, who had been facing him, turned as the two women came into the room. His face was drawn into as convincing a facsimile of stern disapproval as it was capable of, which wasn't very convincing after all. George, as Ruth had said, was a gentle creature.

"Which of you," he snapped, "took the liberty of denying Tyler the house?"

Susan looked at her younger sister. Ruth's face, she saw, was the picture of serene innocence.

"I did, George," Ruth said. "I didn't mean to be presumptuous. But I know how much you disapprove of Ty's views and you weren't here when he called. . . ."

"You were presumptuous," George said sternly. "A man is entitled to his ideas as long as they're honestly held. Ty knows I don't approve; but he knows, too, I think, that it won't make any difference as far as our remaining friends is concerned. I must ask you, Missy, to apologize to Mr. Meredith. . . ."

"All right," Ruth said. "I do apologize, Tyler, for having exceeded my place. I had no right to show you the door of my brother-in-law's house. But if it were mine, I'd do the same thing. My sister and her husband can entertain a traitor and an enemy of the South if they want to—maybe even a coward, since every other man your age I know is already in uniform; but, as for me, I must ask to be excused."

George and Sue stared at her, speechlessly. But Tyler simply tilted back his head and laughed aloud.

"Little Miss Fire-eater," he said. "As a matter of fact, I won't excuse you or at least not any longer than it will take you to change into a riding habit. I mean to

claim the forfeit for your bad manners, Kitten: that is
a couple of hours of your time, during which you'll
listen with a reasonable amount of attention to my point
of view. What do you say, little one?"

Ruth had already drawn herself up to deliver a sting-
ing rebuff, but then, oddly, she caught sight of her sister's face. It had softened, slackened its defenses, so that
the slight quiver of the underlip, the hazed-over glow in
the eyes, the mute longing in her whole attitude, the
half suppressed gesture of appeal—all these spoke through
the silence in a language that any woman not a fool could
interpret; and Ruth Forrester, whatever else she might
have been, was most certainly not a fool.

The thought that ran through her mind she could
not have put into words at that instant; later, having had
time to reflect upon it, she recorded it for all time in
her diary:

"I saw then that George didn't make any difference,
which shouldn't have surprised me, knowing women as
I do. I'm going to have to fight my own sister for Ty,
just as though she weren't married. I don't mean that
Sue's a bad woman or that's she's immoral. All I do
mean, I reckon, is that no woman is moral once the chips
are down. Given the choice between the morals they've
been taught and a man like Ty, the morals can go whistle
up a hollow stump. I don't blame her. I feel the same
way. Can't be so proud of all my burning indignation
over Ty's lack of patriotism; because even I know it's
pure fakery. I'd marry him if he came marching into
New Orleans dressed in blue at the head of the Union
Army and set the place afire. But he's got to be managed

and my sister's dainty claws have to be kept off him. So
I'll have to keep up the flummery. . . ."

Slowly, she permitted her body to relax. Then, gazing
at Tyler, her eyes more enormous and cornflower blue
than ever amid the golden flutter of her lashes, she said,
watching her sister's face paling into misery with that
purely feline delight in cruelty that is one of the dearest
joys of being a woman:

"All right, Ty. Reckon maybe I have been unfair.
'Sides, it's the very first time you ever asked me to go
riding with you. I'm most flattered. Excuse me, all. I
won't be but a minute. . . ."

"See that you aren't," Tyler said.

"You're really going to that midnight service?" Ruth
said. She was referring to her brother-in-law's last remark as they left the house:

"Don't forget the midnight service, Ty. Father Joe is
going to preach the farewell sermon. Kind of an occasion
—our last service in New Orleans for some time. Reckon
it won't take too long to drive the Yankees out of Virginia; but war's a serious business; calls for a mite of
praying. Don't know anybody I'd rather listen to preach-
ing more than your brother. Appears to me the Good
Lord is bound to listen to a Padre as good as he is. . . ."

"Yes," Tyler said. "Yes, Kitten, I'm going. Reckon I
owe that much respect to my brother and my
friends. . . ."

She didn't answer him. She was, at the moment, occupied with turning her mount aside to allow an ancient

cart, drawn by an even more ancient white mule, driven by a still more ancient Negro, to pass.

"My mule is white!" the Negro intoned. "My face is black! I sells my coal two bits the sack!"

Ruth looked at the old man and smiled.

"Isn't he quaint?" she said to Tyler.

"Reckon so," Tyler said. Negroes, as individuals, or as a group, simply didn't interest him. The whole question of slavery bored him profoundly.

"Look at that one," he said, and pointed.

A tall Negro came down the street. He had on a frock coat, and a tall silk hat, both in tatters and covered with soot. On his back was a bundle containing a rope, a sheaf of broom straw, and several bunches of palmetto. His toes, also soot encrusted, stuck out from the torn uppers of his once elegant boots. His trousers were patched and repatched, some of the larger patches being held together with smaller ones of a different color. But the thick coating of soot blended the clashing colors admirably.

"*R-r-r-ramonez!*" he cried. "*Ramonez la cheminée du haut en bas!*"

"What is he saying?" Ruth asked.

" 'Clean your chimney from top to bottom'," Tyler translated. "He's a *ramoneur*—a chimney sweep. A dying breed, he and that Latanier salesman over there. . . ."

"Latanier! Latanier! Palmetto root!" the wizened old Negro was calling. "Get your clothes white! Get 'em white! Finest Latanier!"

"The older *blanchisseuses* use that root instead of soap," Tyler said. "So many of the old ways are going. It's a pity. . . ."

"You aren't doing anything to defend them. . . ."

"Back on that subject?" Tyler mocked. "Look, Kitten, I invited you along for the pleasure of your company, not to explain things to you, whatever I may have said. Useless to explain things to women. The feminine mind is excellent, but it doesn't work in logical patterns. In fact, it hates logic. I could give you a perfectly reasonable explanation that would completely justify my point of view. But it wouldn't change anything. You'd go on feeling about me just as you do now. It's feeling that's important, not ideas or arguments. So, if you want to consider me a traitor go right ahead—as long as you respond properly when I kiss you. . . ."

"Don't you dare!" Ruth began, then she stiffened. Tyler followed her gaze.

"Sue!" he breathed. "What on earth is she doing down here in the nigger quarter?"

"You men," Ruth said contemptuously. She probably came down here because she got upset when you asked me to go riding. . . ."

Tyler looked at her. That was the most beloved of all feminine myths: this hard held belief in the superior subtlety of womanly machinations. Actually, to any man who had made more than a casual study of them, most female intrigues were boringly transparent. He knew the answer to the question he was going to ask before he voiced it. Nevertheless, he said, with the proper degree of wonder:

"And why should she object to that?"

"Because she's still in love with you, you idiot! She only married that tiresome old George Drake because she was mad at you and her feelings were hurt.

Now, she's sorry. She's acting like the dog in the manger; just because she can't have you herself, she doesn't want—"

But that was going too far. Even in the full brashness of her nineteen years, Ruth realized that.

"Go on, Kitten," Tyler said softly. "What doesn't she want?"

"Anyone else to have you," Ruth said flatly. " 'Specially not—me. . . ."

Tyler grinned at her, mercilessly.

"Small chance of that, isn't there?" he mocked. "Seeing as how you consider me a disgrace and a traitor to the South. . . ."

Ruth's eyes were very soft suddenly.

"Ty," she whispered, "It's just that I'm trying to keep you from being—a—an outcast. That would hurt too much!"

"Would it, Kitten?" he asked. "I'll be blessed if I can see why."

"Oh, men!" Ruth said explosively. "Come on—let's follow her."

"Maybe she wouldn't like it," Tyler said.

"I don't care a fig for what she likes. I know where she's going. Bet you a picayune she'll go down Rampart to St. Ann Street. That's where Marie lives. . . ."

"Marie?" Tyler said.

"Marie Laveau. She's our hairdresser. But that's only a coverup, though she's good at it. Actually, she's the darkies' Vaudau queen. . . ."

"Sue believes in that rot?"

"With all her heart. You know how superstitious she

is. Reckon she wants a gris-gris, or some love drops to win you back with. Though what she'll do with you after she's won you, I'm sure I can't see. Maybe she'll get Marie to make her a little wax image of George, and stick pins in it, so he'll waste away to an early grave. Then the comely young widow—"

"Kitten," Tyler said solemnly, "Did anyone ever tell you you have a viper's tongue?"

"Yep," Ruth said shamelessly, "And I know how to use it when I get riled. Oh, come on!"

The cottage that the quadroon queen of the black arts inhabited was very fine. It had been given to her by a wealthy New Orleanais for whom she had done a service. But this service was by no means the usual one rendered by handsome quadroons to wealthy Caucasians. Its details were slightly startling, or would have been any where else except in New Orleans. Marie Laveau had prayed for three hours in the Saint Louis Cathedral, holding three small peppers in her mouth. Thereafter, she had returned to the Cabildo and placed the three peppers under the chair of the presiding judge. Then, to the astonishment of nobody who accepted the interior logic of the back bayou country, the stupified judge had promptly acquitted the son of the wealthy citizen despite the overwhelming evidences of his guilt. The cottage, then, was the result of paternal gratitude.

Susan Drake pushed open the gate and entered the yard. At the door she paused a moment, then knocked. Ruth and Tyler waited until the door had closed behind her; then Ruth skipped ahead and rapped smartly on the door.

It flew open. The woman who stood there was something to see. She was about forty five years old, and the dark silky hair peeping out from under her headcloth was already beginning to turn grey. But her creamy, cafe au lait skin was unlined and her bearing was imperious. Tyler was enough of a Southerner to feel a quick surge of resentment at this. Then he shrugged. His mind, which always quickly dominated his emotions, showed him at once the absurdity of expecting the fawning, entirely faked humility of the blacks from this woman. Even at forty five, Marie Laveau was beautiful. At twenty, Tyler decided, she must have been able to set the Mississippi afire.

"Yes?" she said. Not yessir, yes ma'am; just yes, like a queen speaking to underlings.

"You know who I am," Ruth said. "And this is Mr. Meredith. We'd like to arrange a seance. . . ."

"Sorry," Marie Laveau began, but Ruth cut her short.

"Look, Marie—my sister's in there. We saw her come in. You can take us all at the same time. And I'm warning you, there'll be trouble if you don't!"

Marie Laveau laughed throatily.

"What kind of trouble kin you make me, Miss Ruth?" "Nobody can make trouble for Marie, them. Not even you. I got all them notes you wrote to that Parker boy —ever' living one, me. Copied 'em out real fine. Even he couldn't tell the difference. But the ones I got is the real ones, yes. You want me to show 'em to Mister Drake?"

Ruth's face was stricken. She glanced at Tyler. Then fury leaped into her eyes.

"I—I'll have you whipped!" she said. "I'll get an order from Judge Sampoyac and—"

"Won't give you one, Missy, him. 'Cause Madame Sampoyac will ask him real nicelike not to, yes. Reckon she wouldn't like for the old Judge to see the letters she writ Julien Potier—'specially not the ones where she raves over how good he is at what she thinks he's good at, her. Not that she knows, being married to such an old man. Don't have nothing much to go by, her. Sometimes I feels sorry for you white ladies. Can't have much fun—" she grinned at Tyler insolently, "not having nothing but white gentlemen. . . ."

Tyler grinned back. He liked this middle-aged, handsome witch. Pure evil always appealed to him, especially when it was coupled with such devilish pride.

"How would you know, Marie?" he said.

Marie threw back her tignon covered head and laughed aloud.

"Us mixed bloods got the advantage, us," she mocked. "We just naturally forced into trying 'em, both. You can keep your gentlemen, white, yellow, or brown. Give me a big, buck nigger fieldhand every time!"

"You're perfectly horrid!" Ruth gasped.

"Yep, reckon I am. That's the difference twixt me and a lot of great ladies I know. I *knows* I'm horrid, yes."

"We really would like a seance, Marie," Tyler said gently. It's up to you, of course. I'm not threatening. I'm asking it as a favor. . . ."

Marie smiled.

"That's better," she said. "That's much better. There's

a mighty heap to be said for being a gentleman after
all, I reckon. Come on in. . . ."

Susan stood up as they entered, her face ghost-white.
Sadly she shook her head.

"I expected this of my precious sister," she said. "But
I really thought spying was beneath you, Ty. . . ."

"It was an accident," Tyler said quietly. "Just happened to see you come in. Then I was taken with a
mighty hankering to have my palm read, or the bumps
on my head. Mighty handy thing, knowing your future. . . ."

"Come in here," Marie Laveau said.

The room into which she led them resembled nothing
so much as an altar room. Everywhere there were the
symbols of Catholicism: crucifixes, ikons, beads, statues
of the Virgin and of several Saints. But mingled with
them were the thunder stones, the carved representations
of Damballa, the serpent-god; and an African idol of
such magnificent ugliness and obscenity, that Tyler, un-
fettered as he was by preconceived notions, recognized
it for what it was: a great work of art.

Marie disappeared behind the purple curtains. The
three of them sat there, waiting. . . .

Marie Laveau came back. She had changed into the
robes of a Mamaloi, the high priestess of Vaudau. In her
hands she held cupped a thunderstone, a dark grey piece
of volcanic rock hollowed into a shallow bowl. In the
hollow of the bowl a wick floated on fragrant oil. She
had already lighted it and the flame flickered blue, casting eerie shadows across her face.

It was already dark, but Marie drew the heavy curtains so that not even the lights of the swinging street lamps could enter the room. The only illumination came from the stone bowl.

She sat down, and taking several small bags from a drawer, poured pile varicolored peas out before them. She made cabalistic signs with her hands, mumbling throatily in Gumbo French. Tyler had all he could do to keep from laughing aloud.

He glanced at the women. Sue was staring at all this mumbo jumbo in utter fascination, while Ruth struggled still against it with steadily weakening resistance. Women are strange he thought; the more outrageous nonsense is, the more it appeals to them. He wondered idly about the letters to the Parker boy; but he really didn't care. His fixed approach to the problem of human behavior was that it only surprised him when it was better than he expected it to be. And what he expected of most people was exactly nothing.

"All mixed up," Marie Laveau said. "Can't tell nothing from the peas, no. There's influences in this room working agin me. Got to try something else. Got to make sacrifices. That's more dear. You folks willing?"

"Yes," Tyler said. The two girls nodded, dumbly.

Marie went out of the altar room again. When she came back, she had three white chickens in her hands. As far as Tyler could see the birds were identical.

She held them out. "Choose!" she said.

Timidly Sue put out her hand and touched the one on the left. Ruth chose the fowl on the right. Tyler shrugged. "The middle one's good enough for me," he said.

"Touch it," Marie said. "You got to touch it to make the 'fluences, yes."

Tyler touched the chicken.

Marie laid the three fowl down. Since their feet and wings were bound, they made no effort to move. Then, from somewhere within her voluminous robes, the Vaudau Queen brought out a poignard as thin as a knitting needle. She stretched out the bird that Ruth had chosen, and deftly pierced its skull with one swift stroke. It died at once without a quiver. Which, Tyler realized, was natural enough, since it was the brain that had been pierced. Then, taking a broad bladed knife from the drawer, she slashed the chicken open and began to examine its entrails.

"Well?" Ruth breathed.

"Funny," Marie said slowly. "Never would of believed it if I didn't see it with my own eyes, yes. You going to see hell, Missy; but it's going to do you a mighty heap of good. You going to grow up, you; get to be somebody rightly kind of fine. And it 'pears to me, though I ain't plumb sure, you're going to get what you want—after you done got so you'll deserve it. You going to live a long time and have children and grandchildren. And you're going to be real happy—after you done suffered enough to make yourself worth it, yes. . . ."

"Marie—" Ruth began, but Susan cut her off.

"You've had your turn," she said. "Now it's mine. Please, Marie. . . ."

Again a chicken was expertly slaughtered. But this time when the body was opened, they all drew back, aghast at the stench. The entrails were purplish black.

Marie Laveau sat there, staring at them. Slowly she lifted her eyes to Sue's stricken face.

"You want me to tell you?" she whispered. " 'Druther not me, Miz Sue. . . ."

Sue straightened up, proudly.

"Yes," she said. "Tell me, Marie. I'd rather know."

"You—you going to die, Miz Sue. Not long from now. Maybe two, three years. You going to die all by your lonesome in a real bad way. 'Course you ain't never been real strong—always was a sickly child as I remember. But it ain't that. Don't really know why—but that's what I see. Never no children. Never no real happiness. Lordy, Miz Sue, I'm sorry you asked me, yes! I wish I hadn't of—"

"It's all right, Marie," Sue said gently. "It's better, knowing. . . ."

"Lord God, Sue!" Tyler said. "You don't really believe this rot, do you?"

"Yes, Ty," Sue said. "I've known Marie a long time. And in all these years, I've never known a prophecy of hers to fail. . . ."

"You want your future told, Mister?" Marie said.

"Yep," Tyler said. "Tell me how many yardchildren I'm going to have . . ."

Marie performed the sacrifice. Suddenly she stood up, her face twisted with fright.

"Get out!" she screamed. "You git out of here, you!"

"Me?" Tyler said. "Now what the devil?"

"Look!" Marie said, pointing to the entrails.

"Don't see anything," Tyler drawled.

Suddenly Marie stooped and blew out the stone lamp.

Then they all saw it: the entrails of Tyler's fowl glowed with a soft, subdued phosphorescence.

"Odd," Tyler said. "Still—"

"Look, Mister," Marie said. "Please go. This ain't no place for you. Ordinary people, yes. But not no Saints. . . ."

"Saint?" Tyler said. "Oh, my God!" Then he threw back his head and loosed the great boom of his laughter.

Slowly Marie Laveau calmed. She approached the dead fowl, peered at it.

"You kin laugh," she whispered. "But it's true, yes. I see now you's been a big devil. You done laid with other men's wives. You done sinned and you going to sin some more. Only it ain't going to do you no good, no. 'Cause, Mr. Tyler Meredith, already you been touched by the Hand of God. You don't want to be; but you is, yes. You kin run; but you can't hide. Ain't no hiding place, Mr. Meredith, no hiding place at all. . . ."

"Of all the rubbish," Tyler began.

"I'm done," Marie said. "Please go way and leave me be. This here's a shock. I trys to stay right with God, but Vaudau's trafficking with the devil. And it ain't good when a body with God's mark on him comes in here and faces me. Likely to lose my powers now, me. . . ."

Tyler stood up, grinning.

"How much do I owe, Marie?" he said.

"Nothing! Nary a living cent! Take your money and I'm finished for sure, yes. Just go way, Mister. Go way and don't come back!"

They came out into the dark street. Tyler helped Sue up behind him on his horse. With a swift toss of her head, Ruth mounted before he had a chance to assist her. They rode home without speaking. As he helped Sue down before her husband's house, she stared at him.

"She's right, you know," she said. "There is goodness in you, Ty. Maybe even greatness. Only you fight it. But one day you'll have to let it out and—"

"Oh, come on, Sue!" Ruth snapped. "I've heard about all the silliness I can stand for one day. For goodness sake, come on!"

Sue stood there, looking up at Tyler.

"I'm sorry I shan't see it," she whispered, then: "All right, Ruth, I'm coming. Goodnight, Tyler."

"Goodnight, Sue," Tyler said.

CHAPTER THREE

THE TORCHLIGHTS BLAZED, MOVING THROUGH THE BROAD, straight streets of the Garden district toward the Episcopal church on Jackson Avenue. Ahead of him, and behind, Tyler could see them diminishing into fireflies with the distance, jerking with the cadence of marching feet, while the band boomed "La Marseillaise." He felt the prickle of excitement moving up his spine. It was a thing to remember.

Another man might have surrendered to it. It would have been so easy to forget, to rush forward, as so many others were doing, impelled by the music, the tramp of boots against the cobblestones, the white winged blur of the handkerchiefs that the women were waving from the galleries, to let the intoxication of the moment capture him, and to stand up with the tight knots of other men before the recruiting sergeants' booths on every corner, hand raised to take the oath of allegiance to the new Confederacy, not yet completely born. Even he had to fight it. He had to dig deep into his fund of skepticism, of doubt, into his resistance to all things beautiful, emotional, to resist the pure magic of this moment.

He marched on, grimly. He looked at his brother,

moving at his side. Father Joseph's eyes were half closed;
his lips moved in silent prayer. But not, Tyler saw, the
formal prayers of his faith; no, this was something else
again, something older, purer—the anguished seeking
of a simple man for light, for truth, in a supremely difficult hour. His own private Gethsemane, Tyler thought.

"Joe," he said. "It's not easy, is it? Not the way you
figured it was going to be?"

The young minister looked at him, soberly, slowly.
"It is pure hell, Ty—"

"Figured it would be. Chips all down now. No turning back. Hell of a thing to look at all these boys and
wonder how many of 'em you're going to have to kneel
beside and pray over, while they lie there with their guts
shot out. That's it, isn't it?"

"That's it," Joseph said. "That—and more, Tyler.
I've given my sanction to this, because I believe in it. But
it's a hard thing. I've waked in the night, wondering if
I've done well. Funny. The Scriptures say flatly: 'Thou
shalt not kill.' Without qualifications. Thou shalt not
for any reason whatsoever. And I've got to pray for
boys who'll have to go out and kill, go out and die. Got
to give them hope, make them believe they're justified
in God's sight. But are they, Ty? Is any man justified in
shedding his brother's blood?"

"You're the padre," Tyler said drily.

"I know. Any war's bad enough. But this is something else again. This is fratricide. We're fighting for a
way of life. A kind of living I think is the most noble,
the most gracious ever invented. We're defending civilization against barbarism, but—"

" 'Put up thy sword,' " Tyler quoted quietly, " 'For he who takes up the sword, shalt die thereby. . . .' "

"How else could it be done? To supinely surrender to the money changers, to the despoilers of the temple, is wrong, too. Our Lord used force. He took a whip of cords—"

" 'And the meek shalt inherit the earth,' " Tyler mocked.

"The devil," Joseph snorted, "can always quote Scriptures."

"Yes," Tyler said. "But there is an answer, Padre. Maybe you won't take it from me, but there is. . . ."

"What is it?" Joseph breathed. "Tonight, God knows, I'd take a prayer from Satan himself!"

"Reckon I'd make a mighty handsome substitute for Old Nick. Folks always have held I'm his boy. The answer's simple, Padre. If the bitter cup won't pass, drink it. 'Not my will, but Thine, be done. . . .' "

Joseph lost step, staring at his brother.

"You astonish me, sometimes, Ty," he said. "I wonder if you won't find one day that your vocation is the same as mine—and just as true?"

That's twice tonight somebody has said a thing like that, Tyler thought. Damned if they won't have me believing it after a while . . . But aloud, he said: "It's probably nonsense. Only I'm logical. All I have to do is reason from the basis you usually start from, Joe. Starting from there, granting you your premises, I'm bound to arrive at that. Two and two always make four. That is, if you know what two is. I don't. That's the difference between us. I know I don't know anything. And I don't believe anyone else does, either. Only they think they do. They're lucky. Mighty comforting to have Jesus, Jehovah, Mohammed, Buddha, and Shiva on your side. . . ."

"And one is as good as the other?" Joseph said sternly.

"Quite. It's the believing that counts, not what you believe in. Faith can move mountains. Any faith. Only, sometimes, like Mohammed found out, it's a hell of a lot easier to go to the mountain. . . ."

"Go to the mountain," Joseph said. "That's a good thought, boy. The second good thought you've had to-night. You've helped me. I've been fretting myself over what isn't rightly my business. It's God's, after all. If there's a way out of this blood letting, He'll show it to us. If not, we'll just have to drink that cup, knowing it is His will. . . ."

"Well," Tyler began, but whatever he was going to say was lost in the sudden explosion that erupted from the recruiting booth they were passing. The recruiting sergeant came out of the booth, propelling a man before him with a stiff-armed push.

"Now git!" he roared. "I'm plumb sick of arguing with you, René! How many times do I have to tell you we don't take no niggers? Not even light yellow niggers. For God's sake git, René, before I really gits mad!"

Tyler dropped out of the line of marching men, and stepped onto the banquette. He saw that the fat little man was opening his mouth to protest. That had to be prevented at all costs. The results were likely to be serious.

"But I'm not a nigger!" René Doumier shrieked. "I'm not! I'm not! I'm—"

"Oh, hell!" the recruiting sergeant said, and struck

out savagely. The fat little man sat down abruptly in the
muddy street. His top hat fell from his head and rolled
down the gutter. He sat there, waving his pudgy fists,
and the tears squeezed out from his tight shut eyes. Tyler
came up to him, and bending down, raised him up by the
armpits. His hair was irongrey and slightly kinky. As
Tyler bent over him, the cologne with which it was
drenched in a vain effort to make it approximate Caucasian straightness, rose in a sickening cloud.

René Doumier looked up.

"Tyler!" he said. "Or do I have to call you Marse Ty,
too?"

"You can call me anything except a child of God,
René. What's the trouble, my friend?"

"These—these blockheads! I came to offer my services
to my country, and they refuse me! Me, René Doumier,
the largest slave owner in my parish! I'm a free man! I
was born free, and just because—"

"I know. Just because your mother was a free woman
of color—damned little color, at that—who caught your
father's eye at the Quadroon Ball. Just because your
skin's a shade tanned even in winter, and your hair's
a mite kinky. Doesn't make sense. I've heard it all before.
You're the owner of three hundred niggers. Sans Souci
is the grandest manor house in the Parish, if not in the
State. But, René, man, you're up against some mighty
stubborn facts: to these folks, yellow, brown, or black,
a nigger's a nigger. Why don't you accept it, and kind
of stay out of their way?"

"I do," René whispered. "But to defend my country
is my right."

"You haven't any rights," Tyler said sternly; "Any

nigger, any man of color, exists on the white man's sufferance. You've been mighty damned lucky, René. When your old man died and left you Sans Souci, all folks did was grumble. If he had had any legitimate white children, you wouldn't have stood a hope or a prayer. . . ."

"That, Ty," René said quietly, "was hardly possible since my father lived all his life with my mother in a union that would have been sanctified by the Church if the laws of the State had permitted it, and never bothered to so much as look at a woman of his own race. I was his only son. And he loved me. Mon Dieu, how he loved me! I had it all, the finest clothes, the best horses, a Sorbonne education, everything—"

"Except the acceptance of your father's people," Tyler said. "Everything except what you wanted most in this world . . ."

"You—know too much," René muttered. "Especially the things you've no right knowing, Ty. You'll visit us soon?"

"In a week or two," Tyler said. "I'm pining for a glimpse at Lauriel. You ought to be rightly proud, René. . . ."

"I am. And frightened. She's all I have, Ty. And what's to become of her? What kind of life can she have?"

"A mighty good one, if you'll just come down off your high horse. There are hundreds, no thousands, of free men of color in Louisiana. Some of them highly educated, even rich. Take the Dumas, the Clovis, the Legoastiers . . ."

"You take them. I'm afraid my daughter—won't—"

"Goddamnit, René, you mulattos are worst than white trash when it comes to being down on the niggers. There's something shameful about that. You've no right to hate your own. . . ."

"What," René said quietly, "is our own, Tyler? The niggers hate us. The whites look down on us. Any white, even a red-necked clay-eating ignoramus from the upstate pine barrens. People I could buy and sell by the dozens. . . ."

"That's where you're wrong, old man," Tyler said. "You can't buy them. They're not for sale. Not even we can buy them. They're the freest gosh blamed critters on earth. . . ."

"Free to starve," René sneered.

"Yep. To starve and to sit under a tree all day communing with a jug of busthead. Free to get scrawny towhead brats they can't feed. But free, nevertheless, absolutely free. Because they're outside our world. We don't want 'em; can't use 'em. So they've got a kind of negative freedom of uselessness. And a real freedom based on their pride and their willingness to take on a pack of sixteen wildcats to defend their right to do exactly as they damned well please. Can you say as much? Can I?"

"No," René said slowly. "Still—"

"Still every man living, except maybe your pine-barren whites, is at least a little a slave. Of conventions. Of all the things our pride, our honor, our education, families, friends, the world we live in demand of us. Takes a lot of guts to be free, René. Haven't got 'em, myself. You either. Not even as much freedom as a bucknigger you take a rawhide to. You're enslaved to the desire of being what you're not, of trying to belong to a world that rejects you. Without ever considering whether it's worth belonging to—which I doubt. Wake up, friend, wash that muck out of your hair and let it kink. Be yourself, and a man. And, René—"

"Yes, Ty?"

"Go a mite easier on your niggers. For one thing a good hand is worth money. For another, they aren't going to take it. Not from you. A white man might get away with being as pure damned ornery as you are toward your hands. You can't. Those niggers are bound to resent mistreatment from you more than they would from me, say. I like you. Wouldn't want to find you in a gulley with your throat cut. . . ."

"That won't happen, my old one. Niggers just don't have the courage. That, I think, is what I resent most about being part black—this affair of slavery. . . ."

"Other peoples have been enslaved," Tyler said. "Blonds used to bring high prices in the slave marts of Algiers."

"That, yes. But what other race made such good slaves? The red skins have died almost to the man before submitting. But the blacks—I ask you, my friend. So docile—one half dozen revolts in two hundred and fifty years, even in places where they outnumbered their masters five to one. And every one of those revolts betrayed by a black man at bargain rates, for the price of a pair of boots or a cast-off coat. So of this thing I have no fear. They will never rise against me. And if they do, I shall beat them down like the dogs they are.

But I detain you, my old friend. Yes, yes—pay us a visit. Lauriel will be happy to see you. . . ."

"I'll come," Tyler said. "Au 'voir, René."

" 'Voir, mon vieux," René said, and limped off, enwrapped in his injured pride.

Poor devil, Tyler thought. He's got everything and nothing. Finest cane and cotton lands a man could want. Big house, clothes, carriages, slaves. A daughter too damn beautiful to believe. But no happiness, and no peace. Grateful to me, because I treat him the way he wants to be treated—like a white man. But scared of me, too; because he's afraid Lauriel will throw herself away for my sake. And it would be throwing herself away. Not a damned thing to offer her, except a house on a backstreet and visits in the dark. Lauriel's sweet and lovely and fine. René shouldn't worry about that. He shouldn't think I'm bastard enough to—

He stopped dead, a mocking grin lighting his eyes.

Who're you trying to fool, Tyler Meredith? All right, I am bastard enough to. There are mighty few things that are beyond me. And little Lauriel damned sure isn't one of them. . . .

He moved off, toward the Church, hearing the voices of the boys' choir, soaring high and clear and pure, like the chanting of angels.

He had, of course, missed the formal part of the service. Joseph had mounted the pulpit, and was standing there, looking down at the members of the regiment. Then he started speaking, and his voice came to Tyler, slow, and soft, and deep.

"My friends," Joseph said. "My brothers, my children

in Christ. There has already been too much said about the justice of our cause; and far, far too much insistence upon the ease with which, being right, we shall accomplish it.

"But I say unto you, with the voice of the prophet of old: 'Whom the Lord loveth, He chastiseth.' Our cause is just; we are in the right; but blood must flow and tears be shed before we win the victory.

"It will be a long fight, my brothers, and a hard one. Many times you will know despair; many times will you be tempted—" Joseph paused, his gaze resting upon Tyler's face—"to push aside the bitter cup; but you must hold on, endure. For then the bands will play no longer, and the banners themselves will be shot torn and soiled. And every man in that hour will be alone with himself, and with his God.

"This comfort, then, is all I offer you: that our cause is Holy, and those of us who must die, will die knowing it is so. I pray you bear yourselves as men, in honor, in firmness, and in faith. . . ."

He lifted his hands abruptly in the benediction.

Tyler looked at the others. He had been sure that the fiery enthusiasts of the new regiment had found Joseph's sober, brief sermon disappointing; but now he saw it was not so.

Joe's got to them; that's strange, he thought wonderingly. He was smart enough to appeal to something in them finer than any of the whiskied up spouters could reach. Presented the grim side, and put them on their honor as men. That was intelligent of him. But then, Joe's no fool. . . .

Maybe, he thought suddenly, as he got up from the family pew, I'm the fool. Isn't my belief in my own intellect my own strength, a kind of faith? With as little justification as any other—maybe less? But I can't give it up—not yet. I need to believe in myself. I can't rightly cling to a god that some mighty weak-kneed folks invented because they were scared of the dark. I'm not afraid, not even of the everlasting dark, the silence and the never ending sleep—the notbeing, I reckon. Only effect it has on me is to make me want to cram a powerful lot of living into the time I got left.

Next week, he thought suddenly, I'll go see Lauriel. And every trace of the momentary awe and respect he had felt vanished abruptly from his eyes.

The Doumiers had come out from France in 1795. Lyonais for many generations, they had all the solid, bourgeois virtues of that industrious city. But Louisiana had changed them; by the time Jean Jacques Doumier, René's father, had finally made his grand tour, he found himself an alien and a stranger in the land of his sires. The people of Lyon are a heavy lot; laughter is not one of their gifts. Jean Jacques found Paris more to his liking, took an apartment there, pursued his leisurely studies like the aristocrat he had become, and married the flower-like daughter of an impoverished noble who had prudently kept his head throughout the revolution. He brought his bride, forever referred to, in New Orleans, with awed respect as Madame la Vicomtesse, back to his upriver plantation; lodged her in the cypress and

brick unpainted cottage that had been the home of his
father, and commenced to shut off her view of the river
by building in front of it the imposing Greek revival
mansion which he named Sans Souci. The name, for a
time, defeated him; while she lived he was never without care. Madame la Vicomtesse, moved from the simple
briqueté entre poteaux cottage into the Greek mansion
—the cottage being torn down afterwards to make room
for the separate kitchen, stables, workshops, all the
paraphernalia which made life on a plantation all but
self-sufficient—promptly took to her bed with a series
of ills, real and imaginary, and did not leave it again
until her death, three years later, leaving Jean Jacques
without legitimate heir.

The distinction is important. For, after a year of
being denied his wife's favor, Jean Jacques had already
moved his Quadroon placée from a cottage on the
Ramparts to a neat bungalow on the far reaches of the
plantation itself. There, nearly a year before Madame
la Vicomtesse's death, she, the first Lauriel, after whom
the present Lauriel was named, presented him with a
fat, pale golden cherub whom he named René.

René, strangely, was both darker, and more negroid
of feature than his mother. She wept over his looks; but
Jean Jacques, being French, was delighted. He found
his bastard son enchanting. He was absolutely incapable
of the vitriolic prejudice so natural to the Anglo Saxon
and other Teutonic races. Being Gallic, being warm
and human and absolutely clear, he did not feel himself
hemmed in by blackness, threatened by the alien primitive race among whom he lived. He knew his slaves were

human and treated them as such. Naturally, they adored
him.

What he had, finally, was that good, solid love of self
that has nothing to do with egotism, or even egocen-
tricity. He had nothing at all to prove, and hence, the
mainspring of racism, the need for a scapegoat, the
desire to bolster a faltering self love by contrast and
comparison with a race deemed inferior—and then held
in that position of inferiority by a system of such rigor,
of so many ramifications, social, moral and even physical,
that it was, itself, had its authors been analytical enough
to see it, a complete and sweeping denial of the validity
of their claims—never even entered his head. Chains,
whips, night riding patrols, the denial of books, of learning, the control over religious instruction, are hardly
necessary for the domination of a mindless semi-ape; but
then, logical consistency has seldom been the hall mark
of the Southern mind.

So, when it was pointed out to Jean Jacques that he
owed it to the continuance of his family to marry again
and provide himself with an heir, he answered with
simple astonishment: "But I already have a son!"

His American friends found this point of view completely incomprehensible; the French, while understanding it, did not entirely approve. But Jean Jacques continued to live in calm happiness with his Quadroon
mistress, and to adore his swarthy son and the three
completely angelic daughters with whom his Lauriel
afterwards presented him. They, the daughters, he had
early married off to the sons of the proud and wealthy
free men of color, with which by then, Louisiana was
plentifully supplied.

But nothing was too good for little René. He was petted and spoiled; and educated, unfortunately, far beyond his intelligence. Worst of all, he was left finally, upon Jean Jacques' death, the master of one of the State's greatest plantations, surrounded by envious and hostile whites. The results were disastrous, though the case was far from unique. For, despite the fact that René was no darker than many an Italian or Spaniard, he looked negroid. The other FMC's as the free men of color were abbreviated on the tax collector's records, at least those who owned plantations and slaves, were usually so classified only because their ancestry was known; it could rarely be distinguished by physical appearance. Since not a few of them were offspring of German colonists brought in by John Law's colonization scheme, and mixed-breed women whom the French, with their almost total lack of repugnance toward a black skin, had started bleaching generations ago, blond hair and blue eyes were not rare among them. It was possible, then, for even Anglo Saxon whites to forget that the cultivated French speaking planter whose lands bordered theirs had a touch of the tarbrush. For René, no such escape was possible.

Oversensitive, morbid and proud, he learned his lessons hard. Early in his youth, he so forgot himself as to challenge a white planter. The man had him horsewhipped for his presumption—a kindness, actually, for the Caucasian could easily have had him killed without danger of arrest. He fell in love with the daughter of a neighboring French family; the girl returned his affection. Her father promptly shipped her off to relatives in France, and let René go with a stern warning. No man in Louisiana was by then less free than plump, handsome René Doumier, held close within the prison of his skin.

He turned his savage disappointment upon his Negroes, punishing them for the misfortunes a noticeable trace of their blood had inflicted upon him. He overworked, beat, half starved them. They responded by turning into snarling animals, forever at bay.

He was softened for a time by his marriage to Hilda Grieter, the blonde, blue eyed octoroon daughter of a minor German planter; but even in this his life was twisted by the evils bred in him by rejection: he married Hilda because she was blonde and blue eyed, not because he loved her. Nevertheless he was kind to her, and poor Hilda adored him. She combined the placidity of the Germanic female, with the easy going complacency of the Negress. Had she lived she might have cured him; but one of the yearly epidemics which regularly decimated Louisiana carried her off.

And René was left with his daughter, Lauriel, named after his mother: Lauriel, whose light chestnut hair curled softly about her shoulders, darkened and beautified by her father's heritage, for her mother's had been as straight as the tail of a palomino mare; whose mouth was soft and full-fleshed, instead of following poor Hilda's almost lipless line; and whose eyes were tawny hazel—and who, tragically, combined with all her beauty, more than a little of her father's malaise of soul. Like him, she was more than a little convinced that whiteness of skin was a positive virtue. That this was a distinctly debatable proposition never occurred to her; it, would, perhaps, have done her no good if it had. For the idea of racial superiority is, in the final analysis, a belief, a faith—as impervious to logic as all other faiths—as unshakably irrefutable as all the other props that man, out of his loneliness and his terror, his hunger for importance, his need to deny his nakedness and his temporality—must erect to bolster his dignity and his pride. . . .

But to Tyler she was simply a body, an object having the requisite warm softness, the required firm-fleshed litheness of youth, the innocently provocative movements, the slumberous, languid grace which awoke his all too easily awakened carnality. He would not have liked thinking of her as a person; but the danger of that was not great. Neither did he think of Sue and Ruth as people; he found it ever so much easier to regard all women as dolls and toys for his pleasure. In this, he was, perhaps, right; life is seldom made happier by complicating it. . . .

She, Lauriel, saw him from the main gallery, as verandas are called in Louisiana. She recognized him at once; and upon the instant of that recognition, or perhaps even before it was completed—the signals for the tensing and release of lithe girlmuscle being given prior to the arrival at surety of that intricate mass of grey tissue and nerve fiber finer than any hair which comprised the curious miracle of her brain—she came running, or rather flying, for it seemed to him her feet did not touch the curving stairway which flowed down from the gallery, down toward where he sat upon the rented nag, her face a pool emptied of all expression save alone that of joy.

He dismounted slowly, and put out his arms to her. She came toward him; but just out of reach of his outstretched hands, she stopped.

"No," she said. "I promised Papa, Ty—"

Tyler looked at her. The chestnut hair had the sun in it, giving it the look of burnt honey. The hazel eyes were enormous, with the now emerald, now sapphire blaze of tears, held by some alchemy of her will, trembling on the brink of falling. And her mouth, her mouth—

He stepped forward, taking her, none too gently, into his arms.

Her hands came up, palms outward, hard against his chest. But he, rolling his laughter, unreleased, deep in his throat, increased the pressure of his grasp, until her arms bent at the elbows and she was there against him as helpless as a captive bird.

He bent down and found her mouth. It was hot and salt with the taste of tears. But her hands moved at last, upward against the rough fabric of his waistcoat, past the silken rustle of his cravat to lock finally, in abject surrender about his neck.

The sound of René Doumier's sigh was so soft that Tyler had the impression at first that he had imagined it; but when he turned, the little fat man was there.

"Lauriel," he said sadly. "You promised me. . . ."

The girl turned, staring at her father.

"Yes," she whispered. "I did, didn't I? Forgive me, Papa. It's just—"

"That you're both young and powerfully attracted to one another," René said gravely. "That, I comprehend. But it makes nothing, this comprehension. Facts are stubborn things. This is still Louisiana, still Anno Domini 1861. And my good friend, M. Tyler Meredith remains of English rather than of French descent. Therefore, the kind of behavior my father was capable of— entirely honorable, considered in its own light, is impossible to him, more—unthinkable. You, my daughter, could never be to M. Meredith more than a placée in a hidden house on a back street to be visited in the dark, in secret and in shame. Do not force me to ask M. Meredith whether this is so. He is an honest man. I'm afraid you would not like his answer."

Lauriel turned again to Tyler, her hazel eyes wide with questioning.

Tyler's smile was mocking.

"M'sieur your father," he said in the soft Creole French he had learned as a child, "has right. I have never pretended to be more than I am. . . ."

"Oh!" Lauriel whispered; then, very quietly, she turned away her face.

"Tyler," René said, suddenly dropping the grave formality of his tone. "She's all I have, you comprehend that? I have no wish to play the heavy father of the comedia del'arte, and forbid you my plantation. It would do no good in any case because this headstrong daughter of mine would find some way to meet you. Besides, I should miss you sadly; among the whites, you are the only true friend I have. Therefore—"

"Therefore," Tyler said gruffly, "you're asking me to behave myself. That's it, isn't it, René?"

"That's it," René said.

Tyler stood there, looking at the little yellow man a long, slow time. Suddenly, impulsively, to his own vast surprise, he put out his hand.

"You have my word, René," he said quietly.

René hesitated, searching Tyler's face. Then, quite suddenly, he was sure. He gripped Tyler's hand, hard.

"Thank you, my old one," he said quietly. "Now I must go see after my hands. The lazy black swine, if one leaves them alone for so much as a minute . . ." He paused, looking at Tyler. "I leave you to complete your visit," he said. "I can do that now. For of all the many things you have been accused of, rightly or wrongly, Tyler, not even your worst enemy has dared even imply that you were ever guilty of breaking your pledged word. . . ."

That's so, Tyler thought wonderingly, as he watched the fat little man ride away; but I'll be damned if I know why. It's a thing I've never done, couldn't ever do . . . I've made a god of expediency, and yet I hold fast to this outworn notion that a man must do what he has promised he would. Reckon I don't know myself very well after all. Inconsistency, thy name is man. . . .

He was aware, then, that Lauriel was watching him, her hazel eyes deep and still and sad.

"Tyler," she said, "You shouldn't have promised that . . ."

"I know I shouldn't have," he said. "But the fact remains—I did. . . ."

"And you mean to keep your promise?"

He looked away from her to the brooding loveliness of the house, with its twin stairs like swans' wings under the oak trees.

"Yes," he said slowly. "Yes, Laurie—I do. . . ."

She caught him to her, suddenly; her nails biting into his flesh through all the thickness of his clothing.

"I'm glad," she whispered. "I'm glad and I am desolate —at the same time, Tyler. That is rare, is it not? Only a woman can manage to have opposite feelings at the exact same instant. . . ."

"Take 'em one at a time," Tyler drawled. "Tell me, Laurie, why are you glad?"

"Because otherwise the burden upon me would have been insupportable. If you had not promised, I should have been forced to keep my word to papa alone . . ." She lifted her face to his, the emerald sapphire jeweled mist swimming in her eyes. "And that would have been difficult—no, impossible—But now, with your help, I can keep it; which is why I am glad. . . ."

"And desolate?" Tyler said.

"*Je suis desolée*," she said; "because now I *must* keep my promise. Because there is no longer any escape. Papa talks about disgrace, and dishonor—and I know what he means with my mind. I know also that he is right; that is, my mind does. But my heart doesn't understand: the words are meaningless, incomprehensible. They signify nothing, and are not even real. Being without you is real—I know how that feels. It was bad enough before, when I used to watch the sun come up, after not having slept a wink, praying all the night through that this day

you would come, that I could see you, touch you, even
just be near you, for then I had hope; and sometimes
you did come. But now, if you come at all, it will be
only to torture me with the sight of what I cannot have
—like setting a feast before a starving beggar and chain-
ing him out of reach. And, I fear you will not come at
all. . . ."

Tyler's hand came up gently and stroked the chestnut
hair.

"Wouldn't that be better, little Lauriel?" he said.

"No," she whispered. "Oh no, Tyler! For that would
be a little like dying. More than a little, perhaps. . . ."

Tyler smiled at her, mockingly.

" 'Men have died,' " he quoted, " 'And worms have
eaten them; but not for love. . . .' "

"A man wrote that," Lauriel said. "I don't know who
he was; but I am sure it was a man. You see, Ty, men
don't love the way a woman does: all over, inside and
out, with all her heart and mind and soul and body every
second of the day, and through every dream she has at
night—if she manages to sleep at all. No, Ty, no woman
would ever write such a foolish thing!"

"Right," Tyler said. "It was a man. A very wise man."

"Perhaps. But from my standpoint he was a fool. You
won't take everything away from me, will you, Ty?
You'll spare a few scraps and crumbs of your life for
this off-colored wench?"

"If," Tyler drawled, "anybody else called you that,
you'd cut his throat. . . ."

"You think it, which is the same thing, or almost.
You will come once in a while?"

No, Tyler thought; I won't come, Lauriel. Better the

surgeon's swift slash, and the grating of the bone saw,
than the slow bleeding to death of something that was
rightly kind of fine. Strange, because of this gentle little
mixed breed wench I'll have to change my plans. No—
not change them, speed them up a mite. Going to cost
an arm and a leg, anyhow. The *Pelican's* a damnably
slow old tub; but there's no doubt she's seaworthy.
Wanted to buy a faster boat; but the Government's
snapping the fast ones all up—and the letter of marque
boys. No privateering for me. I'm not mad at anybody. . . .

Still, it's not half bad after all. Time I got out of New
Orleans and to sea again. The blockade's a joke so far.
But it won't stay one. I know those New England boys.
They've got salt water in their veins. The *Pelican* will do
well enough for the first six months. Then with the pro-
fits, I'll have a steam packet laid down in Liverpool
that'll show her heels to anything afloat. If only the
Pelican's engines were worth a tinker's damn—

"Why don't you answer me?" Lauriel said.

"There isn't any answer," Tyler said drily. "I shan't
come, Laurie. If you think I could come here time after
time and keep my horny hands off of you, then you're a
fool. And I don't rightly cotton to fools. Think about it,
Chickee, and you'll see I'm right. . . ."

"You are right, Tyler," she said. "As if that made any
difference . . ." Then she turned her back to him.

He stood there, watching her, while the silence length-
ened between them. She tossed her head, shaking out
her heavy chestnut hair.

"Go 'way, Tyler Meredith," she said, suddenly,
fiercely. "Go 'way! I hate you! I despise you! I—"

Tyler turned and walked to where he had left the rented horse. He mounted, touched his crop to the brim of his hat.

"Au 'voir, Lauriel," he said.

She whirled, and ran to his side, clutching at the stirrup. She was crying.

"No," she said. "I don't! I don't hate you, Ty. I— I—"

He brought the crop down savagely against the horse's flank. The animal bounded off, jerking the stirrup free of her grip. Tyler rode away from there very fast, without looking back. It was, he felt, an act of cowardice; but, all the same, he did not turn his head.

He slowed the nag on the river road, just out of sight of the house. He rode toward New Orleans, sitting loosely in the saddle, the slow clip-clopping of the horse's hooves measuring out the leaden rhythm of his thoughts. Strange, he mused. Never gave much of a damn whether a thing was right or wrong, before. Don't rightly care now. Then, why in the name of hell and high heaven did I make René that tomfool promise? What difference does it make or not make what I do with an octoroon wench?

Does make a difference though. Reckon I'm immune to damn near all emotions except pity. René's been kicked around enough—though a mighty heap of what's happened to him is his own damned fault. Lauriel will get over me. Women always do though they swear to kill themselves, all such nonsense. Adaptable little creatures, damn them. A body can't live with them or without. . . .

Ruth, now—and Sue. Got the advantage there. I'll

be putting back into New Orleans every few weeks, and George'll be stuck up there in Virginia fighting the Yankees. Maybe, he'll be—

He stopped short, unwilling to complete his own thought. But he finished it anyhow, because evading issues and lying to himself were among the very few vices he didn't have.

Maybe he'll be killed. Then Sue'll be free. Rather have her anyhow. Ruth's a beauty; but at bottom, she's a vicious little wench. A man would never have any peace with her. . . .

Better be moseying along. Get on with this business. The *Pelican* isn't much, but she's available. Hell, I can make a fortune before the blockade gets tight enough to count. Lots of ports if things get too rough around New Orleans. Galveston, Wilmington, Charleston, Mobile. . . .

He stiffened suddenly, jerking on the reins. The docile old horse stopped short. The sounds that came over to him were unmistakable: the bullroaring of Negro bass, René's higher pitched tone, shrieking something in incomprehensible Gumbo-French, and between them both, clear and sharp as pistol shots, the sound of the lash.

Tyler spurred the ancient horse toward the sound. He broke through a canebrake, and saw it: the fat, overdressed, ridiculous little man slashing away at a huge Negro, three times his size. The black had a cane knife, three feet of razor-edged machete blade, in his hand. He was coming on toward René, roaring with pure rage, murder flaming in his bloodshot eyes.

He swung the machete, and René was left with the whip handle in his hands, the blade cutting through wood and leather as though through so much cheese. Tyler hadn't time to dismount; he yanked the Colt from his shoulder holster and took careful aim. The black was almost upon René before he fired. It was characteristic of Tyler that he waited so long. He knew the folly of snap shooting, hammer fanning, and all such trickery, which, legends and myths to the contrary, never worked. The idea was to hit what you aimed at, holding true on the exact spot where you wanted to place the ball.

The revolver spat orange flame, and black smoke. The cane knife went spinning from the Negro's fist. The huge black stood there, staring with incredulous wonder at his smashed right hand.

Slowly Tyler dismounted. His voice, speaking, was flat, calm, perfectly controlled.

"Go get that attended to," he said to the Negro. "Get a move on now. Be a pity to lose your right hand. . . ."

The huge Negro stared at him. Tyler stared back, cooly, calmly, obviously master of the situation. Then, very slowly, the black dropped his gaze. He turned and lurched off without a word.

"Tyler!" René got out. "Ah, my old one, you have saved my life! I will never be able to—"

"You ass," Tyler said coldly, "you utterly impossible little ass. I've told you a hundred times you can't get away with this. Goddamnit, man, you're breeding two hundred Nat Turners on your place. It's not your niggers' fault that you can't or won't accept the situation you find yourself in. And to take out on your slaves what you dare not avenge yourself upon my race for, is worse than cowardly; it's the most dadblamed contemptible thing I ever saw!"

René stood there, his pale yellow face greying. Suddenly, ludicrously, two enormous tears squeezed out of his small eyes and ran down his fat face.

"Oh, come off of it, René," Tyler said wearily. "I only tell you the truth as I see it for your own good. Another thing, you'd better sell that nigger. Right now, today. You'll take a hell of a loss, because nobody wants to buy a rebellious slave; but that's better than having San Souci burnt, your throat cut and Lauriel raped by all and sundry. Now for God's sake go home and wash your face. Blubbering is unmanly. . . ."

"We—we're still friends?" René asked piteously.

"Of course," Tyler said. "But I don't know how much longer we'll stay friends if you don't quit being such a damned fool."

"I'll be good to them," René choked. "I hate their stinking black hides, but I'll try. I wouldn't want to lose your friendship, Tyler—you're the only white man who ever—"

"Oh, for God's sake!" Tyler said, and laid a hand on the small man's shoulder. "It's all right, René. I'll be back to see you soon. But for Lauriel's sake, take care. . . ."

"I will," René said eagerly. "I promise you, Ty, I'll—"

But Tyler had already remounted and moved off, toward the river road.

He saw, as he entered New Orleans, a Negro riding a small cart pulled by an evil looking billy-goat. The man was curiously propped up in the cart by an arrangement of cushions and leather straps. He had a tray of rice cakes, and also a tray of those ginger cookies that the Creoles call *estomac du mulatre*, mulatto's belly. Tyler, who had no liking whatsoever for sweets, pushed his hand in his pocket and came out with a silver dollar. He tossed it to the cripple.

"Here, Uncle," he said, "Have a drink on me. . . ."

"Thank you, sir!" the Negro said; then suddenly, he stiffened, his face greying into something like—like terror, Tyler decided.

Now what the devil? Tyler thought. Then he shrugged. Half cracked as well as crippled, he mused, and rode on. But the man's face haunted him. He was sure he had seen it before. He puzzled over it for some minutes before he gave it up.

He returned the nag to the livery stable and walked the rest of the way home. As he entered the house, he was conscious of the oppressive silence. Since the Captain's death, and Joe's departure with the regiment, the house on Poydras Street had been curiously hushed. Even the Negroes tiptoed about their work, speaking in whispers.

Tyler went into the ornate room that had served his father as a study. He crossed to the sideboard and opened a decanter of whiskey. With the glass in his hand, he sank into the great chair with a sigh of pure weariness.

"Funny how scared that crippled nigger looked, he thought; like he'd seen the devil or something. . . .

He turned toward the window, seeing the light spilling out of the sky.

"This," he said aloud, "sure has been one hell of a day. . . ."

CHAPTER FOUR

New Orleans was gayer than ever that summer of 1861. Outwardly, nothing had changed. There were more balls than ever before. Tyler attended a few of the balls, taking both Sue and Ruth with him; Sue, because he wanted to take her, and Ruth because her presence stilled the wagging tongues of the New Orleans matrons.

But in 1861, every ball ended in bursts of pyrotechnical oratory; and since the sure result of this naive, unconscious hypocrisy on the part of speakers more than a thousand miles from the sound of gunfire was to produce near nausea in him, Tyler Meredith stopped going to balls.

Instead, he spent more and more time in the shipyards at Algiers, across the river from New Orleans, trying to speed up the work on the *Pelican*. She was a seagoing wooden steamer of reasonably shallow draft, as beamy as a pregnant whale and as slow as time itself. From her log, Tyler learned that her best speed had been an agonizing seven knots an hour. Coming up the river to dock at New Orleans, her speed had varied between four knots and one, depending on the force of the current. At flood times she hadn't been able to breast the river at all.

83

She was, Tyler recognized, as nearly hopeless as a blockade runner as a man could possibly imagine; but, because of that fact, he had been able to purchase her after every half-way decent craft had been snapped up by the Government and the privateers. He hoped to do something about her speed. In actuality, he had to; nine years of lying at a half deserted wharf out of commission had reduced her engines to a mass of immovable junk, frozen solid with rust, and her hull was badly rotted in several places. The hull was not too difficult: the rotted sections had already been ripped out, and solid, seasoned timber put in their places; caulked and pitched, it was now as good as new. But the engines had to be taken apart, piece by piece, soaked in oil and graphite, and the rust laboriously removed by hand. Dozens of parts were so undersize when the last flake of rust had been scraped from them, that he had to order new ones. And since the engines had been built in England, that meant shopping around the already overworked machine shops to have them made—which took months.

Her boilers, once derusted, were so thin that he was sure even normal pressure would burst them. But a tour of every foundry in the State revealed not one mill capable of rolling plate to the thickness required. He would have to make do with the *Pelican's* boilers as they were, which meant detailing a man to watch the pressure gauge every second of the voyage. With wry humor, Tyler advertised for a preacher for this job, stating that the ability to send up a powerful prayer was its chief requirement.

He worried over the situation most of the summer. And at the end of July, with the news of the Confeder-

ate triumph at Bull Run, jubilant friends urged him to
give up the venture. The war was over, they crowed; all
that remained was the mopping up. But the day after
the battle, Abe Lincoln called for five hundred thousand
Union volunteers. In a week, he had them; and the two
armies stood still in Virginia facing each other, while
brush fire skirmishes flamed in the West; and Missouri,
Kentucky, and the western part of Virginia were slowly
slipping away from the Confederate grasp. More important to Tyler was the Union Fleet's capture, on
August twenty-ninth, of Fort Hatteras and Hatteras
Inlet in North Carolina; the noose of the blockade was
tightening.

He lived in the shipyard, driving the workers. Finally
he hit upon a plan to eliminate as nearly as possible the
danger of the *Pelican's* weak boilers. He invented a simple
mechanism by which the old tub's huge side wheels could
be drawn clear of the water, then had her rigged as a
barkentine, with lofty masts and clouds of sail. On steam,
he would creep her in and out of the harbors; once at
sea, he would draw up the ponderous, resistance-creating
paddle wheels, and crack on all sail. But the innovation
itself cost him two more months. On the eighteenth of
September, riding with Ruth and Sue down to the ferry
landing to cross to Algiers, he could still look forward
bleakly to three or four weeks' more work before the
Pelican would be ready to sail.

On the ferry, Ruth clung to his arm possessively,
gazing up at him with adoring eyes. Sue stood a little
apart from the two of them, her face averted, gazing
stonily down river.

Damn my soul, Tyler thought, this minx is more of a

hindrance than a help. Reckon Sue thinks I've switched over—logical under the circumstances. George was quite a hero at Manassas. But logic never arranged anything much in this world yet. Hero or not, George is still George. Sue figures she's honorbound to love him, now. But honor nor nothing else ever put a bridle on the human heart.

"I'm mighty proud of you, Ty," Ruth said. "Yes, mighty proud. . . ."

He looked at her gravely.

Goddamn, but she's pretty! he thought. Wonder why in hellfire I don't find her exciting?

"Blessed if I can see why, Kitten," he said.

"Simple. Folks had some mighty hard things to say when you didn't join up with the rest of your friends and your brother. Even wrote pieces in the newspapers, hinting you were a coward. But what you're doing is just as brave, and probably more important. You'll be risking your life every day to bring in supplies for the Confederacy. I think that's downright brave and noble and—"

"I," Tyler drawled, "don't aim to risk my life a lick. And if I do, it'll be for one hell of a lot of money, not for the Secesh Government or the Union. . . ."

"Tyler Meredith!" Ruth said wrathfully, "Why must you always spoil things?"

"Don't know. Just fool enough to be honest, I reckon. I'm made different, Kitten. Being brave enough to blow a man's brains out, crack his skull with a musket butt or stick a bayonet through his guts over a difference of opinion seems a mite useless to me—not to mention a sight obscene. And I don't have the slightest hankering to be noble. Got a mighty powerful urge to be rich, happy, and comfortable. Like to drink the finest bourbon, ride the fastest horse and pinch the prettiest bottom in the State. Except these damned hoops make that plumb downright difficult. . . ."

"Tyler Meredith!" Ruth said again, but there was much less wrath in her tone.

"Doesn't it ever occur to you," Sue said slowly, "that society—people in general have some small right to the opinions they hold?"

"Yep. They're entitled to them, Babydoll," Tyler said easily. "Only thing they're not entitled to is to try to force them on me. Trouble is, the dearest opinions of most folks are based on feeling, not brains. Look at the mess we're in right now. . . ."

"Yes," Sue said. "Go on, Tyler. . . ."

"A people, speaking the same language, worshipping the same God, of the same blood, killing each other. Actual blood brothers on opposite sides, meeting in battle. It has happened a dozen times now, you know. And it could have been avoided by a simple exercise of common sense. But that's what we haven't got. We've got honor, nobility, courage—all of which never solved a blamed thing in human history, but always fouled things up worse. . . ."

"You think that it is a disgrace to be honorable, brave and noble?" Sue said quietly.

"Nope. Just kind of silly. Only useful thing to be is smart. Look, Doll, I have yet to encounter one provable instance in the whole record of mankind when right won

out just because it was right. When the right side wins
—and it's rightness is always doggone debatable because the winner writes the histories—it's a pure accident, or a coincidence that the right side happened to
be better lead, better equipped and had more poor devils
to serve as cannon fodder. God, as Voltaire said, is always on the side of the heavier battalions, which is why
the Yankees are going to win this war. . . ."

"Tyler Meredith!" Ruth said.

"Let him finish," Sue said firmly. "I find it kind of
refreshing after all the tub thumpers. . . ."

"There isn't much more," Tyler said. "I just like facts.
And what is fact is that given two men, one a saint and
the other a scoundrel, or two women, one as chaste as the
driven snow and the other a filly off Gallatin Street,
the smarter of the two will always win; and virtue, or
the lack of it, won't have a blamed thing to do with it.
Fact is, I'd bet on the wicked, 'cause that kind of living
sharpens the wits. . . ."

"I won't listen to this!" Ruth said.

"Then don't," Sue said mildly. "There's plenty of
deck space. . . ."

But Ruth stood her ground, glaring at both of them.

"Way I figure it," Tyler said, "It's going to be a long
war, because we've got the better leaders. But they've
got the manpower. And not being stupid, they'll learn.
In fact, they've got time to learn, because even if every
one of our soldiers took three Yanks with him before
he got killed, they'd end up with an army in the field
and we'd be defenseless. We can win damn near every
battle like the British did in the revolution, and still lose
the war. Because they can afford the losses and the de-

feats, and we can't even afford the men we lose while winning. Then, after we're stripped down, with all the captured Yankee battle flags on display in Richmond, there'll be one more battle—the last, the only one that counts. And they'll win that one hands down. . . ."

"Then why do you bother to run in arms and ammunition for our side?" Sue demanded.

"Because I'd get lynched if I didn't. I only buck public opinion when I have a chance to get away with it. But I'm going to stack bales of silk, jewelry, perfume, salt, medicine, and every kind of knick knack that will turn a fast dishonest dollar—in gold—on top of them. The South's fate is sealed. Mine isn't, Babydoll; and I sure Lord mean to make the best of it. . . ."

"You," Sue said, "are probably right, Tyler—but you have no idea how ugly this all sounds. . . ."

"Got a hide like an alligator," Tyler began; then: "Lord God! Look at that!"

The women whirled, following his pointing finger. Then they saw it. A small steamer limped up the river, both masts gone, her funnel shot riddled, two of her long boats smashed, her walking beam making a peculiarly ragged sound because several paddles were missing from one sidewheel, seriously unbalancing her. As she crept closer, they could see her hull had been holed just above the water line by enormously heavy calibre shells.

"Dahlgrens," Tyler said. "At least thirty-two pounders; maybe even a six-inch rifle. That's Navy shooting if I ever saw it!"

The ferry Captain hove to. They could see him leaning out of the pilot house, megaphone in hand.

"Steamer *Henry Lee*!" he bellowed. "What in God's Name happened to you?"

"Union Navy!" the answer boomed back, hollow over the water. "Feds took Ship Island yesterday. Mouth of the river's shut tighter'n a corked bottle! Rowboat couldn't get through now! We've seven dead, and eighteen wounded aboard. You got a surgeon among your passengers?"

"I'll check it," the Ferry Captain said. A few minutes later, he appeared again. "Yep, I have!" he called, "but close as you are to N'Awleans. . . ."

" 'Fraid to wait. Docking'll take an hour with the right wheel half wrecked. Put the Sawbones aboard. He might be able to keep a couple of our boys alive 'til we get in. They're right smart bad off!"

The ferry moved in until her bows were nudging the *Henry Lee*. The crew of the crippled steamer slung down a line, and hauled the wiry, bewhiskered little doctor aboard. Several of them wore bandages, visibly blood stained. Close in, Tyler could see the carnage had been awful. Sue put her face against Tyler's shoulder, shuddering.

"You mustn't try it, Ty," she whispered. "You mustn't!"

"I've got to, Babydoll," Tyler said quietly. Ruth whirled, facing him. She was crying.

"You see!" she said, "I don't care what you say, Tyler Meredith—you are brave! And what's more, you're honorable, too! The next time you talk like that I'm going to slap you, because you're just lying, and you know it!"

Tyler opened his mouth to answer her, but then he

shut it again. There wasn't, at the moment, any answer
that made any sense at all.

That night he rented rooms in Algiers itself. The
business of traveling back and forth between New Orleans and the shipyard was too time consuming. He
couldn't afford it any longer. Finally, early in October,
the *Pelican* was done except for the painting and the
final rigging.

And here, too, the fantastic luck for which Tyler
Meredith was already noted held good. He assembled
his cargo of cotton and tobacco and put the painters to
work day and night. Ordinarily, the painting would have
gone on along with the other work, but Tyler's modi-
fication of the paddle wheel mountings had made so
much debris and dirt that he had been reluctant to begin
it until everything else was shipshape. Now, after midnight, when the last of the workers had gone home, he
stood looking at the *Pelican*. She lay in drydock, between him and the river, and this merely accidental fact
of her relative position was the basis of Tyler's good
fortune.

He had, in the certainty that he would have to run
into the blockaded ports at night, chosen black as her
color. But now, looking at her lying against the moonsilvered waters of the Mississippi, he saw that the already painted bow was outlined against the night as
sharply as a razor's edge, while the rest of the hull,
scraped down to the bare wood, and remaining, therefore, a dirty, greyish white, was all but invisible. He
stared at it, startled. Then he wracked his brains, trying

to remember all his training cruises while at Annapolis.

Moonlight, he thought slowly; white, of course. But when there's no moon? Starlight for instance? Overcast? Fog? Storm?

He stood there, cudgeling his memory. A night sky was black. On land, the blackness met the horizon. But at sea? There was always a rising mist even on the clearest night; and the sea itself was never black at night, but grey even under lowering cloud. Black, which he had casually assumed to be the best camouflage, would make a starkly clear silhouette against the grey-white mist which always divided the grey ocean from the night black sky.

And by day? A white ship sparkled against the sea's deep blue; but it was debatable whether a black hull was any less visible. But grey—grey! Of course. Light grey, just off white, with enough bluish pigment added to the white to kill the sparkle, the reflection. Even on the clearest day, a Union Cruiser would have to be closer than a thousand yards to see her. And in the lightest haze, she could pass almost within range of the bigger guns undetected! Grey then, a light blue grey, a dirty color, just off white. Night or day it would give him an advantage amounting to an additional ten knots of speed. . . .

Ruth swung the bottle of champagne at the launching. City dignitaries, including the Mayor, made speeches praising in extravagant words the patriotism of this private venture.

"There have been those," the Mayor said, "who made free with their criticisms of our fellow citizen, young Mr. Meredith, when he did not immediately join the regiment of which his brother is Chaplain. He has borne both criticism and open insult patiently, when he might have silenced them with an early revelation of his intentions. . . .

"Such was not the path he chose to follow. Loyal to the South, he decided to serve her in his own way—a way, I submit, Ladies and Gentlemen, likely to prove far more valuable to our holy cause than any service, however brave, he might have rendered in the field. The supplies he will bring in from England will arm and nerve our cause; more, he has not called upon the State, or any group of citizens to participate in this venture; but unselfishly risked his personal fortune to prepare this swift vessel—"

Tyler winced. He had been hard put to stand the rest of the balderdash; but to call that ancient tub swift was too much.

"—To transport the arms and ammunition which will prove the lifeblood of our cause. There are those among us, Gentlemen, who owe Mr. Meredith a profound apology; those who were bold enough to question his personal courage. Gentlemen, I hardly need remind you that a squadron of Yankee vessels, totaling nearly fifty heavy guns lies in wait for the *Pelican* a little more than an hundred miles South of here. She is unarmed. Mr. Meredith, within the space of days, will sail this vessel, representing a large part of his private fortune into the teeth of that fleet. Needless to say, he is risking his life under much greater odds than any well armed soldier provided with a good musket and sufficient cover ever faces in the field—"

Tyler heard a muffled sound to his left. He turned and saw that Sue was crying uncontrollably. He took her hand and patted it clumsily, aware as he did so that a whole bevy of middle-aged matrons, self appointed guardians of public morals, were regarding the scene with malicious delight.

"Don't be a fool, Sue!" Ruth hissed from his right. "You're making a spectacle of yourself! You have absolutely no right to cry over him. . . ."

"I know," Sue sobbed. "But I can't help it. They say even a piece of driftwood can't get through now. . . ."

"I'll get through, Babydoll," Tyler said. "I was in that Navy, and I know how they think. I'll have all the advantage, 'cause every minute I'll be doing just exactly what they don't expect me to. . . ."

"But—" Sue whispered.

"Oh, for God's sake, shut up!" Ruth said. "Everybody's looking at you!"

The Mayor concluded his address in a fashion that left even Tyler speechless in admiration. He managed, in a single final phrase, to include our bonny flag, the purity of Southern Womanhood, the Justice of Almighty God, and the Righteous Holiness of Our Cause.

That, Tyler thought, was quite a trick. If speechifying could kill, wouldn't be a live Yankee left 'twixt the Mason and Dixon and the Canadian border!

He heard his name being called, and stood up. The crowd split the heavens with their cheers. He stood there, tall and rawboned, grinning at them. Then he lifted his hands for silence.

"Ladies and Gentlemen," he drawled. "I want to thank His Honor and all the other distinguished gentlemen for their kind words. Half the time I kind of thought they were a mite mixed up—couldn't rightly be talking about me. I'm mighty glad to find out I'm brave and noble and patriotic and suchlike. Didn't know it before. Just figured I was a simple citizen doing a job that's got to be done. Tell you one thing, though: soon as the *Pelican's* fitted out, I want to ask the prayers of all those present, for the daggumed scaredest whiteman in the whole State of Louisiana, not to mention the seven seas. . . ."

The roar of laughter drowned his words.

"And now," he went on, "I want to invite the whole assembled company aboard. There's champagne for them as likes it, and bourbon for them as has more sense; and light wines and fruit punches for the ladies, and snacks for those who all the speechmaking has worked up an appetite. I thank you one and all, mighty kindly. . . ."

"You clown!" Ruth said savagely. "Couldn't you have managed a little dignity?"

"Nope," Tyler grinned. "South's oversupplied with dignity, and short on a sense of humor. Mighty touchy folks, we are. Been able to manage a chuckle now'n then, we wouldn't be playing with a loaded gun in the dark the way we are now. Come on, Kitten, stop being Pure Southern Womanhood, and let's go have us some fun!"

The celebration aboard the *Pelican* was something,

even in a city noted for its celebrations. Men crowded
forward to shake Tyler's hand, and several of them
managed gruff-voiced, red-faced apologies. Tyler accepted them all with unruffled good humor:

"My fault, I reckon," he said. "Should have explained
what I was up to. Did look bad, I'll admit, 'specially
after I sold the river packets to the Yankees to get the
money to buy and outfit the *Pelican*. Never occurred
to me to point out that that deal was damn good poker,
'cause the Feds sure Lord can't bring those nice pretty
boats past either Fort Henry or Fort Donelson without
having 'em smashed to kindling, so they won't do them
a lick of good, while the cash I got sure helped things
along. . . ."

You bastard, he mocked himself; this here is pure
hindsight. If I'd have thought about that, I would have
bragged to high heaven about what a shrewd dealer I
was. But I didn't think about it at the time, and neither
did the Yankees, thank God—else they wouldn't have
bought those packets. . . .

As the champagne, bourbon, and other spirits di-
minished, the hilarity mounted. Before the party was
over, it gave rise to two challenges, due to the momentary forgetfulness on the part of a couple of youngish
wives that they were members of the mystic sisterhood
of chaste Southern Womanhood. Or, as Tyler waggishly
put it: "Maybe those fillies decided to secede and join the
human race. . . ."

At any rate, one was discovered kissing a handsome
young stalwart in a corridor below decks; and the other,
more daring, or with a greater capacity for champagne,

had locked herself and her gallant in Tyler's own cabin. The resulting damages when her husband kicked down the door, cost Tyler nearly fifty dollars in repairs, and two days time. It cost the outraged husband rather more: six months in the hospital—as the result of the two feet of cold steel that had passed through his body—and his erring spouse, who took occasion during his enforced confinement to elope with her gallant, neither of them being seen in New Orleans again. The other duelists were more fortunate. Having chosen pistols, they met under the oaks, both suffering from monumental headaches, unsteady hands and eyes that were far from clear. In the end, the precaution that their seconds had taken—of so undercharging the muzzle loading dueling pistols with powder, that even had one of them accidentally scored a direct hit on a vital spot, the ball probably would have lacked sufficient force to even penetrate the clothing they wore—proved unnecessary; they exchanged five rounds without throwing anywhere near each other, inflicted terrible wounds upon the branches and trunks of the oaks, shook hands and announced honor satisfied.

The work of rigging, which could not be done in dry dock, went on apace. Tyler painted even the lofty masts the dirty off white, seeing how clearly they showed against the night sky. But it failed to help very much. If anything gave the *Pelican* away in the darkness, it would be her rigging. There was nothing to do, however, but to risk it; to depend entirely upon the *Pelican's* engines and boilers was pure suicide.

It was all done finally. A handpicked crew was aboard. Below, twelve burly stokers were already bringing up steam. She was loaded to the gunwales with cotton and tobacco. Nothing remained but to weigh anchor, steam downstream, heave to and make the final dash out in the darkness.

Tyler paced the deck nervously in the first light of dawn, looking at the wharf. Where the devil is Sue? he thought angrily. Surely she won't let me sail without—

The clatter of horse's hooves pounding down the street toward the wharf at a hard gallop came over to him. He looked up. The rider was mounted side saddle; voluminous green riding skirts billowed in the wind. She was slashing at her mount with her crop.

Now, who the devil? Tyler thought. Neither Ruth nor Sue can ride like that. . . .

Then the trim little hat flew off and bounced behind the rider on the neckcord; a moment later, a mass of hair streamed free like a banner, light chestnut, almost dark golden in the morning light.

"Lauriel!" Tyler groaned. "Oh, damn it all!"

He went down the gangway to meet her. He helped her down from her mount, holding her as if she were a thing infinitely fragile and precious in his arms.

"Ty!" she whispered, "I—I brought you—this . . ." Then, shyly, she gave him the little tissue-wrapped package. He opened it and found a hand embroidered scarf. The workmanship was exquisite, for Lauriel had made it herself. Her skill with the needle, Tyler knew from the numerous handkerchiefs, cravats and mufflers she had already given him, was extraordinary.

"Thanks, Chickee," he said. "I'll wear this every time

I smell a gale a-rising . . ." Then, looking at her, he saw she was crying very gently, without making any sound at all.

"Don't take on so, little Laurie," he said with gruff tenderness. "I'll be back, big as life and twice as ugly. Just you wait. . . ."

"You," she sobbed, "were going away without even saying goodbye. It was only by accident—" She stopped short, staring at him. "Or was it?" she whispered "Papa usually reads the papers in his study; but yesterday he left *L'Abeille* and the *Picayune* in the foyer, where I'd be sure to see them. They both had glowing accounts of the launching of the *Pelican* and announced that you'd be sailing today. . . ."

"Then you think he did it on purpose?" Tyler said.

"I know he did! He wanted to shock me, to let me know exactly where I stand with you—as if I didn't know that already—"

"And where, Chickee, do you stand?"

"Exactly nowhere," Lauriel said, and hid her face against his shirtfront.

"Now, now, Laurie," Tyler said, "You know better than that. Reckon the reason I was going to sneak off was that you're a mite too close to my heart for comfort, considering the circumstances. But don't you worry your pretty head about me, Chickee. Ain't a Yankee born who can—"

"Mister Meredith," the voice, coming from just behind him, was pure ice, "If I may take the liberty of interrupting this charming scene. . . ."

He turned. Ruth stood there, wrath blazing in her eyes.

"I'd come to say goodbye," she said. "But that appears hardly necessary right now. You've had enough good-byes for this trip. Anyhow, I brought you this note from Sue. I kind of convinced her it was wiser for her to stay home. . . ."

Tyler grinned.

"Thanks, Kitten," he said, and put the note, unopened, in his breast pocket. But Ruth did not leave.

"You might present me," she said. "I've lived in and around New Orleans all my life; but I don't recollect ever having seen this—person before. And that, Tyler Meredith, is plumb, downright strange!"

"Hardly strange, Mademoiselle," Lauriel murmured. She was, Tyler saw, in full possession of herself again; and the light of battle was gleaming in her eyes. "There was scant chance that we should ever meet. We don't even live in the same world. You see, my father is René Doumier, of whom even Mademoiselle has doubtless heard. . . ."

"René Doumier?" Ruth began. "Not—not that ridiculous, little, fat yellow nig—" She stopped short, staring at Lauriel.

"Yes," Lauriel said simply, "that ridiculous, little, fat yellow nigger—who owns Sans Souci, the finest planta-tion in the State. Who is the kindest and best of fathers. And who," Lauriel smiled very slowly, "taught his daughter that the mark of a lady was the kind of man-ners she exhibited under stress. And now, if Mademoi-selle will excuse me, I will say goodbye to Mr. Meredith, who, for all his faults, is at least a gentleman. . . ."

She turned slowly, deliberately, and going up on tip-toe, kissed Tyler's mouth. She took all the time in the world about it. It was, Tyler reflected wryly, one damned fine show. . . .

" 'Bye, Tyler," she whispered huskily. "I'll see you when you come back. It's nice knowing you. A privilege, really—the one man in all Louisiana who doesn't let the color of his hide affect the kindness of his heart. . . ."

She turned then, and walked with enormous dignity to her horse. She mounted with easy grace, fitting the smart little riding hat aslant over one eye.

"Au 'voir, Captain Meredith!" she said. "Adieu, Mademoiselle . . ." Then she was off in an exhibition of superb horsewomanship that was a pure delight to see.

Tyler turned back to Ruth. He grinned mockingly. "Well, Kitten," he said, "aren't you going to kiss me goodbye?"

Ruth backed away from his outstretched hands.

"Don't you touch me, Tyler Meredith!" she said. "Don't you ever dare!" Then she turned and fled up the wharf toward the street, just as the sun came up over the roofs of New Orleans. . . .

Tyler climbed to the bridge, and read the note from Sue. It was stiff, formal, and said exactly nothing. He tore it into pieces and dropped them over the side. A moment later, the speaking tube began to squawk:

"Chief Engineer Hargraves reporting, Sir," the ghostly voice came up to him. "We're up to pressure and await-ign your orders. . . ."

Tyler turned to Reed Clayton, his young Second Officer.

"Order the lines slackened off," he said.

Reed picked up the megaphone, and pointed it toward the dockhands beginning to gather on the quay.

"Slacken off, bow lines!" he roared. The dockhands unwound the heavy hempen lines from the moorings. The bow slanted out toward midstream.

"Slacken off, aft!" Reed called.

The *Pelican* moved out, muddy water showing between her and the wharf. The lines tightened, broke water, glistening, taut now, ruler straight.

"Cast off, fore and aft!" Reed cried.

Tyler picked up the speaking tube.

"Quarter speed, forward," he said calmly. It was an effort. Inside, he was shaking with excitement.

The wheezy, ancient engines took up a slow, ragged beat. The paddle wheels turned over once, twice, yellow white water cascading from them. The lines splashed clear, the crew drew them in. The walking beams began their bone-jarring thumping. The *Pelican* started out toward midstream, moving at an agonizing crawl.

Tyler spoke into the tube again.

"Half speed ahead," he said. The thumping increased in volume. The shoreline swam backward past them at a perceptible rate.

"Speed?" Tyler demanded.

"Just a minute, Sir," the Executive Officer said. He went aft. The drag float was tossed into the water, bobbing in their wake. Reed counted the knots in the logline slipping past the marker on the stern as the float dragged it over. He returned to the bridge, saluted.

"Six and a half, Sir," he said.

At half speed! Tyler exulted. Then he remembered that they were pointing downstream, riding the current.

The exultation faded. They'd have to make the open sea before he could really determine her speed.

"Give me the wheel, Mister Myers," he said to the pilot. He wanted to get the feel of her. Normally, no new or refitted vessel ever braved the sea for a voyage of any real length without a shakedown cruise. But there was no time. The hundred ten miles between New Orleans and the Gulf would have to serve for that.

Two hours later, Tyler was satisfied. The *Pelican* was reasonably maneuverable. But the engines were cranky, temperamental, and the boilers were near disasters. At three-quarters speed, they began to clang alarmingly, so that Tyler was forced to cut her back to half speed again.

"Picketboat off our port bow, Sir," the Second Officer reported. "Shall I hail her?"

"Yep," Tyler grunted. "Might as well find out what we're up against."

"Blockade's broken!" the picketboat's officer called back gaily. Cap'n Hollins' fleet gone'n chased the Yankees clean back to Washington! You can break out in daylight if you want to!"

"Hear that, Captain?" the Second Officer said. "We're in luck! That Hollins is a corker!"

"Wait a minute," Tyler said slowly. "There's something a mite off here. Know how many ships Hollins commanded?"

"Let me see," Clayton said. "There's the *McRae*, and her engines are damned near bad as ours, the *Ivy*, the *Tuscarora*, the *Calhoun*, the *Jackson*, and the ram, *Manassas*. Six, sir. . . ."

"All of 'em light craft," Tyler said, "except the *Ma-*

nassas. All of them put together mounting fewer guns than one Union cruiser of the *Brooklyn* class. And we know for a positive fact that both the *Brooklyn* and the *Richmond* are down there. The *Richmond* mounts twenty two nine-inch guns, Lieutenant. By herself she would have been more than a match for Hollins' squadron."

"You think they're—lying, sir?" Reed Clayton whispered.

"Exaggerating. There's been a scrap all right. Maybe the *Manassas* did a right smart bit of damage—and the Yanks withdrew. But not very far, Reed, and not for very long."

"You, Cap'n," Reed said ruefully," have more damn respect for the Yankees than any man I ever saw. . . ."

"Know 'em, son. Those boys down there are the grandsons of the men who damn near whipped the British Navy in 1812 with nothing. They come from families who have been seafaring folks since before America became a nation—more than an hundred years before in fact; and beyond that from men who had salt in their veins for a good thousand years on the other side of the pond. We'll give them a good fight on land, because we are a race of hunters, crackshots, and above all horsemen—our cavalry is already the world's best, bar none —but at sea, we're plumb, downright out of luck, son. . . ."

He did not notice, in speaking to his young Executive Officer, how easily he had fallen into the traditional paternalistic attitude of seafaring men. In fact, he was less than five years older than Reed Clayton; but already he was addressing him as "son." Reed neither noticed nor minded. It was, as far as he and the rest of the crew were concerned, a perfectly natural thing. In three more days they would be referring to Tyler affectionately as "The Old Man," and grumbling good naturedly at his orders.

In the middle of the day, they passed Hollins' little squadron, steaming upriver toward New Orleans. Tyler ordered his signalman aloft to wigwag the message: "Congratulations on your victory! Signed, Meredith."

Captain Hollins' message flickered back, spelled out by the bright signal flags:

"Head of passes free. Yankees still at the mouth. Take care. Hollins."

They came, after fifteen hours' hard steaming, to the head of the passes, the spot where the Mississippi broadens into a bay two miles wide, and the various passes reach out to the Gulf through the spongy morass of the lower delta like the fingers of a hand.

Tyler had the *Pelican* anchored there, and descended with the Second Officer to the chart room. The navigator was a brisk, bespectacled young man with imposing sidewhiskers of the type that Major General Ambrose Burnside of the Union Army was later to give his name, reversed, of course, into sideburns. As yet, they had no name, but on a young man under thirty, and being fiery red, they were a sight to see, proving a source of endless amusement to the *Pelican*'s entire crew. To make it worse, the navigator's name was Hartley Fry. It took the irreverent junior officers and crew less than a day to transform that into "Hardly Fried;" and from that to "Half Baked" and other variations.

"Fry," Tyler said, without ceremony, "could we get past Ship Island before daybreak?"

Both of the young officers stared at him.

"Ship Island, Sir?" Fry whispered.

"Yes," Tyler drawled. "Could we?"

"No, Sir," Fry said briskly. "Not even if we ran out at full speed, which our boilers, begging your pardon, Sir, couldn't take. We'd be directly abeam of the island in full daylight, Sir, from here. At half speed, we still wouldn't even have raised it before the sun rose . . ."

"But Ship Island, Sir!" Clayton gasped.

"Exactly, son," Tyler said. "Where the Union blockaders are based. The last point on the compass they'd expect us to head for, especially not inshore between the island and the coast of Mississippi. . . ."

"Inshore!" Reed exploded. "Lord God, Sir—that's suicide!"

"I can make this a direct order, Lieutenant," Tyler said. "But for the last time on this voyage I'm going to explain a decision to you. After this, you'll just have to take me on faith. Look here—" he pointed to the chart; "stands to reason that the Yankees are fanned out around the mouths of the passes, seeing as how Hollins chased them back to the sea. If he hadn't done that, nothing could have gotten through here. Now which pass, if you were a Yankee Commander, would you guard the least, or even leave unguarded?"

"This one, Sir!" Fry said eagerly, pointing to the pass that led directly toward the east, straight toward Ship Island. "Only a damned fool would—" He stopped suddenly his face as red as his whiskers.

"Right," Tyler said calmly; "only a damned fool would sail directly for the enemy's base. So we're going to be damned fools, triple distilled. Nothing on earth throws a man off more than the unlikely, the least expected. We weigh anchor late tomorrow evening, Gentlemen, and go by Ship Island before dawn, day after tomorrow. Pray God there's a mist; because even in the lightest fog, the *Pelican* can't be seen at cableslength."

It was a thing to remember. They broke out of the pass while there was still light enough to see by. Half a mile out into the Gulf, the lookout's voice rang out:

"Yankee Cruiser off the sta'board bow!"

Tyler lifted his long brass telescope. The cruiser leaped into view. Her crew were loafing about the deck. The rigging was decorated with their washing.

"They don't see us," he said. "Keep on the same course, Lieutenant. . . ."

"Lord God, Sir!" Reed said nervously. "They must be blind! I can see them just as plain. . . ."

"Our color, son. We sort of blend in with the sea and the sky. Glad of this chance to test it. Seems to be just about right. . . ."

Reed looked at his Captain admiringly.

"Captain," he said, "don't you ever get a little bit scared?"

"Son," Tyler said solemnly, "I'm so scared right now that my stomach's doing the St. Vitus dance. But I learned a long time ago not to give way to it. That's the principle thing. But I'll give you a word of advice, Lieutenant: If you ever draw a birth aboard a ship whose

Captain hasn't got gumption enough to get scared—resign. I've met quite a few men in my time who were absolutely fearless, and they all had one thing in common: they didn't have a damned thing between their ears except solid bone. . . ."

"We're dropping her astern, Captain!" Reed said.

"Good," Tyler grunted, watching the dim shoreline to the North crawling almost imperceptibly backward, half lost in the evening mist.

"It's getting dark," Reed sighed. "Lord, Captain, I don't reckon I've ever been so glad to see night fall. . . ."

"Me neither," Tyler said. "Go below, Lieutenant, and get some rest. I'll take this watch. . . ."

"Aye, aye, Sir," Reed Clayton said.

Four o'clock in the morning, they raised Ship Island. They crept up the channel between it and the Mississippi shore. The reasoning upon which Tyler based this apparently insane choice of course was actually quite sound: Blockade runners, once they had broken out of the inlets, stood for the open sea, intent upon losing their pursuers in the vast waste of water. He was sure that the Federals had a twenty-four hour lookout on the seaward side of the island, scanning the horizon for a plume of smoke or a sail. But on the channel-facing side, the watch was apt to be sporadic, if not non existent. The Union Navy had nothing to fear from that side, and they knew it. Even a raid of small boats, stealing in to do as much damage as they could, then beating for cover was scarcely possible. The Mississippi shore opposite the island was naked. The long range Navy guns could smash such an attempt in the launching. Even a night

raid had so little chance for success as to be not worth
consideration by Confederate Commanders straining
every nerve to transform river packets, ancient derelict
hulks, towboats, anything and everything that floated,
into a fleet. Their terrible scarcity of materials would
make them take many a long thought before risking
what they had for so little and so uncertain gain.

Tyler, with his cynical conception of human nature,
was gambling that the sentries, if any, posted on the
Mississippi side of the island, would have long since
fallen into the habit, from sheer boredom and inactivity,
of sleeping their watches through.

Still, it was a gamble. He knew it, and so did the crew.
Not a man aboard the *Pelican* slept. The off watches
crowded the decks, staring at the low bulk of the island,
black against the night sky. No one talked. The thumping of the walking beams, and the paddle splash were
louder than thunder, loud as the trump of doom. They
were, all of them to face pursuit, to see the Yankee shells
raise white geysers all around them, to watch the pro-
jectiles from the long range rifled Parrots smash their
decks to kindling; but never again were they to experience anything like the icy terror of that night when
they crept safely through the channel, through the whole
blockading fleet, without anything happening at all.

By daylight, they were standing out to sea, with a
brisk breeze three quarters astern. Tyler ordered the
engines stopped, the paddle wheels retracted, and every
inch of canvas cracked on. Under that cloud of sail, the
Pelican logged seven full knots, two knots faster than
she could steam. They headed southward toward Ha-

vana, under the British flag; for Tyler had taken the precaution of having the *Pelican* registered at Liverpool by
his English cousins.

Strange, he mused, the little things that decide a man's
fate. Life was hard in Ireland, so the Captain, rest his
soul, and my Uncle Tim decided, all of a sudden over a
bottle of Irish whiskey in a Dublin pub, to go to England
to better their chances. Started a mercantile business on
nothing, half starved for years. And, being Irish, naturally
they had to quarrel. Captain Pat took ship on the first
craft available for the States. But what do you call the
fact that the Clipper *Mary Ann* was bound not for New
York, where he wanted to go, but for New Orleans,
which he hardly knew existed? Chance, fate, the sure
Hand of God? A man's life is based on things like that.
If the Captain had ever got to New York, I'd be a
Yankee, probably an officer by now, aboard a cruiser of
the blockading fleet. . . .

Instead, I'm a Southerner bred and born; and my
cousins are more English than Yorkshire pudding. Took
me three weeks the first time I was in London to understand them when they talked. Sounded like a foreign
language. Don't reckon they quite understand me all the
time, yet. Funny, but the Captain and Uncle Tim both
prospered after they split up. Good thing, too. I'm going
to need their help when I get to England, financially and
otherwise. Wonder if Cedric's got an extra among all
those music hall actresses and dancers he's always got in
tow? Don't know how long it'll take to get new engines
and boilers fitted; but I don't aim to have me a dull
life. . . .

They made Havana without difficulty. But a brief

check at the purchasing offices revealed that the price of cotton had risen not at all. Tyler had very little intention of selling his cargo in Cuba anyway, being sure that he could get much more for it at Nassau in the Bahamas, or in England itself. After four days—most of which were spent in rounding up the crew, given liberty for the first time in a Latin port, out of the saloons, jails, and whorehouses of Havana—they sailed for Nassau, changing course completely so as to give the Yankee captains of the blockading fleet standing outside of the three mile limit the impression that they were inward bound from England. The Northern captains were not above stopping a British vessel sailing on a course to or from the Confederacy, flag or no flag; but they let those inbound from England alone, until after they sailed again from Nassau. Then, if their headings indicated a Southern port, they gave chase, sure that the English craft were loaded to the gunwales with arms and ammunition for the Rebs, as they usually were. It was all very slipshod. Chasing one craft, they left the harbors wide open for dozens of others. More, in the fall of 1861, the North did not have enough vessels to adequately patrol even half the major harbors of the Confederacy, not to mention three thousand miles of coast, and the islands of the Antilles. Blockade running was a game, and was to remain one until late 1862. But, by the spring of sixty-three, if still a game, it was one of the most dangerous sports ever invented by man.

At Nassau, the other blockade runners gasped at the *Pelican's* lofty rigging and clouds of sail. Tyler was repeatedly advised to cut the masts down to just above the lowest yardarms, and use them only as lookout sta-

tions. More, he was shown the new method of rigging
the boats on a level with or just below the gunwales,
thus eliminating another eye catching detail. The *Pelican's* color was approved of, but some of the English
craft had adopted an even lighter shade of grey, which,
Tyler saw, was even harder to see, so he had her re-
painted while in port. But he left his rigging standing in
the melancholy certainty that the *Pelican's* engines and
boilers would never survive an ocean voyage.

The pinch of short supply of cotton was only barely
beginning to be felt. Prices had risen very little. But,
everyone assured him, by the spring of 1862, he would
be able to name his own price for a bale.

He stood out for sea, headed for England. The Yankee
cruisers trailed him for miles but did not open fire. That
early in the struggle, they had not commenced their
fixed policy of stopping every vessel of whatever registry
that crossed their path. In November, 1861, they were
still making some pretense of observing international
maritime law.

Twenty seven days later, the *Pelican* slid into a berth
at Liverpool. There was intense excitement at her arrival, for Tyler boldly broke out the Confederate flag.
Cotton brokers flocked aboard, intent upon snapping up
her cargo. Despite the fact that there was, as yet, no
actual shortage of the fiber, they bid against one another,
sending the prices high enough, because of their antici-
patory fears for next Spring, to make the voyage a
financial success exceeding all Tyler's expectations.

The cargo sold, Tyler set out for London, leaving
Reed Clayton in charge of the arrangements for putting

her in drydock, buying new engines and boilers, cutting
down the masts until she became a pure steamer, and
many other small details.

Cedric and Vivian met him at the station. Despite the
fact that they were blond while he was dark, anyone
with half an eye could see the relationship. They all had
the rough hewn Meredith bone structure.

"Uncle Tim's well, I hope?" Tyler said. "I've got
to see him. This blockade running is going to be big! If
all of us were to organize a company—"

"Already organized, old boy, "Cedric grinned; "Devil
of a fine craft is being laid down next month, fastest
bloody steamer you ever did see. Long and narrow,
shaped like a knife blade—You're to command her, of
course. . . ."

"Great!" Tyler exulted. "Where are the plans? I
must—"

"Pity he's so dueced American, isn't it?" Cedric sighed.

"Rather," Vivian said. "But perhaps we can civilize
him, given time. . . ."

"Oh, for heaven's sake," Tyler began, but a certain
gleam in Cedric's eye stopped him.

"Thought you'd be a bit sick of business and that
sort of rot," Cedric drawled. "There's a little dancer I
happen to know . . . Seems to me, the shipping business
could afford to wait a day or two. . . ."

Tyler looked from one of them to the other. A slow
grin lighted his eyes.

"It can," he chuckled. You're dadblamed right—it
can!"

CHAPTER FIVE

Tyler came awake in the ghostly light of morning. He lay there, watching the London fog blow in the open window, rolling into the room in clouds of dirty grey. He was glad he wouldn't have to sail to England any more. This was his second trip across, though, since Reed Clayton's driving energy had made the refitting of the *Pelican* with new engines and stout boilers possible during their stay in England on the original trip in November, it had been a much better and faster voyage than the first. Poor Reed. He didn't like to think about that . . .

Still, braving the Atlantic was no fun, especially in winter. He had spent half the voyage below, inspecting the patches that Chief Engineer Hargraves had installed to plug the shell holes the Yankee cruiser had punched in her hull the night Reed Clayton died. Of course, they had held; and lightly loaded as they were, most of the cargo heaved over the side to outfoot that persistent Yankee, they had made the trip handily, arriving about the middle of January, 1862. But he wouldn't have to cross the Atlantic again. Cedric and Vivian had already dispatched two large, slow cargo vessels to Nassau. From now on, the *Pelican* would ply only between Wilmington and the Bahamas.

He tried to lift his head, but he could not. There was a legion of tiny fiends, equipped with sledge hammers, crow bars, and steam drills, at work inside his skull. He put both hands on the top of his head, holding down hard to keep it from coming off, reflecting that Cedric, at the dinner party at his diggings, must have served as the *piece de resistance* old calvary boots. Made of the hides of long deceased polecats at that, he added.

He didn't remember the details of the party at all. There had been a number of exceedingly pretty minor actresses and music hall performers there; but their faces were a blur to him, now. He wasn't interested in trying to remember them. There was something else he should remember, something hellishly important—

He lay there, competing with the imps, cudgeling his brain for the memory. Today was—the last day of January 1862. That was important; because tomorrow was the first of February and—

Good God! He leaped from the bed and swayed upright, the fog swirling coldly about his naked body. The first of February! The *Pelican* sailed tomorrow, and here he was in London instead of in Liverpool where he belonged!

He stooped, picking up his scattered garments, keeping one hand cautiously atop his head to guard against the very real possibility that the top of it would come off. He straightened up with great care, and dropped them one by one on the foot of the bed. As he did so, he noticed that something was amiss. The last garment he held in his hand was—feather light, silken, lace trimmed.

He stood there, staring at it with owlish solemnity, then inch by painful inch, lowered his eyes to the opposite side of the bed. A cloud of bright red hair was spread out on the pillow. The face under the hair was indisputably pretty; that is, it must have been pretty the night before. It was one of Tyler's hardest held beliefs, based upon much experience, that no woman on earth is pretty before eleven o'clock in the morning. This one lay on her back, and her mouth had fallen open. She snored, gently. He could see, a detail which surely had escaped him the night before, that her teeth were irregular and far from white. Moreover, she was plump to the point of being ample, and Tyler preferred women almost as thin as he was himself. "Ever see a fat filly win a race?" he always demanded of his friends who insisted upon a more generous endowment of feminine charms.

He wondered idly what her name was; but gave it up as being an item of no importance. What was important now, was to get the hell out of his lodgings without awakening her. He began dressing with elaborate caution; but in the middle of his preparations, he kicked over a footstool with a crash like thunder. The girl snored on. A twenty-one gun salute would not have awakened her.

Thereafter, he made better speed. After he was shaved —a feat he accomplished not without the shedding of a considerable amount of blood—and dressed, he pinned a ten pound note to her pillow. That, he reflected, should take care of a hansom cab to her home, and whatever damages she might have sustained in the course of the evening. If there were any damages. He didn't know. He didn't remember a blessed, living thing about it.

On the train, going down to Liverpool, he was conscious of a feeling of depression. He couldn't understand that. The headache was gone, having succumbed to a pot of black coffee and a reasonably hearty breakfast. He felt tired; that was all. And he had escaped unscathed from his brief, unremembered encounter.

Still it was a fool trick, he told himself angrily. Fat, simpering filly, whose name you don't even know and—

And the whole thing was so blamed meaningless. That's it. A thing's got to have some meaning. Strange. I've outgrown myself, I reckon. Can't accept useless things any more. Or enjoy them either. Not even the animal coupling in the dark of two bodies empty of tenderness, or joy, or love. I've gone beyond that. Damned if I haven't crossed the line. . . .

He had. He couldn't figure exactly when he had gone over the hump, plunged over the invisible dividing line; but sometime during this last voyage he had crossed it, one of the days he had crept the *Pelican* southward from Wilmington, North Carolina, her rigging shot away, one engine out, six full days of constant manning the bilge and donkey pumps; the night, perhaps, he had read his first service over the *Pelican*'s dead, and watched their canvas-shrouded bodies splash over the side, and sink, weighted, into the sea's everlasting darkness. But he had crossed it. That was sure.

Perhaps it had been the night young Reed Clayton died, his belly ripped open by a shell splinter, walking toward Tyler, holding his entrails in with his two hands, saying, very quietly, as Tyler eased him gently to the deck: "I'm afraid I'm done, Sir. . . ."

Perhaps then. Almost surely then.

In Africa, he thought wryly, a boy must kill his lion, stand with glowing coals pressed under his armpits without yelping before they'll accept him as a man. Reckon we're a mite less obvious—that's all. . . .

Coming up the street to the wharf where the *Pelican* lay, he thought of one more thing; not even a very important thing really; but just the last tiny drop to make his cup of bitterness run over:

"Do the best you can, Old Boy," Cedric had said. "There's been a bit of grumbling among some of the stockholders over the loss of the last cargo. Nothing to worry about, of course. City blokes. Hinting that you might have shown more daring. Rot, coming from them. They'd get seasick at the sight of water. Viv and I will put a hawser on them; but get the next lot through, won't you—so we'll have a talking point?"

Damn them, Tyler thought angrily. Damn 'em all to hell!

A crewman, scrubbing down the *Pelican*'s deck as he came aboard, turned to another.

"What's happened to the old man?" he whispered. "He sure Lord looks like hell!"

The *Pelican*, creeping through the fog-shrouded channel, sounding her whistle at one minute intervals to avoid collision, a danger to which the very effectiveness of her camouflage rendered her particularly liable, was scarcely recognizable as the vessel that had sailed down the river from New Orleans in October of Sixty one. Equipped with new and reliable engines, and boilers whose plates were even thicker than her old ones had originally been, she no longer sported lofty masts and clouds of canvas. Her poles, bare except for one yardarm and a crowsnest each, were only a little taller than her smokestack. She was a steamer now, pure and simple; for, although Tyler out of caution had retained a couple of flying jibs and the mainsails, for her yards, even he scarcely anticipated using them. Bereft of the towering rigging, she could not be seen at cable's length on a dark and foggy night. . . .

There were, of course, drawbacks; the new engines were the same make and horsepower as the old—her speed, now a full seven knots, owed its increase only to the fact that the new boilers could maintain the pressure to drive her full speed ahead without danger. And seven knots, against Yankee cruisers that could steam seventeen fully loaded, was pitiful.

One improvement had been added which promised to be a real lifesaver. Her forward deck had been covered with a rounded turtleback so that when she ploughed into the mountainous waves of the Atlantic, she shed water like a duck instead of shipping it by the ton as she had done on her previous voyages. She was a sound and seaworthy craft, and would serve as well as possible while the *Captain Pat*, as it had been decided to name the new craft, the first true blockade runner of Meredith and Associates, Limited, of London, Nas-

sau, and Wilmington, was being built. The new vessel,
twice as long as the *Pelican* and half again as narrow,
would be driven by engines having four times the horsepower. She, too, would be a sidewheeler, as getting
screw propellers the size and weight that she would
require was still a difficult matter in 1862.

By now, having profited by the mistakes and experi-
ences that he, himself, had had, as well as those of other
blockade runners to whom he had talked, Tyler had
been able to organize the affairs of Meredith and Associates in a much more practical fashion. Accordingly,
two large and sea-worthy vessels had been dispatched to
Nassau and awaited him there. These would make the
run between Nassau and England, enabling the *Pelican*
to confine her activities to plying between Nassau and
Wilmington. The firm was already building a warehouse
at Nassau; Tyler's cargoes would be stored there until
they could be transhipped.

The system had its advantages: It would keep the
Pelican constantly at sea, since the six hundred forty
miles distance to Wilmington could be covered in a
matter of days; by eliminating the necessity of sailing
the *Pelican* across the ocean each trip, and keeping the
two great vessels constantly at that task, the amount of
cotton run into England could be enormously increased,
not to mention the profits, amounting to more than one
hundred thousand dollars in gold per voyage, both
from the sale of the fiber in England, and from the de-
livery to the Confederacy of the supplies for which the
new born nation was already in desperate need.

But, from Tyler's personal point of view, his own

system had one major, agonizing drawback: his chances
of seeing New Orleans again, perhaps even for the duration, were exactly nil. His own honesty had brought
this about: when the question had been raised of running
the *Pelican* into his native city, he had been forced to
admit that the chances of success were just about non-
existent. The Union Navy again had a fleet not only
at the mouths, but at the head of the passes; not one
major cotton factory was in operation in the city, due
to the utter impossibility of shipping the bales out. Every
other mercantile establishment in the city was already
closed and shuttered. Tea and coffee were quite literally
worth their weight in gold; medicines had all but disappeared; the loss of life through sickness was appalling.
Pins and needles were actually priceless; a house would
be turned upside down from top to bottom if one happened to be lost. Silks, perfumes, laces, fine-toothed
combs, soap, had all vanished. Since, in the entire Confederacy, there was only one saline deposit of any
consequence, that of Saltville in southeast Virginia, salt
had been the first commodity to become a thing of the
past. In all these deprivations, New Orleans set the
pattern that the rest of the South was to follow; for that
city suffered the melancholy distinction of being the
first and only port where the blockade was one hundred
percent effective; geography betrayed her; a river, even
the mighty Mississippi, was much easier to block than
a bay.

Tyler had all this information in letters from both
Ruth and Sue. Mail continued to get through, overland
to Galveston or Mobile, then out by blockade runner.

He described these sad details to his cousins, his uncle, and the other Englishmen who had invested in the venture; suppressing only the one that Ruth had written, which seemed to him the epitome of the tragic comedy of man's fate: the highborn New Orleans lady, a friend of the Drake's, who sat weeping in their parlor, because the last fine tooth comb in her household having succumbed to hard usage, and soap being impossible to procure, she had discovered only that morning that her children had lice in their fine, blonde hair. . . .

His honesty defeated him. Since other men had invested considerable portions of their fortunes in Meredith and Associates, he could not suppress the facts he had learned from other blockade runners: that Galveston and Mobile, both of which would have permitted him a flying trip to New Orleans between sailings, were all but useless from a commercial standpoint. Heavily blockaded from the sea, and able to draw but scant supplies of cotton from the interior, these ports were already doing less than one tenth of the business done at Charleston and Wilmington. Wilmington, then, it must be. . . .

Hundreds of miles from Sue. He did not add, as he might have earlier, from Ruth, from Lauriel. He did not think of them at all. That too, was a measure of the distance he had travelled; he was no longer prepared to accept substitutes, no matter how lovely or fine.

Now, crawling out of the Channel into the fog-shrouded waste of the Atlantic, he was moved to the wry reflection that God, or fate, or something was taking damned good care of George Drake. George,

mild, gentle George had been cited several times for
bravery; while several of the fire-eaters, notably Titus
Claiborne, had been cashiered for cowardice, and were
back in New Orleans, singularly chastened and silent.
George, men said, bore a charmed life. And damn me
for a sinner, Tyler added, if the charm doesn't extend
to the protection of his wife's virtue. Better like that, I
reckon. I've changed; but damned if I've changed that
much. . . .

The *Pelican*, being one of the stoutest vessels afloat,
rode out a whole series of gales on her way across. She
slid into her birth as Nassau thirty-one days later, without even having seen a Yankee cruiser. Tyler checked
her cargo for damage. Above and beyond the arms and
ammunition he was obliged to bring in, every available
inch of cargo space was crammed with silks and laces,
French perfumes, pins, needles, and every other kind of
luxury goods designed to catch the feminine eye. He
had brought no salt, because it was heavy and bulky,
and no medicines because the profit on them was slight.
The goods he had brought beyond the war materials
could by no stretch of the imagination be considered
of any service to the Confederacy. On the contrary,
since by March, 1862, the Confederate currency was
already suffering from the disastrous results of inflation,
and Tyler had no intention of accepting anything but
gold, he and the other blockade runners were contrib-
uting to the wreckage of the country's economy by
taking specie needed to purchase the sinews of war in
payment for feminine fripperies.

Nothing had been damaged. He noted the items on

the list the Supercargo had given him. Going back to his cabin, he caught sight of his face in the mirror.

"You bastard," he whispered. "You goddamned miserable bastard!"

He went ashore, moving past the mountains of cotton bales that covered the wharves, into the swarms of blockade runners, cotton factors, shipping agents, Confederate deserters, Northern spies, gamblers, pickpockets and occasional whores that filled the streets of what, two years ago had been a quiet island town, asleep with the lethargy of centuries. Half an hour later, he was drunk.

He stood out from Nassau the morning of March Fourth, suffering from a fiendish headache and in an absolutely vile state of temper. The crew, of course, suffered from this; but by now they were quite accustomed to the 'Old Man's inexplicable alternations of mood. It made little difference in any case; he had learned his trade by now. Headache or not he crossed the Gulf Stream exactly at two o'clock in the afternoon, so that Fry could establish the *Pelican's* position by chronometer, escaping the adverse influence of the Gulf Stream's current upon his dead reckoning. They crawled along, taking soundings every hour, which checked against the depth readings on the charts, enabled the navigator to keep well inshore without danger. At nightfall, the flaring fires of the saltworks on the shore served the same purpose; morning found them off the Florida coast.

Seven days later, they were still a long distance from Wilmington, and ploughing into the teeth of the damnedest gale it had ever been Tyler's hard luck to witness. As a result, instead of running through the blockading fleet at night, they sighted the tall masts of the blockade's flagship in the full light of dawn. Tyler hove to, and called a conference of the officers. Collins, the new Second or Executive officer, who had replaced Reed Clayton, stood up and said frankly:

"Cap'n, I'm scared. My vote is to put back to Nassau and try it again some other time. . . ."

Tyler looked at Chief Engineer Hargraves.

"Well, chief?" he said.

"Nope," Hargraves drawled. "We might have a sight more coal in the bunkers than it would take to run her in at full speed through those Yankees. But as for going elsewheres, begging the Lieutenant's pardon, we couldn't even get to Charleston."

"Reckon that settles it," Tyler said. "Collins, detail some hands to see that everything is battened down and secure. Hargraves, how long do you think the boilers would take it, if we tied down the safety valves?"

"Damned if I know, Sir," Hargraves said coolly. "But as for me, don't appear to make much difference if the boilers blow, or one of them cruisers puts a thirty-two pounder in amongst all that gunpowder we got stored aft. Tie 'em down and be damned, I'd say."

"Good," Tyler grinned. "One more thing, gentlemen: I'll put a longboat at the disposal of anybody who thinks the risks are too great. A Yankee jail has got one advantage over hell—it's only temporary. And I'll freely state right now that I'm not casting any shame on a man who'll accept the offer. . . ."

Collins reddened to the ears.

"I'll stick with my ship, Sir," he said.

"Good, son," Tyler said. "All right, gentlemen, let's ride her in. . . ."

They moved in, straight for a gap in the line of blockaders. In the middle of it, the broadsides of two frigates stared them in the face from a distance of two hundred yards. Afterwards, Tyler decided that it was this that had saved them; neither vessel dared fire for fear of hitting the other. But once the *Pelican* was safely ahead, they opened up with the Parrott bowchasers; white geysers as thick as doric columns stood up all around the *Pelican*.

"Shall I bring her in on alternate tacks, Sir?" the helmsman said; "Might throw their aim off. . . ."

"Hell, no!" Tyler said. "Cut our speed like that and they've got us. Hold her to the line, son!"

He heard the sickening crack as the foremast went. Looking aft, he could see that both stacks were pouring smoke through an hundred shrapnel holes. Then she heeled wildly, the deck shuddering under their feet, as a shell from a rifled Parrott slammed into the forward hold at the water line.

Tyler picked up the speaking tube.

"Man your pumps, Hargraves," he said. His voice, speaking, was very quiet, almost serene.

No one had time to pay out a logline. If they had, they would have been astonished. The *Pelican* was making ten knots, despite her wounds. Behind them, a swarm of fast cruisers were broiling up, light, handy craft, capable of nearly double the frigate's speed.

"Collins," Tyler said solemnly, "You know how to pray?"

"Cap'n," Collins said, "If I didn't, I'd sure learn mighty damn fast!"

Tyler could see the Second Officer's lips moving in silent prayer. Might help, he thought, and it damned sure can't do any harm. . . .

He heard then, the whining whistle of shells passing overhead; and looking back, he saw the white geysers rising close to the bows of the foremost frigate. A second later, her tall foremast splintered off just above the lowest yardarm. She lost seaway, while swarms of Yankee sailors ran up with axes to cut the mast and cordage free. He turned forward, seeing incredulously the smoke rising from the forty-pounders of Fort Fisher on the headland. Another salvo passed overhead, shrieking like a thousand derailed express trains. The shell bursts straddled the second frigate neatly; she fell back, and they were under the fort's guns, and free. The cruisers didn't dare come in. One hit from Colonel Lamb's heavy Whitworths could blast any one of them clear out of the water.

"Collins," Tyler grinned, "I don't know what you told the Lord, but it sure was effective."

"Sir," Collins groaned, "I promised Him if He'd bring us in alive, I'd give up whiskey and women for the next four trips. It's going to most kill me, Sir; but damned if I'm not going to keep my word!"

They moved into quarantine station, where the bustling little medical officer came aboard. There had been some Yellow Jack at Nassau; but apparently no one had been ashore long enough to catch it. The doctor pronounced himself satisfied and they crept up to the dock.

As the goods were being swung ashore, Tyler noticed a tall, enormously fat man standing there, watching every move through a pair of square-cut steel rimmed glasses.

"Son," he said to Collins, "reckon you better go find out what that Dutchman's up to. Report back to me. I don't like the cut of his jib. If he doesn't have a reasonable explanation for being where he is, we'd better send him packing. . . ."

"Have we the right to do that, Sir?" Collins asked.

"Hell, no. But we can ask him mighty politely to leave. If he doesn't, a note to Colonel Lamb will bring a couple of guards down on his neck in one hell of a hurry."

"Aye, aye, Sir," Collins said.

In ten minutes, the Second Officer was back.

"Says he's a cargo broker, Sir. Offered me one hundred thousand dollars for the lot of the speculation goods," Collins said.

"Paid damned near that much for 'em," Tyler said. "Reckon I'll have a word with this party, myself . . . Of course, it's really the Supercargo's business; but I've got a lot of my own money tied up in those goods. . . ."

He went down the gangway with no apparent haste.

"I'm Captain Meredith," he said. "What was that offer you made for the 'spec' cargo?"

"One hundert tousand!" the fat man beamed. "Fine offer, *nicht wahr?*"

"Reckon I'm getting a mite deaf," Tyler drawled. "Didn't catch your name, Sir—"

"Mister Zinnlouf, at your service," the fat man grinned. "As I wast saying—one hundert tousand, das ist goot, yes?"

"Still deaf," Tyler said. "But before you go on, Mister Zinnlouf, I better tell you I've been running stuff into Wilmington since last fall. . . ."

"Ach, so?" Zinnlouf said. "In that case, one hundert fifty—"

"Never could hear figures under five," Tyler said mildly.

"Five hundert tousand?" Zinnlouf roared. "You crazy, Kapitan?"

"Nope—just a mite deaf. But not blind. Know exactly where the auction sales room is. You want me to show it to you?"

"Ach, Gott!" the German said; "but you Kapitans get worser every trip! Two hundert tousand?"

"I," Tyler said, "prefer to do business through the usual channels, Zinnlouf. But thanks, anyhow, for giving me an idea of what current prices are. Goodday, Sir. . . ."

"Goot day!" the fat man spat, and stomped off the dock.

"That was quick, Sir," Collins said, when Tyler was back aboard. "No sale, eh?"

"Nope, son," Tyler said; "but I'm rightly grateful to that Dutchman. He went to two hundred thousand. Means we'll get five with ease at the auction. How's Hargraves coming with the repairs?"

"Got a temporary patch in, Sir, but he says we'll have

to partially beach her for him to put in anything that'll stand a sea. He's waiting for us to unload; when she's light enough, he wants you to run her on in. . . ."

"That means a few days in Wilmington, then," Tyler said. "Well, son, there are worse ports. . . ."

"And I gave the Good Lord my word," Collins groaned.

"I didn't," Tyler grinned. "Reckon I'll make you official prayer for the ship, Collins; sure will take a heap off my shoulders. . . ."

"Cap'n, Sir," Collins said. "That's plumb, downright unfair!"

"Yep, it is," Tyler said. "But then, what isn't in this world?"

The next day, after the *Pelican* had been beached to repair the hole the frigate's shell had torn through her hull, Tyler and Collins attended the auction of the speculation goods. Tyler, though his salary as Captain was five thousand dollars a month, had the added advantage of being a stockholder in the firm. He had not only chosen the goods, depending upon his cynical knowledge of the workings of the feminine mind, but had invested heavily in them. How well he had chosen was proven almost from the instant the auction opened.

A big man, who weighed, Tyler estimated, two hundred forty pounds, climbed upon a chair. It creaked dangerously under his weight. He had a stub of a cigar stuck in the corner of his mouth. It was unlit, and throughout the entire auction, he did not remove it.

"Cargo of Meredith Associates Limited!" he bawled. "Now on sale! You gentlemen know the rules—no shin-

plasters accepted. Sales are cash—in gold. First I'll entertain bids by lots; if there are no takers, by items. Now,
gentlemen, what am I offered for all the silk?"

His assistant, a tiny man with a long white beard,
wearing a skullcap made up of Confederate banners,
held up the shimmering cloth. The brokers went wild.
They were, Tyler saw, nearly all central Europeans,
and the English spoken by some of them was completely
incomprehensible.

The bids came in, silently. A waved handkerchief, a
nod sufficed as the auctioneer cried out the prices. Collins, who had never seen a cargo auction in a Southern
port, was speechless with astonishment. Tyler was more
than a little surprised himself, though he concealed it,
well. Things must be getting mighty bad, he thought.

In a shade under one hour, the *Pelican*'s entire speculation cargo, that is the privately owned goods over and
beyond the arms consigned to the Government, was sold.
And goods for which Meredith's purchasing agents had
paid about ninety seven thousand dollars in London and
Paris, were sold in that space of time for a shade under
six hundred thousand—in gold. Tyler made some rapid
mental calculations: the *Pelican* if she were sunk tomorrow, had already brought him and the other partners
one hundred fifty per cent clear profit on their original
investment, including the money he had spent on her
purchase and outfitting.

"Well, son," he said to Collins, "reckon I'll be moseying along. You armed, boy?"

"Why, no, Sir," Collins said; "I didn't think—"

"Wilmington," Tyler said, "is one of the roughest

damn ports on earth today. A man's life isn't worth a picayune after dark. These thugs will do you in for a nickel-plated pocket watch. Here, son, take this—it ain't much, but it'll serve. . . ."

He gave the young officer a double-barrelled Derringer, bored for forty-four caliber slugs, and a pouch containing balls, paper cartridges and percussion caps.

"Hit what you aim at, boy," he growled. "You won't get a chance to reload. . . ."

"What about you, Sir?" Collins whispered.

Tyler opened his coat. Beneath his armpit nestled a Colt revolver, its barrel sawed off to a mere stub.

"Won't hit the side of a barn at any distance," he said; "but, then, if you have to use one of these things, distance sure Lord ain't what you've got . . . Be seeing you, son. . . ."

Whatever else might have been in short supply in Wilmington, whiskey certainly wasn't. But after two drinks, Tyler found, unaccountably, that his craving for it was gone. Good thing, he thought. Tomorrow, maybe, I'll feel like a human being. . . .

As he turned to leave the bar, he felt two soft hands gripping his arm. Even before he looked at her, the cloud of cheap perfume enveloped his head.

"Dearie," the coarse, whiskey sodden voice, said.

She was absurdly young, not yet twenty, and decidedly pretty, under the rice powder and the paint. Tyler's eyes lit up; then, suddenly, they clouded, and he was seeing not the pitiful, ravished face of this desolate child; but that of the girl in London, mouth agape, and snoring, her hair spread out like a coppery cloud against his pillow's muted white.

He put up his hand to break her grip.

"Sorry," he began, but she interrupted him.

"Lord, God, Cap'n," she whispered huskily, "don't turn me down! I haven't turned a trick all night—and Tim'll beat the living hell out of me!"

Tyler pushed his hand into his pocket and came out with a twenty dollar gold piece.

"This fix things, honey?" he said.

"Lord Jesus!" the girl said, "You giving me this, Cap'n—for nothing?"

"Not for nothing," Tyler said. "In part payment for my sins, past, present, and future. Go on, take it. . . ."

The girl stared at the gold piece, and the tears gathered in her eyes, spilling over her lashes and ploughing two sticky furrows through the chalky mess on her face.

"You—you sure you want me to have it, Sir?" she said.

"Sure, Baby—if it'll earn you a good night's sleep, I'll be just as happy," Tyler said.

"You know how much that's worth in paper?" the girl said. "Four thousand, four hundred dollars—Confederate—enough to get me out of this town, back home to the hills where I came from. God bless you, Cap'n. . . ."

"Don't mention it," Tyler said and turned to go, but she clung to him still.

"Cap'n," she said; "one more favor. Walk me to the station, won't you? I'm scairt. Most in generally the officers is nice, but them sailor boys—that's why I ain't been able to make no money. They's so rough; and some of 'em is downright cruel. . . ."

Why not? Tyler thought. Since I'm not in the market for this particular brand of shoddy goods, no reason

why I shouldn't extend my new bent for sickly sentimentality a little further—

"Come on, Baby," he said kindly. "Let's mosey along."

He saw, as he neared the station, crowds of drunken
sailors, each with his painted doxy in tow. A young
officer had two, one on each arm. When he came closer,
he saw that the young officer was Lieutenant Collins,
his own Second in Command.

"Howya, Cap'n," Collins burbled. "Having fun, Sir?
Me, too—reckon you think I'm no good seeing as how
I promised"—His face screwed itself suddenly into a
caricature of seriousness. "S'pose the Good Lord'll forgive me? I meant well, but—"

"The flesh is weak," Tyler said dryly. "Of course He
will, Collins. I'll put in a good word for you. . . ."

"Thankee, Sir," Collins said drunkenly. "Goodnight,
Sir, and don't take no Confederate bills!"

Tyler left the girl sitting in an isolated corner of the
station and started for his lodgings. Fool, he cursed
himself, sentimental damned fool. She was pretty and—

I didn't want her. I've lost my taste for casual loves,
paid for or donated. Something's got to me, burrowed
under my hide. Reed's death, I reckon. Men die. What's
the odds if it's by taking a shell burst in the gut, or by
the weakness of old age? We're designed to be stinking
carrion, food for worms. Death's an irrelevancy, as
far as human behavior is concerned. Only—

He died so well. With dignity. With—with grace.
Good Lord! I'm using Joe's language! But what other
language is there to use? If man is an animal, nothing
more, everything we've done, everything we've built,

becomes a cheat, a snare, an illusion . . . And God damn it, he did die well! Food for the fish—all right; but he went out like a man. "For Thou hast made him but little lower than the Angels, and crowned him with glory and honor . . ." I'm drunk, I must be! I'm not and it's true; there are things that count. Like grace, and dignity, and honor, and pride. And love—that passeth understanding. And not a damned one of them can be bought with the dirty gold I sold Reed Clayton's life for . . . Funny. I bought a sight of happiness tonight by giving away a little of the money I've gone through hell for. Reckon the only things we keep finally, the only things we can take with us into the silence and the dark, are the things we give away. "For he who saves his life shall lose it, and he—"

Lord God, Lord God—let go of me—I'm not ready yet, I cannot stand—

He stumbled blindly through the darkness his eyes scalded by the rush of tears. He mounted the stairs to his room; but even then, lying in his bed, it was no good. Not even the night was refuge, nor the dark shelter; he lay, defenseless and alone, with no place to hide, feeling in his heart the slow closing grip of invisible, yet matchlessly tender hands. . . .

CHAPTER SIX

THERE WERE TOO MANY THINGS TO THINK ABOUT: Hargrave's voice flat, and absolutely without fear: "I've done the best I could, Cap'n, but them so called ship's carpenters ain't worth a damn. She'll ride out an ordinary blow; but if we run into weather anything like as dirty as the gale we met coming in, that patch ain't going to hold . . . Overhauled the donkey engine for the pumps just in case. It's in tip-top shape. We can stay afloat—with luck, if the patch gives. But, begging your pardon, Sir—I'd like to ask a favor in the interest of my own neck, and that of every mother's son aboard: Don't take on a full cargo. We'll make less money; but a mite lighter, we'll stand a hell of a lot better chance of getting in alive. . . ."

That, and his own decision: "Hargraves, you said we could get into Nassau with the anthracite you've put aboard?"

"Yessir. At half speed. Maybe, three quarters . . ."

"Allowing for a run at full, past the blockaders?"

"Yessir. But not allowing for having to outfoot a Union cruiser on the high seas as has happened a couple of times before. That's why I ordered that bituminous to kind of help things along."

136

"Chief, you know how much smoke that damned bituminous coal will send up?"

"Yep, Cap'n—enough to bring every Yankee vessel twixt here and China down on our tails. But there wasn't any more smokeless, and I don't aim to use that soft coal unless I have to. 'Pears to me, we'll be a hell of a lot better off, clipping off seven knots, than hove to out of fuel, smoke or no smoke. . . ."

"We haven't run into a cruiser at sea in a long time," Tyler mused, "and that soft coal weighs a damned sight more than the cargo in the forward hold. . . ."

Hargraves stared at him.

"Cap'n," he said quietly, "Money is rightly fine, and I appreciate it as much as the next man; but it don't spend so good in a Yankee jail, not to mention at the bottom of the ocean. . . ."

"I know," Tyler said, "but I'm not a free agent, Chief. The company in London is mighty demanding. The more money I make them, the more they want. I'd like us to be around until the *Captain Pat* is finished. I want to command that vessel—and there's been more than one veiled threat of getting a new Captain who is more daring. . . ."

"Daring! Lord God, Sir! You saved them the bloody vessel on that run when we lost poor Clayton; I don't see what the hell—"

"I own the *Pelican*, Hargraves," Tyler said, "and we heaved the precious cargo over the side to make it. Lots of complaints that time. I was accused of acting in my interest instead of that of the company."

"If you hadn't of," Hargraves growled, "we'd of lost

the vessel, cargo, and crew. Damn them, I say. It's us who're risking our hides, whilst they set on their fat behinds and—"

"We'll chance it, Chief," Tyler said. "Don't put on the soft coal. Can we sail tomorrow?"

Hargraves stared at him a long, slow time.

"Yes Sir, Cap'n," he said.

That—and the visit that he and Collins had paid to the "Blockade Store" to which the entrepreneurs had consigned the goods they had bought at the auction. They had gone out of simple curiosity; but afterwards they were sorry. One of the good things of life, one of the things to be cherished is the illusion of feminine sweetness and gentility. But it is an illusion: the human race is no exception to the rule that the female of nearly any given species is more deadly than the male. If, Tyler thought grimly, a man wants to witness female savagery at its naked worst, a blockade store is the place to see it.

The rows of poor women without the bales of Confederate money it now took to purchase the simplest article, standing there with the unashamed tears streaking their faces, while their more fortunate sisters, shrieked, clawed, and fought like tigresses over a scrap of silk, a flagon of perfume. The women, perhaps weakened by the monotony of the diet they had to subsist upon, fainted, and were laid atop the counters to prevent their being trampled by the others. It hadn't been pretty.

"Lord God, Sir!" Collins had said. "Let's get out of here!"

They had to use force to do it. Applied as gently as possible, but still—force.

Too much to think about. He had been among the first in his class at Annapolis. Among the things that sustained him was a deep and quiet pride in his seamanship, more, in his profoundly professional knowledge of the tactics of naval warfare. He had sailed from Nassau comfortably borne up by that pride; but he had arrived at Wilmington to find that he, and every man trained as he had been, were as extinct as the dodo. For, four days after he had slipped out into the Gulf Stream, an iron barn roof on a raft had crept down past the Norfolk estuary and murdered half the Union fleet at Hampton Roads. Murdered them, because solid shot bounced up and away from sloping four-inch-thick iron plates like peas striking a tin roof, while she smashed in their wooden sides with her prow; cut them to ribbons and splinters at point blank range, invulnerable to their broadsides; the others were saved by nightfall and the miracle that no spinner of tales would have dared to invent, the arrival, that same night, of an over-turned cooking pot on a shingle, called the *Monitor*. It had double the thickness of the Rebel ironclad's armor, with a turret which whirled and spat balls heavier than the world had ever seen before, and a deck so low, awash actually, that no gunner alive could hit it fairly; and the battle that rocked the navies of the world thundered to a draw; the fleet was saved—by the very existence of the *Monitor*; by the genius of a Swedish engineer called Ericsson, inventor before this, of the screw propeller.

All Tyler knew was doomed. All the great ships he loved, with their proud sails, were finished, for "the laws of physics were unphysick't, wood sank and iron floated"—and the days of wooden ships and iron men were done.

More, two fine naval officers had visited Annapolis, during his studies there, the brothers Buchanan. And one of them had commanded the Rebel ironclad, *Virginia;* while the other, still in the Union blue, had gone down in the hell of flame aboard the wooden frigate, *Congress,* cut down by his own brother's fire.

Too many things.

The stop, this afternoon at the fumigation station, required by Wilmington and Nassau now, with yellow fever ravishing both ports—and the arrival aboard of a squad searching for deserters. The Confederate soldier was brave; perhaps, by and large, the bravest the world had ever seen. But by early Sixty two, he was beginning to receive the letters, tearspotted and ill spelt: "Pete done run away and jined up. Ain't nobody here to git in the crop, can't stand no more to hear Lucy crying from hongry and nothing in the house to give her. 'Fore God, son, if you don't come home, we all going to die!" And he, Johnny Reb, who nine times out of ten had never owned a slave, was beginning to dimly apprehend that this war, actually fought over the interests of a tiny ruling class, benefited him not at all. So already, in April 1862, the first thin trickle of deserters, never ceasing, always growing, until by the Fall of Sixty four it would be a flood, by the Spring of Sixty five, an inundation.

They had found the boy, seventeen or eighteen years old, hidden among the bales in the center hold. His

coughing and sneezing from the smoke of the fumigation had betrayed him. They had marched him ashore;
and there, suddenly, he had made a break for freedom.

Tyler saw his knobby knees come up, his thin legs
pumping like pistons, his arms flying like some animated
scarecrow. His blond hair, uncut for months, trailed out
behind him. The sergeant turned to his men, and nodded.

"Fire," he said, speaking flatly, calmly, not shouting
or even raising his voice; and they, all of them raising
as one man, their Enfields, ripped out a ragged volley,
the smoke pluming up from the muskets half hiding
them, and only the tongues of orange flame stabbing
through. The boy stopped. He hopped on one foot, in
a grotesque dance step, then crumbled, becoming suddenly and oddly boneless. The Sergeant walked slowly
up to where he lay, and, seeing the boy's extended right
leg jerking convulsively, he drew out his Colt dragoon
slowly, leisurely, and pointed it at the back of the boy's
head. Tyler saw it jerk in his hand. When the smoke
cleared, the boy's right leg was still.

He turned just in time. Collins was clawing at the port
window, his big Navy Colt already in his hand. He was
crying, his boyish face twisted with rage and grief.
Tyler came up from his seat, and caught the Second
Officer from behind, pinioning his arms.

"Lemme go, Cap'n!" Collins sobbed; "Goddamn it,
lemme go! Going to kill that bastid! Going to! Nothing
but a kid, a green, scairt kid—like my little brother!
Cap'n, for God's love. . . ."

"Mister Collins," Tyler's voice was ice. "Give me
that gun. And that's an order!"

Regular Navy discipline had its advantages.

"Aye, aye, Sir," Collins whispered, and loosened in Tyler's arms.

Too many things to think about. And nothing to do now, but to wait until it was dark enough to run through the blockading fleet. To wait, and to think, the two most painful labors in all the world.

The night favored them. There was no moon, and the fog lay thick over the face of the waters. They crept at half speed down the New Inlet channel, moving out amid the Union fleet. They saw, time and again, the heavy spars of a frigate rising through the mist; but they crawled by, sometimes at cable's length, and broke through into the open sea.

The next day dawned fair, and the next, and the next. The fourth day came in with rain, and an endless series of line squalls. Still, they did not slacken speed. But all the fifth day the barometer fell, and on the sixth, they were plunging into the teeth of a gale, off the Florida coast.

Tyler watched the water break white over the turtle back. The *Pelican* wallowed in the trough of the seas, rising skyward, plunging head on through tons of water, shaking it off, plunging again, rolling like a dying dolphin, pitching sickeningly, agonizingly; her timbers groaning so that he could hear them above the shriek of the gale. A new motion had got into her: she would rise until her bow was pointed skyward at a fifteen degree angle; and hanging poised there, she would start to roll; the two motions, the roll and the pitch, wrenching her until the juddering of the planking could be felt through the soles of his seaboots.

He picked up the speaking tube; then put it down again. He went below, clinging to the spiral ladder, until he reached the murky hell of the engine room. He stepped down into water half way to his knees. He heard the thump of the donkey engine, the hiss and gurgle of the pumps. Hargraves came up to him.

"Bad?" Tyler said.

"Bad enough. She's leaking all around that damned patch. Water's gaining on us. I could keep her afloat if I could seal off that forward hole. But seeing as how it's full of mighty valuable cargo. . . ."

Tyler did not miss the sarcasm in his tone.

"Chief!" a voice roared. "Number three furnace is going! We better do something mighty damn fast. . . ."

"Number three feeds the donkey pumps, Cap'n," Hargraves said, and waited. He didn't need to say anything more. If the donkey engine went, the steam pumps would gurgle into silence. Even with the hand operated bilge pumps, the *Pelican*'s end would come in a matter of hours.

Tyler walked over to the Chief Engineer's speaking tube.

"Collins," he called, "Detail the whole damn offwatch to unload the forward hold. What? Heave it over the side, of course. What the hell else can we do with it?"

"Thanks, Cap'n," Hargraves said. "I'll seal the forward hold off. Even with it flooded, we can make headway. . . ."

"Number three's gone, Chief!" the black gang cried.

"Man the bilge pumps!" Hargraves bellowed. "Hop to it, and look alive!"

Tyler climbed back up to the bridge. Collins was standing there, watching the grey mountains of water toss the bales of cotton skyward.

"My fault," he whispered. "I broke my word to the Lord. . . ."

"Oh, come off of it, Collins," Tyler snorted. "Bad luck's a thing you've got to expect in this business."

They plunged on, riding the crest of one wave, hanging there, shuddering, then crashing down with such an impact that Tyler was sure no timbers on earth could take the strain. The speaking tube's squawking caught his ear.

"Hold's sealed," Hargraves' voice came over calmly. We're gaining, Sir. I'll have number three going again in half an hour. . . ."

Nightfall found the gale rising. Tyler nodded to Collins and went below.

"Chief," he said, "What about the coal?"

Hargraves shrugged.

"If it slackens off tomorrow, maybe," he said. "If not, reckon you better tell Collins to pray some more. . . ."

"I'll do my own praying, thank you," Tyler said and went back topside.

Some time before morning, the winds died. For some hours, the seas continued, heavy, but, by midmorning, they were creeping South under a serene and smiling sky.

"That does it, Sir!" Collins grinned. "Appears like the Good Lord ain't mad with me after all. . . ."

"Reckon not," Tyler began, but the speaking tube interrupted him.

"Cap'n," Hargraves said, "Can you meet me in the chart room in about five minutes?"

"Right," Tyler said. He went down at once; but Hargraves was already there ahead of him.

"I was asking Mr. Fry for our position, Sir," he said. "He's gone topside to shoot the sun with his sextant. . . ."

Fry came bustling in.

"Good morning, Captain," he said, drawing himself up to a rigid salute.

"At ease, Fry. Where the hell are we?"

"Longitude, seventy eight degrees fifteen minutes," Fry began.

"I know that, gawddamnit! What I want to know is how far North are we?"

"Latitude," Fry whispered, "twenty nine degrees, eighteen minutes. . . ."

"A wee stretch south of St. Augustine, ain't it, Sir?" Hargraves said.

Tyler nodded. The two men looked at each other. Neither of them said anything. Fry stared from one face to the other.

"Begging the Captain's pardon," he began, "I don't quite see—"

"Well, Chief?" Tyler said.

"Maybe. We'll be sweeping the coal dust up from the bottom of the bunkers with a broom, Sir—before we sight land. You ship them sails on, Sir?"

"Yep. Two flying jibs, a foresail, and a main. I can rig a spanker aft. Think it'll do?"

"I'm an engineer, Sir. Never did ship aboard a sailing

vessel. I was a riverboat man before, and after that, ocean vessels. Course we always carried sail as well as steam, but I never had nothing to do with canvas. . . ."

"The wind's usually right, down there, Sir," Fry said. "We'll hit the tradewinds in two more days. . . ."

"Thanks, Fry. Hargraves—"

"Yes, Sir?"

"My apologies," Tyler said.

"No need for that, Cap'n," Hargraves said. "You took a chance 'cause them John Bulls was crowding you. But life's just one damn gamble after another. And, Cap'n—"

"Yes, chief?"

"I've sailed under many a good Cap'n. But damned if you ain't the whitest man I've ever shipped with. Don't you worry, I'll bring this tub in if I have to burn everything above decks including Fry's whiskers!"

They crawled southward under both steam and the pitiful amount of canvas they could spread on the truncated masts. The sails added perhaps a knot to their speed; but, under the circumstances, even a single knot was not to be sneered at. The Florida shoreline crept backward with agonizing slowness; but now, some two hundred fifty miles from Nassau, they were beginning to have hope.

Tyler stood on the bridge, peering ahead of him. He heard, slow and drawn out, the lookout's cry:

"Sail astern! Three points to port!"

He, turning, had the glass already to his eye. The rigging of a Yankee cruiser leaped into view, a large one of the James Adger class; and with that cloud of sail aiding her engines, she was making two knots to the *Pelican*'s one.

He picked up the tube. His voice, speaking, was filled with unutterable weariness.

"Full speed ahead, Hargraves," he said.

"But, Cap'n—" Hargraves' voice came back hollowly; "the coal!"

"Damn the coal. There's a Union cruiser three miles aft, Chief, and coming on like all hell. . . ."

"Aye, aye, Sir," the Chief Engineer said.

The engines took up a double beat. The wake boiled whitely. The sails on the horizon were increasing in size more slowly, now.

"Speed?" Tyler said to Collins.

The Executive Officer ran aft. He was back in minutes.

"Eight knots, Sir! Those sails do help!"

"Not enough. That Yank is still gaining. We'll wait a bit and see. . . ."

They ran on, through a sunlit sea.

"Cap'n," Collins said; "She faster than us without sail?"

"By three knots—and all that canvas is giving her a hell of an advantage. . . ."

"Suppose we were to change course, Sir—run into the wind. Wouldn't she have to take in sail?"

"Yes; but so would we. We just aren't equipped for tacking . . ." He looked aft. Then very suddenly, he spoke to the helmsman. "Put her about," he said; "on a sta'board tack. But do it so slowly that the Yankee'll follow us. . . ."

"Aye, aye, Sir," the helmsman said.

"But, Sir," Collins whispered, "You said she's three knots faster on steam alone. . ."

"She is. But she's two thousand tons burden, and she draws a hell of a lot more water than we do. I'm going to run inshore, where she can't follow us. . . ."

"But fast as she is, she'll be there waiting when we come out," Collins said gloomily.

"We do seven knots—loaded," Tyler said quietly.

Collins stared at him.

"Lord, God, Cap'n," he said; "Not again!"

"We'll draw six feet less water," Tyler said, "and do ten knots, equal to that Yankee's speed. With the new boilers, Hargraves can push that up to twelve for quite a while before we have to blow off steam. Two knots aren't much; but—"

"I should of," Collins whispered, "I should of kept my word to the Lord. . . ."

All that day the chase kept up, the *Pelican*'s wake littered with a mass of bobbing bales.

"Cap'n," Hargraves said, standing on the bridge beside Tyler, "You better keep some of that cotton for fuel. . . ."

"That bad?" Tyler said.

"That bad. I got her up to twelve, like you said. And it's nip'n tuck whether we're going to run out of coal first, or have to blow off pressure to keep from blowing up. . . ."

"But we're leaving her," Tyler said. "Look!"

"In the wrong direction," Hargraves said quietly,

"away from Nassau, so's to make her take in them sails. . . ."

"Put her about!" Tyler barked. "We're light enough now—even with the wind three quarters astern we ought to have maybe one knot advantage. . . ."

Collins licked a finger and held it aloft.

"We got 'em, Sir!" he shouted. "Wind's shifted! It's dead abeam, now!"

The duel went on. Tyler kept watching the sky, hoping for darkness. The settling dusk was the slowest in all the world. Then, just on the edge of the night, at a range that Tyler would have sworn that no gun in the world could carry, the cruiser opened up. Opened up and hit the *Pelican* squarely with the first shot.

It was, of course, pure luck. Nobody could shoot like that. Every gunner knew you had to straddle a target to get the range, throwing first over, watching the splash through the glasses, correcting, throwing the second short, and then elevating the gun again to a point between the two settings to come anywhere near what you were shooting at. Pure luck—but enough to finish them.

He saw the flash of flame from the black hulk of the cruiser, silhouetted against the darkening sky. And the next instant, the bridge crashed into splinters, the air filled with ugly slivers of glass; and behind them, and ahead, rose a wall of flame.

Tyler picked himself up and groped his way to the speaking tube. The wheel was smashed, and draped over it was—

The shreds and tatters of what had been a human

being. The bulkheads were splattered with ugly splotches that ran and ran, except the places where they weren't red, but pinkish gray, or dark with patches of hair . . .

"Hargraves," Tyler barked. "Can you hear me!"

"Yes, Sir!" Hargraves shot back.

"We're hit—bad. Put the emergency steering gear to work. I'll give you the headings. . . ."

It was then that he heard the groan.

He dropped the tube, and his foot slipped on the sticky wetness, so that he fell headlong; he raised his head, and saw it. Inches before his eyes, Collin's trouser leg lay, the cloth shredded, the cloth, and the leg under the cloth, both in long strings of fiber and flesh, and pulverized bone.

He tore at his belt, ripping it off. He got it about the boy's leg above the knee, and twisted it, cruelly. The red torrent slowed to a steady ebb. He knotted the belt and stood up. He saw, with one part of his vision, the crew rushing forward, dragging the hoses; with another, he saw the shell geysers rising all around the *Pelican*. He clapped his hand on the shoulder of one of the firefighters.

"Get me the surgeon," he said.

They carried Collins below. Tyler couldn't leave the wrecked bridge. In five minutes, they had the fire out; and then, just as the cruiser, closer now, yawned to port, to loose a broadside; the tropic night crashed down. Tyler heard the jangle of the shells passing overhead, saw their bursts pluming the grey sea. But he stood rock still, calling out orders to the engineers, riding her inshore with two leadsmen in the chains taking soundings every

minute, until the cruiser could no longer see to fire. Then
he went below.

He looked at the surgeon.

"Shock," the surgeon said. "If I can keep him alive
until we hit Nassau, there's a chance. And, Cap'n, you'd
better strip down and let me have a look at you. There's
an awful lot of blood—"

"His, and the helmsman's," Tyler growled. "Stay with
him, Doc—"

He went back to the bridge. He stood there, staring
out into the night.

"Don't know what You want, Lord," he prayed, "but
save that boy, and You got it. My life, any service I
can render— Anything, God, anything at all. . . ."

The dawn came up clear, with a rising wind. Tyler
ordered the sails set; but when the crew pulled on the
lines they parted in their hands, burnt through. Tyler
walked forward. The jibs and the fores'l were a mass of
charred tatters. The main and the spanker alone remained.

He visited Collins every hour. The boy was unconscious at first. But later, he opened his mouth and
started raving.

"I promised! I gave the Lord my word, and I broke it!
Now we're on fire and sinking, and the Cap'n—the best
damn Cap'n in the world is dead, and I killed him! I
killed him! Me!"

"Look, son," Tyler said, the unashamed tears bright
in his eyes; "I'm not dead, I'm—"

"I killed!" Collins shrieked. "I broke my word and
killed the Cap'n—"

Then he lapsed into silence.

The surgeon shook his head.

"Can't we make a little more speed, Captain?" he said.

"No," Tyler said, and went back to the smashed bridge where the engineer was supervising the repairs to the gear.

"Coal?" he croaked.

"Two hours more, maybe," Hargraves said.

Tyler turned and went back to his cabin. He spent those two hours on his knees in prayer. When he regained the deck, he saw sailors with axes, chopping away at the turtleback.

"Mr. Hargraves' orders, Sir," they said.

Tyler nodded and turned away.

Two days later, they sighted Nassau. The turtle-back was gone, the wooden superstructure, both masts, and all the boats but one. The crew were hacking away at the forward decking.

"Chief," Tyler said into the tube, "Nassau's in sight—got steam enough to make it?"

"Yes, Sir!" Hargraves' voice came back; but Tyler felt at that moment a hand laid on his arm. He didn't turn his head. He knew who it was. He even knew what the surgeon was going to say.

"Collins?" he said.

"Yes. Ten minutes ago. I'm mighty sorry, Captain, I—"

Tyler strode away, down the ladder, and forward to the bow. He stood there, seeing the low buildings of

Nassau, growing, spreading on the horizon. Then he raised his eyes. They were like coals. Like ice.

"What good are You?" he rasped. "Even if You're there—what bloody, damned good are You, after all?"

Then he turned very quietly, and went back to his cabin.

In Nassau, they had to cut the seaboots off of him. He had kept them on seven days and nights, and his feet were so swollen they had to cut the leather from his flesh.

But there was no means to cut away the thing that festered in his heart.

CHAPTER SEVEN

TYLER SAT AT A TABLE OUTSIDE A NASSAU PUB. HE HAD a broad brimmed panama on his head, and native sandals on his feet. They were still too tender to bear the touch of leather. He lifted his glass of dark Bahama rum, and sipped it slowly. It burnt going down with a good burning.

He watched, idly, the tall, blond young Britisher weaving his way through the crowd, coming toward him. When the man was close enough, he stiffened.

"Viv!" he called. "What in the name of God—"

His cousin slipped easily into the other chair and put out his hand.

"Thought I'd have a look at things close at hand," he said. "Cedric, of course, is tied up. Business. This time the business' name is Pamela. . . ."

"Never changes, does he?" Tyler chuckled. "He'll be chasing fillies in a wheel chair at the age of eighty . . ." His smile faded. "You can tell the truth, Viv," he said flatly. "You were sent over to check up on me, weren't you? Just in time. I've lost another cargo, and two damned good men. You want my resignation in writing, or will my word do?"

"Neither. Don't be so bloody sensitive, old boy. That

situation is under control. There was rather a bit of criticism. City blokes. But both Cedric and I have seen
service in Her Majesty's fleet. We know what you're up
against. Ced took time out from his pursuit of the fair
Pamela to gather some facts and figures. D'you know
that we're the only company operating who've never
lost a ship? Silenced the city men deuced effectively.
You should have heard him. He should run for Parlia-
ment; he certainly has the flair. . . ."

"Good," Tyler grunted. "Now what?"

"You might offer me a drink. Or I'll buy you another." Vivian turned in his chair. "Waiter!" he called.

"I still would like to know where we go from here,"
Tyler said. "The *Pelican*'s a mess. It'll take two months
to put her in shape again. . . ."

"I know. Saw her this morning. Damned fine show,
Ty. Saga of the sea, and all that sort of thing. You should
be British."

"I," Tyler said, "put my ship in jeopardy, and lost
my Executive Officer, and the best helmsman I've ever
had, because I so overloaded her that I had no reasonable
margin for fuel, Viv. That wasn't seamanship. . . ."

"But it was business. The two things conflict. Of
course they don't know about this in London, yet; but,
since Ced and I have added a number of Naval men to
our stockholders, I can assure you that seamanship will
take precedence in the future. As for the *Pelican*, sell
her. We'll reimburse you for any loss you take. . . ."

"That'll put Meredith Associates out of business. She's
the only runner we have. . . ."

"Just the point, old boy. The *Pelican* is not, and never

was suited for running the blockade. When the *Captain Pat* is finished next Spring, we'll have the vessel for the work. Her designers guarantee seventeen knots. . . ."

"Hell, Vivian," Tyler said, "how do you know the war won't be over by next Spring? New stockholders, or old ones for that matter, aren't going to sit still while—"

Vivian tossed a banknote on the table and stood up.

"Come take a stroll with me, old boy," he said. "There's something I want to show you. . . ."

Tyler picked up his heavy malacca cane and got painfully to his feet.

"It had better be good," he growled, "if I have to walk to see it. . . ."

"It is," Vivian said. "Come along. . . ."

Ten minutes later, they stood on a quay. Vivian pointed to the vessel tied up alongside. She was long and exceedingly narrow. Her prow was shaped like the point of a scimitar. She had a single, telescoping stack, and huge sidewheels. She was called the *Sea Witch*, and even tied to the quay she seemed to be making twenty knots.

"Like her?" Vivian said.

"That's a boat?" Tyler asked incredulously, "or a flying machine?"

"You like her?" Vivian persisted.

"Very much—far as I can see. Why?"

"I bought her this morning. After, of course, getting the expert advice of your man, Hargraves. . . ."

Tyler's eyes lit up.

"When do I take her out?" he said.

"You don't. Not for two months anyhow. She goes into drydock tomorrow."

"Now, what the hell?" Tyler said; "You're losing as much time as you would with the *Pelican* and—"

"Ending up with a better vessel. I got her for a song. She belongs to a company of merchants from Liverpool. They sold her after her crew finally, and justifiably, mutinied."

"Justifiably?" Tyler growled.

"Yes. That hull's paper thin. She's one of the first vessels actually built for blockade running, and they overdid it. She'll do nineteen knots over a measured mile in fair weather. Actually, ten is all her Captain ever dared get out of her. And the crew got bloody sick of manning the pumps on *every* trip. . . ."

"Yet you bought her," Tyler said.

"On Hargraves' advice, remember. On the condition that I put her in drydock, and let him supervise the strengthening of that hull."

"Hargraves," Tyler said, "is the best there is."

"So it seems. He's wonderfully fond of you, too. I think the two months' time is worth it. She'll be heavier and slower. Fifteen knots, Hargraves thinks; but that's five more than they ever dared push her."

"And eight more than I could get out of the *Pelican*. Good. But what the blazes do I do with those two months?"

"Take a vacation. You need it. Pardon the frankness, Ty, old boy; but you look like hell. Come back to London with me. I've given Hargraves an open account and full power of attorney, and Cedric, I'm sure, will find you another redhead. That last one got married. . . ."

Slowly Tyler shook his head.

"If you don't mind, Viv," he said, "I'd rather go home.
"It's been a long time since I've seen New Orleans . . ."

"As you like. But isn't that rather dangerous?"

"No. I can ship aboard a craft bound for Havana and
run into Mobile from there. Then, overland to New
Orleans. Sort of roundabout; but it'll get me past the
Yankees."

"Rather stiff squadron off Mobile, what?"

"Not any more. Not enough ships go in and out to
make it worth it. Too hard to buy cotton there; com-
munications with the interior are doggoned poor. . . ."

"All right, then. If you're not back in two months,
I'll run her out under another skipper. Might even go
along as super-cargo. I'd like to see a bit of this show. . . ."

"You'll find it loses its charm damned fast," Tyler
said.

It was, as he had thought, not too difficult. There were
delays and a thousand and one annoyances; but he
reached New Orleans on the twelfth day of April, 1862,
having come overland from Mobile to Baton Rouge,
and down river to the Crescent City. He brought with
him two valises and a large trunk. It was the size and
weight of the trunk that caused the majority of the delays
and the inconveniences that he suffered. But he fought for
it grimly, with bribes in gold to the Confederate officials,
hard words, and once with his bony fists. In the end, it
was worth the trouble; for the two valises held his

clothing, while the trunk was packed to the brim with tea, coffee, and that commodity literally beyond price in the blockaded South—salt. He had managed to squeeze in a bolt or two of silk and one of velvet, for Ruth's last letter had complained bitterly that they were in rags. The contents of the trunk was his home-coming gift to Ruth and Sue. . . .

He stopped first at the Saint Louis Hotel, for his home had been closed; with no Meredith left in New Orleans, it was hardly worth while to keep it open. Tyler had wanted to free their remaining few slaves; but his acute knowledge of the state of the public temper forbade that. Instead, he had loaned them to Sue for the duration. After having bathed, shaved, and changed his travel-stained clothing, he proceeded to rent a buckboard, had the enormously heavy trunk loaded in it, and set out for the Drakes' house.

The melancholy aspect of the city startled him. On his way from the river to the hotel, he had passed one deserted warehouse after another; and now, moving through commercial streets that had always been, from his earliest memory, packed with throngs of humanity, he was astonished to see that all the stores were closed, their windows shuttered, and scarcely a soul was in sight. Looking down, he saw some fine blades of grass peeping up between the cobblestones. He had seen ships sunk; the *Pelican* had twice been hit by heavy fire; he had lost two young officers of whom he had been very fond; but nothing had ever impressed him as much with the power of the Union blockade as the sight of grass growing in the streets of New Orleans.

It was his own Cato who opened the door for him
at the Drakes'. At the sight of his young master, Cato
burst into tears of pure joy. Tyler put an arm around
the aged Negro.

"Now, now Cato," he said. "No need to take on. I'm
back; big as life and twice as ugly. Mrs. Sue at home?"

"Yessir!" Cato spluttered, beaming through his tears.
"I go git her right away, Mr. Ty! Lord, Lord, Lord, I'm
so glad you's back! Me'n Bess done worried the Lord
right smart over you—specially since we got the news
that Marse George is in the hospital. Them Yankees done
shot him. He's right pert bad off. . . ."

"That's so?" Tyler said; "I'm mighty sorry to hear it,
Cato. Now, if you'll tell Mrs. Sue I'm here. . . ."

"Yessir!" Cato said. "You wait right here in the
parlor, Mister Ty . . ."

Tyler stood with his back to the door, looking about
the room. Nothing about it had been changed—except
the fine drapes were gone. The women had been forced
to cut them up to make dresses. He moved aside, so
that he could see the doorway reflected in the mirror
while remaining himself in shadow. He heard the whisper of her footsteps coming on, running almost, thinking sardonically: Just like before, but this time I can
see. . . .

Gazing into the mirror, he saw her come to a stop.
For a moment, seeing the ravages of a year of privation
upon her, seeing how thin and wan she was—she who
had always been so fragile as to scarcely seem a part of
this world, he almost surrendered to the pity that rose
in him. But he checked the impulse and waited.

Her hand flew to her throat like a captive bird; and

she, standing there, looking at him, fell into the trap he had prepared. Thinking he had not heard her, could not see her, was unaware of her presence, she rested against the doorframe a long, slow time, and permitted her eyes to fill up with such an excess of tenderness, of pure, hopeless longing, that almost it shamed him; almost he could not bear the sight of it.

Almost. He turned very slowly and faced her.

"Sue," he said solemnly, "did I ever tell you that you're the most beautiful woman in all the world? And that I love you with my whole heart?"

It was, the mocking, pitiless part of his mind told him, very nearly true.

He came toward her, seeing, as he did so, the crystalline rush of her tears. She did not move, or speak. She waited there, the adoration in her face, an illumination, a glory; and made no resistance when he took her into his arms.

"Ty," she whispered, "Your hair—your hair. . . ."

Her fingers came up, touching the white wings, spreading along his temples, and the broad swath of silver dividing the darkness of the heavy hair atop his head.

"How you must have suffered!" she wept.

"With a thousand miles of ocean and the Yankee fleet between us?" he growled, "what would you expect, Sue?"

Then he kissed her, very slowly and gently and tenderly and expertly; finding almost instantly the response he sought: the sweetsighing warmth, the soft adhesion; even, finally the quiet, completely unconscious demand, the supplication, the unuttered, unutterable, "More, more—"

He released her and stepped back; but she surged forward, and hiding her face in the hollow of his throat,
cried very quietly and terribly in an absolute agony of
hopelessness; while he, holding her, stared across the
spun gold crown of her head into her sister's stricken
face.

"You," he said mockingly, "have the damnedest habit
of showing up at the wrong times, Kitten. . . ."

Sue whirled, seeing her sister's face ghost white, the
nostrils flaring, the blue eyes as hard as ice, and as cold.

"There were ten thousand men killed and wounded
at Shiloh," Ruth said, her voice flat. "Among them was
a man named George Drake. 'Seriously wounded,' the
telegram said. Perhaps he *is* dead by now. But you might
have waited for official notification, Sue."

"Ruth," Susan implored.

"Even so," Ruth went on, "I was raised in the belief
that a year was a decent interval for a widow to wait
before entertaining a suitor. That is, knowing that she
actually is a widow—having at least seen her husband's
grave. . . ."

"Ruth, Ruth!" Susan wept. "You don't understand!"

"I understand perfectly. I just came back from the
hospital. Not many wounded, we're too far from the
war for that. But lots of sick and dying men. They—
they're all so hopeful, Sue. They keep talking about
going back to their sweethearts, and their wives. Confident, too. Not one of them dreams that they might come
back to find the woman they loved and trusted—in
somebody else's arms. . . ."

"That," Tyler said coldly, "is quite enough, Ruth."

"Enough?" Ruth snapped. "It's a sight too much to

my way of thinking, Tyler Meredith! You shirked your
duty to your country to make yourself a fortune in a
safe and easy fashion. You might, I think, have the common decency not to try to seduce a soldier's wife. Leave
my sister alone, you hear me! You've enough to occupy
your time. It's easy for you, seeing as how you're not
even discriminating. Go back to your easy lights o' love
—like, for instance, your yellow nigger wench!"

Tyler studied her a long time, and very calmly.

"You, Kitten," he drawled, "are the dirtiest fighter I
ever met—and I've met some dirty ones in my time. No
holds barred, eh? All right. I can't stop you from being
mad, 'cause that's your right. What you haven't any
right to do is to place a piece of jealous female cussed-
ness on the basis of high and mighty morality. I love
Sue. Always have, always will. I don't try to justify
that. Don't have to. The fact that I'd sell my life, my
future, and my hope of heaven for her is justification
enough. . . ."

"Ha!" Ruth snorted.

"But you," Tyler went on imperturbably, "can't
attack her on a basis of a moral code you'd toss out of
the window in five seconds flat—if you haven't already
—to get what you want. Don't much cotton to moralists.
The majority of them got that way out of envy anyhow. And while we're talking so dadblamed frankly,
I'll freely add that Lauriel Doumier isn't rightly responsible for her ancestry, since she didn't pick her
parents, is one of the prettiest girls I know, and certainly
the sweetest, next to Sue, I ever ran across. . . ."

He felt Sue stiffen in his arms.

"Would you—marry her?" Ruth sneered.

"In a minute," Tyler said calmly, "if I were in love with her, which I'm not; and if there were anywhere in this benighted land of ours, North and South, where it could be done—which there's not, either—"

"Convenient, isn't it?" Ruth said. "So now, much to your regret, she'll just have to go on being—your mistress. . . ."

He felt Sue's hands come up, frantically to break his grip; but he held her against him, hard.

"Another low blow, Kitten? The only thing I regret about little Lauriel is that she's not my mistress. Never has been. You know why, Ruth?"

"I," Ruth said, "can't possibly imagine."

"Nope. Don't reckon you can. You see, Lauriel really is decent in the precise way you're talking about, despite the fact you don't rightly understand it. That's one thing. Another is, I wouldn't hurt her for anything on earth, which, considering man's inhumanity to man, and the damned near obscene laws we live under, is all I could do. The third reason is I kind of like and respect her fat fool of a Pa. But the last reason's the most important: I've lived a mite too long, and been through a damned sight too much to have divided fancies or a vagrant heart. I love Sue—period. Nobody else. Rightly or wrongly, there it is. You don't like it. All right; I'll accept that. What I won't accept is your lying about the reasons why you don't like it. You make a pretty poor out at defending George Drake whom you despise, Kitten, or female virtue, when your own, wouldn't bear any too close scrutiny. If you don't believe the things you're saying, you're a hypocrite. If you do, you're a

fool—neither of which breed I cotton to. Now be a good
girl and have the niggers bring in that trunk I got outside. There's a few things in it for both of you. . . ."

"I," Ruth said, "can do without anything you might
have brought, Tyler Meredith!"

"You can," Tyler chuckled, "but you won't. Now
run along and tell them. You might find it a relief from
being so dadblamed tiresome. . . ."

Ruth whirled and marched away from them, as stiff as
a soldier on parade.

"Ty—" Sue whispered, "Did you mean all those things
you said?"

"What things, Babydoll?" Tyler said.

"About loving me—with all your heart. That you'd
give your life for me, and—"

He held her at arms' length, looking into her eyes.

"Yes, Sue," he said very quietly. "I meant every
blessed living word."

"But you can't!" she said wildly, the anguish moving
through her voice. "We can't—I—"

"*We* can't, Angel?" Tyler said.

She hung there, against the circle of his arms, looking
at him. Her eyes, at long last, were naked and defenseless.

"Yes, Ty—we. You accused Ruth of being a hypocrite
and a fool. What does that make me? I married George
in bad faith, although I didn't know it then. I entered
into the most solemn contract known to man, loving
not my bridegroom, but another man—you, Ty—with
all my heart and mind and soul and body. I do still. More
than ever—worse than ever. The greatest battle of the

war has been fought. Ten thousand killed or wounded
on both sides—and George was among the wounded.
But I've lain awake all these nights wondering, not
whether my husband has died of his wounds but whether
you had been drowned in a storm, or sunk by a Yankee
ship, or captured. You—not George . . . Have you any
idea how I've suffered when he turned to me in the
night to take me in his arms? Have you, Ty?"

"Sue," Tyler whispered. "For the love of God!"

"Oh, I am sorry. I didn't mean it like that . . . Or
maybe I did. Maybe I wanted to get back at you a little
for the way I felt hearing Ruth talk about—that girl.
Is she really very pretty, Ty? Some of them are, I
know."

"Lauriel," Tyler said flatly, "is one of the loveliest
creatures who ever drew the breath of life."

"Oh. And you are fond of her, aren't you, Ty?"

"Very. But I love you. There's a difference."

"And you really haven't—you've never—?"

"Oh, for God's sake!" Tyler said. "I never lie un-
necessarily, Babydoll. I've a lot of faults, but that's not
one of them. If you insist upon my saying it, I never
have, and I have no intention to. Look Angel, have
your people bring that trunk in. Apparently, Ruth isn't
going to. . . ."

"All right, Ty. But—"

"But what, Sue?"

"What are we going to do, Ty?"

"Get on a boat for England. George'll give you a
divorce. He'll have to—"

She looked at him, her eyes tear bright.

"No, Ty," she said quietly. "We can't—"

"Why can't we? What earthly reason can you give
that—"

"No earthly reason, Ty. Divorces are forbidden—by
Our Lord Himself."

"Oh, hell!" Tyler said. "Look, Babydoll—I'm going
to be here for two months, maybe longer. You know
what's going to happen in that length of time?"

"Yes, Ty: Nothing."

"Nothing? You're mighty damned sure of yourself,
aren't you?"

"No, Ty. I'm not. There isn't a sin on earth I wouldn't
commit for your sake. It's you I'm sure of. Because Marie
Laveau was right: you have great goodness in you. All I
have to do is to ask you—for George's sake, who is truly
your friend; for my sake—even for your own—"

"Then don't ask me!" Tyler said viciously.

"I must. I do. Please, Ty—don't take me in your arms
—not too often. Don't kiss me as you did today—not
ever. Don't ask me to run away with you. Don't hurt
me and shame me. You could, you know. I—I haven't
any defenses against you. None at all. Except your own
goodness—and your honor. . . ."

"Honor!" Tyler laughed bitterly. "Oh, good Lord!"

"Yes. You have them, you know. Honor and goodness and decency and greatness of soul. It's strange you're
so ashamed of them. You even try to hide them from
yourself. But all the same they're there. Please, Ty—"

"Oh hell," Tyler said. "Let's go get that blamed trunk
in, Babydoll. . . ."

He heard, as he rode back to the hotel, the babble of
excited conversation in the streets. Over and over again

the same words: The Yankee Fleet. Forty four vessels, three hundred and sixty nine guns, at the mouths of the passes, waiting to get over the bar to steam upriver to take New Orleans. Shiloh Church. Pittsburg Landing. Island Number Ten. Fort Henry. Fort Donelson. Island Number Ten. Lord God, they've got damn near the whole river! Shiloh, Shiloh, Shiloh. Albert Sidney Johnson, dead upon the field. Beauregard. Beauregard. Ten thousand fallen. Shiloh. Corinth. Shiloh.

George Drake was with Beauregard. George Drake and Joseph Meredith. Father Joseph Meredith, Chaplain, Fifth Louisiana Rifles.

I wonder, Tyler thought, how Joe made out?

Joseph Meredith, Chaplain, was at that moment kneeling beside the bunk of a dead man in the hospital at Corinth. He had read the service for the dead five times that morning. Five days after Shiloh the wounded were still dying. Even the walking wounded, men who had reported to the Medical corpsmen on their own two feet. He no longer paid much attention to the stench of gangrene. Not that he was used to it; no man got used to that smell. It was just that his mind was occupied by other horrors to which the smell of living flesh festering was as nothing; it was deep down inside him, at the upper apex of his ribs a knot had formed itself of quivering flesh and jangled nerves, which one day soon he would have to examine, and the name of that knot was fear.

Not physical fear, for Father Joe was the bravest of the brave; but something else—something he could not put a name to. A complicated unit composed of many things: of horror, and disgust and incertitude. And for the first time, doubt that their cause could succeed. For— in that rough parallelogram of hill and scraggly wood where Lick and Snake and Owl Creeks boxed off a battle ground, and a tiny white chapel called Shiloh Church, and a steamboat dock called Pittsburg Landing were given by man's brutality, stupidity, savagery, courage, heroism, and honor, chance immortality—he had seen for the first time Union troops who when beaten, did not run; commanded by Generals, whom he, in common with every Southerner alive, hadn't believed the North capable of producing. And one of those Generals was called Sherman, the other, Grant—christened Hiram Ulysses at birth, renamed Ulysses Simpson by the inexplicable mistake of the registrar at West Point. A mistake almost calculated to add to his glory, since it gave the newspapermen a convenient handle: U. S. Grant— United States Grant; and after Fort Donelson, "No terms except an unconditional surrender can be accepted . . . I propose to move immediately upon your works . . ." Unconditional Surrender Grant. A small, unkempt, untidy man, who put his cigar stub in his teeth before he put on his clothes, and through whose veins ran not blood, but ice water, double distilled.

Father Joe, who made a point of honor of advancing under fire with his men, had seen Grant in that battle. Pinned down by fire with the regiment, he had seen a horse killed under the Union General; Grant, rising from the mud, not even brushing it off, signalled for another; mounting, a sharpshooter's ball took off his hat, he rode on, bareheaded; another took a patch of cloth from his

coat between his side and his arm; he ignored it, giving
orders without even raising his voice more than was
necessary; still another clipped the insignia from his
shoulder. He slouched down, the unlit cigar stub in his
teeth, searched in his pocket until he found another insignia, pinned it on, not in defiance of the sharpshooters
about whom he didn't even give that much of a damn,
but that the bewildered troops of Sherman and Hurlbut
and W. H. L. Wallace might recognize his authority and
respond instantly to his commands.

Seeing that, Father Joe began to know the meaning
of fear: We shall never beat that man, unless we kill
him. And why—he thought in aching wonder, seeing
the tall tree just to the right of Grant that had not one
of its thousands of leaves remaining, every one of them
cut from the branches by the incredible volume of rifle
fire—have we not already killed him—if he is not protected by Divine Providence? I've prayed, I've prayed—
Oh, God, are You truly on our side?

It wasn't a good thought to live with. And seeing
Albert Sidney Johnson—the greatest General the South
had produced, next to Bob Lee—reel from his saddle,
dying of blood lost from a wound where a minié ball had
cut an artery in his thigh, a perforation so slight, and so
little painful that he had ridden on, ignoring it, not
knowing that his life itself was pumping out upon the
redtide, Joe had found it hard to dominate his new and
subtle terror, even as he knelt in the dappled shadows of
the glade and prayed at his General's side. Grant lived
under unbelievable fire. Johnson died by a chance shot
from beaten, disorganized troops. God was in His heaven,
but all was not right with the world.

The rest of it was horror: the Confederate private, not quite eighteen who grinned at him cheerfully as he scraped the Union soldier's brains from his musketbutt with his bayonet. You, Joseph reflected, got used to blood. Blood was, after all, a familiar thing. But the sick pink grey of brain tissue, and the bloodslimed white of guts where a trooper lay, his, and those of his mount's entwined . . . The gully that bisected the field, running from the first, ankle deep in blood; and later, a gully no longer as first one side then the other surged across it, trampling on the bodies of the dead that filled it level with its rim and even piled above the edge—the dead, and not quite dead. In the lulls between the volleys, you could hear them crying.

He could feel his lips moving in silent prayer; but he could not hear his words; he could not even shape them in his mind. Words came to him finally, not, oddly from the scripture or even from the Book of Prayer; but from Shakespeare:

"My words fly up; my thoughts remain below—
Words without thoughts, never to Heaven go—"

I've seen it all, he said, he thought; there can be nothing worse. But there was; and in the precise sense to get to a man of his temperament and his training.

He knelt beside the young butternut clad officer, writhing on the ground—a little out of the line of fire, because the battle had swept on toward the landing. A little group of privates watched.

"Father," the Lieutenant said, "Am I hit where I think I am?"

"Yes," Joseph said. "Yes, my son—"

"Turn your head, Father!" It was an order, ripped out

in the crisp voice of one accustomed to command. Joe
saw the officer's hand groping for his sidearm, and hurled
himself forward to stop him. But the privates grabbed his
arms, holding him back, hard:

"Leave him be, Padre! He's got the right. I'd do the
same damned thing if it was me. . . ."

And he, unable to face it, turned his head, feeling inside his own guts the soft, curiously muffled sound of
the shot.

Where are our teachings? And where Our God, when
a man values the lusts of the flesh more than his life?
Where?

And then, just once—on the second day, after Lew
Wallace had come up on the double at midnight with
seven thousand blue clad troops to replace the other
Wallace, W. H. L., killed yesterday upon the field, and
to stay Grant's right; Lew Wallace a not too bad General
in spite of the fact that he regarded war as grist for his
mill, transforming the sights and sounds of Shiloh into
the military passages of his *Prince of India;* getting here,
perhaps, the first vague glimmerings of *Ben Hur,* the
exception perhaps to the general rule that writers should
not be allowed into uniform: war is not for imaginative
men; for imagination and cowardice go hand in hand;
after "Bull" Nelson, Crittenden, and McCook came up
with three divisions of Buell's troops, dooming Beauregard who had taken Johnson's place, with the one thing
that nearly always doomed the South: the Union's ability
to put not one, but three fresh armies in the field to replace the one slaughtered the day before—the one for-
lorn example of saving grace:

He had knelt beside a dying New Orleans lad, young Devereux, the Senator's son. And raising his eyes, he had looked into the muzzle of a Yankee musket held steady on his heart. He felt no fear. What he did sense, dimly, below the threshold of consciousness was a surge of hope: It'll be over, and I am glad . . . Not that he formed the thought so clearly; it was against all his training and a sin.

Then a musket swipe had knocked the Union soldier sprawling, and another blueclad boy stood tall against the man made lightnings.

"Damn it! Don't you see he's a Padre?"

"Padre or not—he's a Reb, ain't he?"

"Yep. Go ahead, shoot him, you bastid! But if you do, I'm going to blow your brains out, and stick a bayonet through your miserable guts to boot! What are you waiting for—go ahead!"

And the other had slunk off. The tall Yank had crossed the bullet splattered space, and knelt beside Joseph in the mud. So confused was the fighting that even such things were possible.

"Mind if I say a prayer for him, Padre?" the boy said solemnly; "Don't think Our Father cares what color suit a man comes to him in. . . ."

It was over then; the attack broken against the guns at Pittsburg Landing; the blueclad wave coming on, led by Sherman, crying: "Give them hell!" in a voice gone cracked. And they, the boys in grey and butternut brown, fleeing, but not in disorder, covering their retreat to Corinth with discipline, precision and skill. But four thousand men, blue and grey, lay dead upon that field, four times that many wounded. And nobody could ever say again that Yankees would not fight.

That, and the prayers for the still dying. The prayers that served for what? That and the sick, tingling knot of quivering nerves that forbade food and drink; that murdered sleep.

And worse, the words that moved inside of him, un-uttered, unrecognized, unformed, that he sensed, he felt; but which to say was very death; the words his brother perhaps had said for him a few weeks ago, creeping his crippled ship into Nassau harbor:

"What good are You? Even if You're there, what good?"

He could not shape them yet; but he was closer to them than he knew.

Riding alone, on the nineteenth of April, Tyler Mere-dith was unaware of the stares of the people he passed. It was not alone that his horse, rented for the two months stay from an upriver planter who had made a hobby of breeding Arabians, was magnificent; but masculine attire of such quiet elegance had vanished from the South, months ago. Some, particularly women, were, after being caught by the obvious things, held by his appear-ance: his silvery temples, and lean, sardonic face were something to see.

More, he was once more operating on the basis of the hard cynicism and native arrogance that had formerly sustained him. Collins' death had come as a reprieve for him. He had been drifting into what had been for him

dangerously uncharted waters of the spirit; but the failure
of his prayers for his young friend's life, had restored for
him the validity of his old philosophy: "Men are, at bottom, swine; women, but toys and vehicles for male lust;
act upon the certainty of human dishonesty, greed,
vanity, and frailty, and you can never fail. . . ."

Restored it; but only in part. At the core of his being,
the new doubts gnawed. He could not allow them to rise
to the surface; he had to force them down, shout them
down, destroy them by behaving more cynically, more
ruthlessly than ever; convince himself once more by
the success of actions based upon that cynicism, that
ruthlessness, that all else was sentimentality, weakness,
and folly. . . .

Hence his ceaseless siege of Susan Drake, halted now,
temporarily, by the needs of the hour; these needs, being
actually at bottom dictated to by nothing more than his
aching hunger to silence the questioning of his heart.
He did not need money; he was already by April, Sixty
two a millionaire; the coup he was planning, by which
he stood to double his fortune was motivated by no such
obvious drive as necessity, or even greed. He would not
permit himself to examine his reasons; he was afraid to
face them.

The thing he was doing was quite simple: Having
learned that nearly every planter near New Orleans was
planning to burn his cotton in the event that Farragut
succeeded in his attempt to silence the Forts and sail upriver to take the city, he was using his drafts on the Bank
of England, the only paper worth its face value in the
South, to buy up all the cotton he could, and store it

in a hidden depression on René Doumier's undeveloped forest lands. He hadn't asked René's permission to this; the fiercely patriotic little Quadroon would have damned him off the grounds had he dared. Using rented wagons and Negro labor, surplus since the official curtailment of the crop, the cotton lands being not yet converted into food growing, he detoured around René's entrance, and entered the wild outlands the little planter never visited, by a game trail widened with cane knives to permit the passage of the wagons. But, while his plans went well, they had not produced anything like the results he had expected: Many a planter, father or brother of a boy dead at Shiloh, quietly and with dignity refused to sell despite Tyler's bland lies that the cotton would be shipped to England to purchase supplies for the Confederacy. Some of them were intelligent enough to realize the impossibility of his getting it to England. The only way, they pointed out, for him to profit from the affair, would be to traffic with the enemy—and despite all his assurances to the contrary, they would have none of his scheme.

They were, of course, right. Tyler held the firm conviction that the color of any man's money, like the color of his blood, was always the same. One of his most treasured possessions was the proof that he had never taken up arms against the Stars and Stripes. He had already destroyed the records of his blockade running, sure that the Union Commander would regard them as tantamount to military service against the Union. He was fully prepared to pose as a loyal Union man. To that end, he gathered the clippings from the newspapers he had saved, in which several writers had attacked him in print for his disloyalty to the Confederate cause—all of them, of course, prior to the launching of the *Pelican*. The news about that event, and the later clippings praising his services, even, some of them, apologizing for their hasty judgments against him, he burnt with Machiavellian glee.

For he was sure that the city would fall. In this, with gloom in their hearts, many loyal Confederates agreed with him.

But—to profit from his venture to the extravagant degree he hoped to, he had to secure more cotton than he had been able to buy. When the idea of how to get his hands upon it came to him, he moved with characteristic thoroughness: He at once set about hiring additional wagons and squads of Negroes from their owners. That he was able to do so was due to the monumental stupidity that characterized the Confederacy's conduct of foreign affairs: With the grandiose idea of forcing England and France to recognize her, the New Nation had tried to aggravate the anticipated shortage of cotton in those textile manufacturing countries by asking the planters to drastically cut the acreage devoted to the crop. Nobody in the South knew, or bothered to find out, that England had so great a surplus of raw cotton in 1861 that she profited by the war to the extent of selling it to the Yankee millowners; and that moreover, she was wise enough to sharply encourage the increase of the acreage of cotton lands in Egypt. France, indeed, suffered; but with her hands tied to her Mexican venture, she was but the tail of the British kite. The policy, then,

failed dismally; the more so because no one had the fore-
sight to suggest that the planters devote the idle lands
and slaves to the production of foodstuffs. Some of them,
of course, had done so out of simple common sense, but,
since one of the prime examples of man's vanity has
always been his insistence upon calling "common" the
most uncommon of human faculties, they were few.
Tyler, then, could hire any number of heavy wagons and
prime hands, languishing in forced idleness because of
the Government's policy.

Then he spent a few days among the saloons, dives,
barrelhouses of the worst section of the city, recruiting
as his lieutenants, the idle, dissolute riffraff of that law-
less town, aided in this by the fact that he knew many of
them personally, having constantly pained both his
father and his brother in his youth by the delight that
he had found in the company of vagrants, blackguards,
and thieves. "They," he used to say, "are a damned sight
more interesting than the quality, Joe. And smarter. It
takes brains to live without working—and they sure
Lord have more fun."

On April nineteenth, the day that the guns of the two
Forts tuned up disharmoniously, replying to Porter's
mortar vessels which were already lancing the sky with
the high, looping trajectory of their shells, throwing
them over the bend of the land beyond the willow trees,
to crash into the forts, Tyler was ready with his plan:
He would lounge ostentatiously about the town, be seen
by as many people as possible while flying squads of
blacks, led by his white trash lieutenants, would descend
upon the plantations and snatch by main force the bales

from the burning. The white men would be masked; the Negroes would never be sent to any of the plantations from which they themselves came. The lieutenants were schooled to give the impression that they were Union sympathizers, acting upon orders from the Federal Commander.

That this was stealing, Tyler admitted to himself, making only the highly irrelevant defense that he was only taking that which, having been destroyed, would not have benefited its owners anyhow.

Tyler would have much preferred spending his entire time with Sue; but it was imperative that he be seen as much as possible in public. He had no intention of having his name connected with the great cotton raid. Knowing that sooner or later, after the war, the control of the city would revert to the hands of native sons, he meant to perform the delicate task of profiting from the approaching disaster, while remaining *persona grata* with his victims. Accordingly, he frequented the bars, barrel-houses, dance halls, gambling palaces, and all other places of public assembly.

On April twenty fourth, with the news that Farragut was safely past the forts, Tyler gave the signal to a small ratty-looking man who during those five days had always managed to be in the same saloon at the same time that Tyler was; always keeping carefully apart from his employer, and never indicating by word or deed that there was any connection between them. The man left the bar at once, and Tyler, along with several acquaintances and friends, strolled down to the levees to wait. There was a rush of confident talk:

"They got more ships than us. But we got the *Manassas*, the *Louisiana*, and the *Mississippi*. It'll be Hampton Roads all over again; only this time they won't have the *Monitor* to save them. . . ."

"Heard tell the *Mississippi* ain't rightly finished; nor the *Louisiana*, though she's further along. . . ."

"Don't worry your head. The Tift brothers will have them down here in no time—and when those ironclads tear into that wooden fleet—"

The *Manassas*, Tyler thought, a converted tug so slow that she can barely do two knots upstream. The *Louisiana*, which, headed South on her trial trip, had been passed by the driftwood borne in the same direction by the current; and which, when put about by her commander and headed North, had been swept downstream when she tried to breast the river, moving backwards at three knots an hour with her engines at full speed ahead. The *Mississippi*, a magnificent job, but immovable because her machinery isn't even in working order yet. . . .

But he didn't say it. He just waited. And the river filled up with the tall masts, and the black-crossed yard-arms of the Yankee Fleet. The *Mississippi* came downstream, a sheet of flame, fired by her builders. The *Louisiana*, unable to steer or maneuver, had been tied against a bank and used as a fort; but, because her builders had had so little knowledge of design that they had cut her gunports so low that her guns could not be elevated to throw any distance beyond point blank range, Farragut had simply steered his fleet out of range and paraded contemptuously past her, leaving her tied up, helpless to interfere. The *Manassas* had done some damage; but even her iron was not equal to the weight of Union fire. The *McRae* went down in sight of the quay. The other Confederate gunboats were scattered or sunk. And New Orleans, largest city of the Confederacy, was doomed.

The mob went wild. They started firing the cotton on the quays. They set afire the few ships tied up along the docks. They screamed, cursed, smashed store windows, looted. And the gunners aboard the tall Yankee frigates, patted the breeches of their guns and grinned at them. And the rain came down in torrents.

Tyler left the waterfront and hurried to the Drakes' home.

"I've come to offer my services," he said to Sue and Ruth, "in taking you out of the City. New Orleans has fallen. . . ."

They stared at each other, white faced. Then Sue spoke very gently.

"No, Ty. This is our home. I—I've met a few Yankee officers before the war. In spite of what people say, I don't think they've ceased being gentlemen. . . ."

And nothing Tyler said could move her from her stand.

He rode, swift and secret that night, out to the game trail to check up on the failure or the success of his cotton raid. It had been, he found, eminently successful, due to

the rain that made igniting the slow burning bales all
but impossible; due to the absence of the planters, gone
down to New Orleans to witness the unbelievable with
their own eyes; due to the cowardice of the overseers in
charge, Northerners themselves, for the most part.

As he paid off his raiders and dismissed them, he was
struck by two strange facts: the absence of one of the
chief scoundrels among them, burly Tennessee McGraw,
never a man to separate himself from a dishonest dollar,
and a subdued red glow in the sky.

"Where's Tennessee?" he growled.

"Don't know. Seed him a mite earlier heading this
way; but I ain't seed hair nor hide of him since. . . ."

"I did," another spoke up. "Said he was going over to
see about the fire. . . ."

"What fire?" Tyler said.

"The plantation house. Tenn vowed it were afire; but
you done give us strict orders—"

"What plantation house?" Tyler spat. "There's hardly
a house between here and—"

"That's what I mean. The big house on this here place.
Told him it warn't our business. Fire draws folks, and
you told us to keep out of sight, once we had the
cotton. . . ."

"Good God!" Tyler said. "All right, get those niggers
back home! And if a word about this stuff leaks out,
somebody is going to end up dead!"

He was in the saddle before he had finished speaking.
But long before he reached Sans Souci, he knew he was
too late. The house was a hollow shell of firegutted
bricks, from which even the whitewash had been blis-
tered. Inside, the fallen floors and rafters smouldered sul-

lenly. It would be days before he could enter it to find—

He rode slowly through the grounds. The sugar mill, the cotton gin, the presses, the slave quarters, barns, stables, everything had been burnt to ashes. Not a soul was in sight.

Then, beside the well, he came upon the answer. Near the well, René's body lay. He had been decapitated. Both arms had been hacked off at the shoulders. Other things had been done to him too that Tyler lacked the will to discover by turning him over. The head was not to be found. The arms lay near by, each ring bearing finger chopped from his hands.

Tyler sat there, shuddering, fighting the nausea rising within him. Then he drew his pistol and went to look for Lauriel.

He did not find her. Not that day, nor the next, nor even the next when the fire had cooled enough for him to search the house. There were no bodies in the house at all. The Negroes, taking advantage of the news of the arrival of the Yankee Fleet, had had their revenge and gone. Taking Lauriel with them? Tyler turned white at the mere thought. But the patrols that guarded the roads against runaway slaves had ceased with the Union victory; he could find no trace of René Doumier's murderous blacks.

Nor, though it was not until the next day, that it occurred to Tyler to look for him, of Tennessee McGraw. Only two things would have caused that greedy beast not to show up for his pay: death—or a woman.

And other than René's pitifully mutilated corpse, there had been no bodies at Sans Souci at all. . . .

CHAPTER EIGHT

T YLER MOVED THROUGH THE CROWDS ON ESPLANADE Street, in front of the Mint. Inside that building, Captain Bailey of the United States Navy, and Farragut's Flag Lieutenant were conferring with Mayor Monroe and ex-Senator Pierre Soulé. The conference, like the ones to follow it, was proving fruitless: Mayor Monroe insisted that as a civilian official he had no power to surrender the city to military forces. That was the duty of General Lovell, he said; and as the General had fled the city with his troops, he didn't see what he could do.

Meanwhile, the mob stood in front of the Mint, and howled for blood. "Don't let them out! Kill the damned Yankees!" they roared.

Tyler glanced toward the river. The frigates stood tall, their guns at ready, loaded with enough grape and canister to make the streets swim with blood. This, he decided, was not a healthy place to be. Farragut was hewn of solid oak, and his guts were ironclad, Tyler knew. Kill those Yankee officers and there wouldn't be any New Orleans left. He started to move off through the crowd, when he saw old Pierre Soulé appear on the portico. The mob roared out a welcome, splitting the heavens with their cheers.

Soulé lifted his hand, pointing his hypnotic forefinger at the crowd. The finger trembled, and the silence of death descended upon Esplanade Street.

"Sons of Louisiana!" M. Soulé began in his marked French accent.

Tyler grinned. Old Soulé could handle them; in a few minutes the danger would be over. He slipped from the crowd and resumed his search. Nowhere among all that mob of men, was there any sign of the hulking, ill-shaven, rough-clad form of Tennessee McGraw. Nor in any of the other crowds wandering drunkenly through other streets. Tyler stood still, thinking.

Under ordinary circumstances, he could have called together a posse on his own initiative to search for the fugitive slaves. Even though René Doumier was a colored man, the great dread of servile insurrection that had hung over the South since the successful revolts in Haiti, Nat Turner's bloody rebellion and the raid of John Brown, would have turned out hundreds of planters, not so much in René's behalf, but in their own self-interest. But the times were out of joint: the fall of New Orleans had superseded all other considerations. More, he could not institute such a search without jeopardizing himself. The first thing that would have come to light would be the immense pile of stolen cotton, guarded by his own slaves.

There was, moreover, no proof that the Negroes had made off with Lauriel. Increasingly, Tyler was beginning to doubt it. They, his Southern trained mind told him, would have subjected her to multiple rape, cut her throat and left her there, secure in the belief that white indignation over their crimes would be tempered by the reflection that she was not, after all, a member of the master race.

No. It was that bastard McGraw, he thought. He got there in time, and took her away. And more than likely out of New Orleans, figuring that he'd have both me and the Yankees to deal with. . . .

Nevertheless, he continued his search. He passed word among the underworld, that any sight of McGraw was to be reported to him instantly. He canvassed every low dive, barrelhouse, pretty waitress saloon, bar, and whorehouse in the old city. To no avail. McGraw, and Lauriel, had vanished as though the earth had swallowed them up. Still, he walked on, rechecking the places he had already visited.

By so doing, he missed witnessing history being made, Southern style. That afternoon, a detachment of Marines came ashore and planted the United States Flag atop the Mint. And one William Mumford earned himself eternal fame by climbing the building and pulling it down. A few days later—when Benjamin Franklin Butler, forever to be known to history as "Silver Spoons" Butler, and later, even as "Beast" Butler, General in command of the Union forces—came ashore, he gave Mumford a drumhead courtmartial and hanged him; thus unintelligently supplying New Orleans and the South with a martyr.

Forever after, generations of Southern school children would read the moving story of the impetuous youth defending his city's honor. And nobody at all would point out to them that the youth was forty-five years old at the time of his feat, or ask the very simple question: what

was a man, agile enough to climb to the roof of the Mint,
doing in New Orleans in civilian attire when thousands
of his fellows were dying along the whole width of the
flameshot, echoing front?

By the first week in May, when the Union troops of
Ben Butler were firmly in control, Tyler had reluctantly
given up his search for Lauriel. He had other things to
occupy his attention; and, among these, the chief was
General B. F. Butler. At the end of the first ten days
of the occupation, Tyler was sure that Butler was his
man.

But how to reach him? He couldn't simply call at
Headquarters. To do that would be to damn himself
forever in New Orleans. There must be some other way.
He haunted the streets near the St. Charles Hotel, where
Butler had officially established himself, waiting for a
chance. And in those disordered days, it was not long
in coming: He was present at a fight between Yankee
troops on leave, and a group of New Orleans citizens.
When the blueclad swarms descended upon the civilians,
clubs swinging, he stepped up to the Lieutenant in charge.

"Would you please arrest me, too?" he asked politely.

The Lieutenant glared at him.

"Move along!" he spat. "You weren't in this scrap—
you're much too neat. Why the hell should I—"

"I've an important communication for General Butler,"
Tyler whispered. "I can't just call on him. It would ruin
everything. . . ."

The Lieutenant was quick.

"Secret Service, eh? Very well. Guards!" he roared,
"Arrest this man!"

And Tyler had the satisfaction of being paraded off to jail, along with the rioters, between rows of outraged citizens, many of whom knew him well enough to call out as he passed:

"Don't worry, Ty! We'll get you out even if we have to storm the jail!"

"It's all a mistake," Tyler called back. "Don't do anything rash, boys. I'm sure I can straighten this out myself. . . ."

He was allowed to cool his heels in jail all day. That night, to his vast astonishment, Ruth came to see him. Ruth, not Sue.

"I—I brought you a note from Sue," she said. "It's my fault she's not here. She's longing to come. But I convinced her it wasn't wise, Ty—"

Tyler grinned at her.

"But for you to come was wise, eh Kitten?"

"Yes. I'm not married, so people won't talk so much. And Ty—"

"Yes, Kitten?" he said.

"I'm sorry I spoke to you and Sue like I did. I was just plain jealous. Don't reckon it's any good trying to hide —how I feel about you. I was unfair. If I was married to a creature like George Drake and you came along, I'd do the same thing. . . ."

"Now, Kitten," Tyler admonished, "I like George. I think he's mighty white. . . ."

"He is nice. I admit that. It's just that he's so—so dull! But I didn't come here to talk about him. Ty, is there anything I can do—anyone I can see, to get you out of this mess?"

"No, Kitten," Tyler said; "I reckon I can straighten it out by myself. . . ."

"Ty," she whispered, "I've rightly enjoyed the tea and coffee and the salt, just like you said I would. That was mighty sweet of you. And I've got to apologize all over again for saying you shirked your duty. I knew better when I said it; I was just poison mad. Then Sue told me the stories of how you lost your two Executive Officers, and ran the *Pelican* into Nassau, burning even your lifeboats to try to get that boy in alive . . . I—I cried, Ty. You're the finest man I know—or that I ever will know, I reckon . . ."

"Don't say that, Little One," Tyler said gently. "I'm just a poor lone critter, trying to get along. . . ."

"Why did they arrest you, Ty?" Ruth said. "Everybody in town is up in arms about it; but nobody knows the reason. . . ."

"Damned if I know, Kitten. From what I can gather, they seem to think I'm a Reb spy. . . ."

"Oh!" Ruth gasped. "Then they might shoot you—or hang you like poor Mumford!"

" 'T'ain't likely. They haven't one iota of proof against me. Tell me, Kitten, anybody ever find out who stole all that cotton the night the Yankees came?"

"No. But all the same everybody knows who it was—"

"Who, Child?"

"General Butler's agents. He's been stealing everything that's not nailed down, ever since he got here. Folks say he even stole the silver spoons at an official dinner he was invited to. . . ."

She was interrupted by the tramp of booted feet

through the corridor. A sergeant and two guards, armed
with rifles with bayonets fixed, came toward the cell.
Ruth turned ghost white at the sight of them.

"Ty!" she whispered; "Oh, Ty!" Then she surged
up, pressing her face through the bars, clinging her mouth
to his in an agony of grief and terror. The Yankees stood
there watching it, and grinning.

"Kiss him again, Miss," the Sergeant said. "Make the
best of it. 'Cause when the Gen'l gets through with him,
he ain't going to be around for nobody to kiss. A pity—
a girl pretty as you are, shouldn't ought to have to go
around wearing black. . . ."

"Oh!" Ruth gasped. "You—you beast!" Then she
whirled back to Tyler. "They won't kill you!" she
sobbed. "They won't! I'll get Papa's pistol and shoot
that mean old General myself if they try it!"

"Now, now, Kitten," Tyler said. "Don't take on. The
Sarge's just plaguing you. Aren't you, Sarge?"

"Yep," the Sergeant grinned. "Just trying her out to
see whether I had a chance. You're a lucky man, Mister
Meredith. All right, Miss, you can kiss him one more
time—'cause he's got to see the General now. . . ."

Ruth kissed Tyler then with such fervor, that he
drew back, staring at her.

"You're *that* fond of me, Kitten?" he said.

"Fond?" she said. "Fond! Oh, good Lord!"

The Sergeant unlocked the door, and marched Tyler
out. Just as they were about to move off, Tyler remembered something.

"Kitten," he said, "You never did give me that
note. . . ."

"Oh," she whispered. "No, I didn't. Here it is, Ty. . . ."

As he took it, he could see the pain moving, deep in her eyes.

Benjamin Franklin Butler was a sight to see. He had only one eye, and that one wandered persistently off toward the corner of his head. He was fat, and getting bald. Sitting there, behind his desk, he resembled nothing so much as a pink, blue-clad frog. At his side, the young Lieutenant who had arrested Tyler at his own request, stood.

"This the man?" General Butler said.

"Yes, Sir," the Lieutenant said.

"Very well, Lieutenant, you may go. Mr. Meredith, will you have the goodness to take a seat?"

Tyler sat down.

"Cigar?" General Butler said, shoving forward the box.

"Don't mind if I do," Tyler said.

The cigar was excellent. Tyler studied it. Very slowly, the General smiled.

"I took the liberty to have your room at the St. Louis searched. If my men were overzealous, you'll be paid for the damage. These—clippings. Interesting. Union man, eh?"

"Yes, Sir," Tyler said.

"Or damned careful to make it appear you're one. Which, Mr. Meredith?"

Tyler looked at the General with interest. Whatever else he might be, B. F. Butler was nobody's fool.

"I," he drawled, "could hardly have had those items

printed, General. Any printer still operating at that time, would have kicked me out of his shop in the first place, and reported me to the Reb Secret Service in the second. Then, it's not easy to find the kind of paper they print newspapers on, nor the exact typeforms of a half dozen different sheets. . . ."

"You've got a point," Butler grinned; "and besides that, I had these issues checked by our Intelligence from the original files for those dates. The clippings, for which you can be thankful, are genuine. . . ."

What I can be thankful for, Tyler thought grimly, is that you didn't check the later dates of the same papers. . . .

"But," the General went on imperturbably, "they sure changed their tune, later. Blockade running must be very interesting as well as profitable especially to a man so successful at it that even our own naval commanders have named him Captain Rebel. You didn't imagine, did you, Mister Meredith, Mister Captain Rebel Meredith—that I'd limit my investigation of you to the dates of such an obvious plant? I have your whole biography. Quite a boy, weren't you? Tell me, Meredith, why were you sent down from Annapolis?"

"The usual thing," Tyler said; "a girl. You can check it there. It's in the records. And, General, begging your pardon, you've just cleared your name with one citizen of New Orleans. I know now, you never stole anybody's spoons!"

Butler threw back his head and roared with laughter.

"What makes you so sure, Captain?" he said, wiping his eyes.

"You're too damned smart. If you'd wanted to acquire

spoons, you'd have figured out how to take possession of a warehouse full. A spoon or two wouldn't have interested you at all—"

The General controlled his wandering eye with an effort.

"Blockade running's a Federal offense, Meredith," he said.

"I know. Subject to a prison term if you're caught doing it—which I wasn't. You have clippings indicating I launched a vessel to go blockade running. That proves intention. I also have the intention to seduce every good looking housewife in town; but not even their husbands can shoot me 'til they prove I've done it. . . ."

"You," Butler said, "have a head on your shoulders, yourself, Meredith. All right, let's quit fencing. What did you want to see me about bad enough to have yourself arrested to get here?"

"Cotton," Tyler said.

General Butler got to his feet.

"Cotton?" he whispered. "Where is it?"

"Hold on a minute, General," Tyler grinned. "That's the question that's going to cost you money. I've got the bales. Several tons of 'em. And they're hid so damned well, that I'd have a hard time finding them myself. . . ."

"You know I have the right to seize Rebel cotton as contraband of war," the General said sternly.

"Rebel cotton. Not my cotton. I've never broken my oath of allegiance to the Republic. I've never taken up arms against—"

"You," Butler roared, "ran the blockade, and that makes you a Reb!"

"Does it? Interesting point; but it won't hold water.

Number one, you say I ran the blockade. I say I didn't.
You produce clippings to say I outfitted the *Pelican* for
blockade running. I'll produce a bill of sale showing
where I sold her to an English outfit at Nassau. Number
two, blockade running, for argument's sake, is a violation of neutrality, but hardly bearing arms. If it were,
it would make Rebs out of a hell of a lot of Englishmen
and Yankees. So let's drop the blockade running, shall
we? What you do, is go find some one who ever saw
me in grey or butternut with a musket in my hands. Then
you seize my cotton—if you can find it; and realize
if you do find it, it'll be soaked in turpentine and burning like hell. . . ."

The General stared at him a long, slow time. Then he
smiled.

"You, Meredith," he said, "are a man after my own
heart. Never thought I'd meet a bigger crook than I am.
Congratulations. How much?"

"A million dollars in Federal notes," Tyler said easily.

"You're crazy!" the General said.

"Nope. That cotton's worth at today's prices two and
a half million dollars at Nassau—more'n that in Massachusetts. I can't get it to Nassau, nor Massachusetts. I'm
offering you, General, one and a half million dollars
in clear profit. Take it or leave it. The cotton's worthless to me, now. But I'll burn it before I'll let it be
seized. . . ."

"I can clap you in jail until my men find it," Butler
said.

"And have another Mumford case on your hands?
Besides which my niggers have orders to burn it the first

time *one* Yank shows up. Come now, General, haven't you found out by now, I'm worthy of your steel?"

"You are," Butler said slowly. "You'll take my draft?"

"Hell, no! Where the blazes could I cash it?"

"Then it'll take me some time to raise the money."

"I," Tyler said, "will be here. . . ."

"How will I see you?"

"Have me arrested again—on suspicion. In fact, General, I'd appreciate it, if you'd throw me into jail every once in a while anyhow. It sure makes me popular with these Rebel fillies. . . ."

"You're lucky," the General said. "They cross the street to spit in my face. I'll put a stop to that, though. Meredith—"

"Yes, General?"

"It's a deal. But how am I going to be sure you'll deliver?"

"You pay me five hundred thousand in cash. Then I'll ride along with your boys to show them where the cotton is. You send the other five hundred thousand along with one of your men. When the cotton's loaded in your wagons, I get the rest. . . ."

"I've got to trust you with a half million? How do I know you won't skip?"

"How do I know you'll pay me the other half?" Tyler said. "Besides, where could I skip to? I'd have to have a pass, issued by you, to get out of this town. And if I tried to sneak out, way you've got things buttoned up, I'd be dead—especially since from here on in your guards are going to be instructed to pay me extra special attention. That's it, General—honor among thieves. You trust me; I'll trust you. Done?"

"Done," Ben Butler said, and put out his hand.

Tyler was arrested twice more, each time, actually for conferences with the General. Ben, because he was too well known to his Massachusetts colleagues, was having a devil of a time raising the money. Both conferences were nothing more than attempts on his part to get Tyler to name a more reasonable figure—say two hundred fifty thousand. But knowing the value of his booty, Tyler refused to reduce his price. He was aware that General Butler was actively searching for the cotton; but this did not trouble him much. Even if the fat old scoundrel found it, it would be destroyed; and all Tyler stood to lose by its destruction was the time, effort, risks, and not inconsiderable money he had put into his raid. That would be painful, but hardly fatal. He could afford to gamble those things against the fortune he'd receive if he won.

"Why is General Butler always having you arrested?" Sue asked.

"You know," Tyler grinned, "I think the old rogue likes me. He has me hauled in, accuses me of everything up to drawing detailed plans of Abe Lincoln's outhouse for the Reb Secret Service, then challenges me to a game of poker—which I let him win to be on the safe side. And, anyhow, everytime he throws me into the hoose-

gow, my stock goes up with the people of New
Orleans. . . ."

"You value that, don't you?" Sue said. "Why, Tyler?"

"I mean to live here after it's all over. It's my town,
and I love it better than anything on earth—except you,
Babydoll. That's all I want out of life: a nice house, a
little comfort—and you. . . ."

"That," she said very quietly, "is hardly possible,
Ty. . . ."

"Who knows?" he said. "There's a war going on,
Babydoll, and—"

She surged toward him, suddenly, and laid her hand
over his mouth. Her fingers were like ice.

"Don't say that, Ty!" she breathed. "Even to think it
is wicked! God listens to thoughts like that, and punishes
them, too. There is a war—in which George is fighting.
He's a brave and honorable man and a good and faithful
husband. I have no complaints against him. Only against
myself. I must complain against my own dishonor. . . ."

"Dishonor?" Tyler growled. "Hell, Baby, you hardly
ever even so much as let me kiss you!"

Susan looked him in the face a long time, and very
steadily.

" 'As a man thinketh in his heart, so is he,' " she quoted
bitterly. "By that measure, Tyler, I'm an adulteress a
thousand times over. . . ."

"Sue," he got out, and crushed her to him. She hid her
face against his throat.

"No, Ty," she murmured brokenly, "I take some comfort in the fact that I haven't done the deed—largely
because you haven't really pressed me; because you've

been gentle and understanding. George has been wounded twice now, in the service of his country. I—I cannot permit you—or myself to wish his death even in thought. You know why, darling?"

"No," Tyler growled, "why?"

"Because the Hand of God is long. And His mills grind surely. You—you're going back to the war. To an ocean where storms rage, and there are Yankee cruisers waiting off every port. In an unarmed vessel, like the one which twice now has been smashed by cannon fire, killing two Executive Officers of yours, as well as seven members of your crew. And if I permitted either of us to wish harm to George, on that instant God's protection over you would cease. If anything happened to you, Ty, I'd—"

"You'd what, Angel?" Tyler prompted.

"I'd die," Sue said calmly. "Even if I can never have you, there is a joy in knowing you're alive and somewhere in the same world with me. . . ."

"Sue," Tyler said. "Sue—Baby. . . ."

But Ernest, the butler, interrupted him.

"Marse Ty," he whispered; "there's a passel of Yankee soldiers waiting outside. The Cap'n's in the foyer; 'lows he knows you's here. You follow me, and I'll slip you out the backway, and—"

"No, Ernest, thanks," Tyler said. "They haven't a thing on me and they know it. Better to go along with them and get things settled. . . ."

"Damn' old Yankees," Ernest grumbled. " 'Fore God, I wish—"

"Ernest!" Sue said, sharply.

"Yas'm, Miz Sue. I'm sorry. But they do git a body riled. . . ."

Tyler stood up.

"So long, Babydoll," he said.

"Oh, Ty, Ty," she wept, and ignoring the Negro's presence, took him in her arms.

To Tyler's astonishment, instead of taking him to General Butler's headquarters, the Yankee troops clapped him unceremoniously into jail. He languished there for four days, from the first to the fourth of August. Ruth and Sue both visited him; but he had no comfort to offer them.

Nor for that matter, for himself. He had lingered in New Orleans long past the time he should have rejoined his ship, in hope of gaining his fortune, and of finding some clue to Lauriel's whereabouts. In neither had he had any success. And now—the only answer to this was that Ben Butler had found the cotton; found it, and prevented the Negroes from burning it. Perhaps when the thing was done, he would be released; perhaps not.

On the morning of the fifth, the General, himself, came to Tyler's cell. He was not alone. With him were five guards, and a towering hulk of a man, uncombed, unkempt, unwashed, and ugly as homemade sin: Tennessee McGraw.

Tyler's knuckles whitened about the bars.

"You bastard!" he said quietly.

"Thanks, Meredith," the General laughed. "I wanted to make sure that Mr. McGraw, here, wasn't lying. Public spirited citizen, Mr. McGraw. He's going to point out to me where a cache of Rebel cotton is hidden. Of course he'll be rewarded amply—a thousand dollars. Generous of me, isn't it?"

"You fool!" Tyler roared at McGraw. "You know what that cotton's worth?"

"Not a dime to you'n me," McGraw said, "seeing as how neither of us kin git hit outer here. An' I could use a thousand dollars. . . ."

Tyler looked at him.

"All right," he said tiredly, "to hell with the cotton. Where's Lauriel?"

McGraw laughed evilly.

"Where you'll never find her," he said. "But don't worry your nice gentlemanlike head 'bout her none a-tall. She don't want to see you. She useta cry over you at first; but she done stopped that. You see, you rich, 'ristocratic bastid, she done found herself a man!"

Tyler's hands, striking, blurred sight with the speed of their motion. His fingers closed around McGraw's throat, bit in. But five guards were too many. They managed to tear his hands loose before McGraw's face turned completely blue.

"You," Ben Butler chuckled, "are an impetuous lad, aren't you, Meredith? Don't worry, when the thing is done I'll release you. With a pass to leave the city, which I must insist upon your using. I have a few men, unfortunately, who have rather nervous trigger fingers. And if they're sent to bring you in—a most regrettable accident just might—"

Tyler looked at him very steadily.

"I was wrong," he said. "The name fits: 'Beast' Butler. Yep, it sure Lord fits. . . ."

"But such a cunning beast, eh, Captain Rebel?" the General laughed. " 'Til tomorrow, then. . . ."

When, late the following afternoon, he was ushered into the General's office, he could see from Butler's face that the attempt had failed. But he didn't move a muscle. The General looked at him, and picking up his pen, wrote rapidly. He held the paper out to Tyler.

"Here," he growled. "Your safe conduct through our lines. You have forty eight hours to tidy up your affairs, and kiss Miss Forrester, or Mrs. Drake—or both, good-bye. I'd advise you that you make the best of it. . . ."

Tyler stretched out his hand for the pass. Then he calmly took a cigar from the open box on the General's desk.

"Tell me, Ben," he drawled, after he had lit the stogy. "You get that cotton?"

"No. Some of it. Your Negroes were zealous. I was forced to take them into custody. They'll be useful, working the confiscated lands. . . ."

"And McGraw?" Tyler said.

"Mr. McGraw," the General said, smiling a little, "is no longer with us. He was a little—impetuous. Took upon himself to kill two of your Negroes. Naturally my men had to shoot him. The Northern press has a most kindly attitude toward the 'Colored Brother'. It wouldn't have done if his crime went unpunished. . . ."

Tyler's face whitened.

"Oh, my God!" he whispered.

"Now, now, Meredith," Ben Butler said, "McGraw was scarcely a friend of yours."

"No. But—there was something he had—he knew that I—"

"A girl? A tasty yellow wench named Lauriel? You Southerners really like your dark meat, don't you, Meredith?"

Tyler did not answer. He just stood there, looking at Ben Butler.

"You've your pass," General Butler said. "Use it. However, out of recognition of your services to me, and the pleasure I've had from your company—which I mean truly, Meredith, and without sarcasm—you just might stop a day or two in Baton Rouge on your way to where ever you're going. . . ."

"Baton Rouge?" Tyler said. "Did McGraw say—?"

"Only that he came from there. Goodbye, Mr. Meredith, Mr. Captain Rebel Meredith—and thanks. . . ."

Tyler grinned.

"You're entirely welcome, General," he said.

Tyler did not follow General Butler's advice. He left for Baton Rouge that same day. Before he reached it, history itself, took a hand in his affairs. Lady killer Earl Van Dorn, one of the handsomest men in the Confederacy, and a fine general—whose inability to resist a pretty face or a well turned ankle were to cost the Confederacy his able services, and him his life at the hands of an outraged husband—launched an attack on Baton Rouge and drove the Union Forces to the river. He might have smashed them there, but he waited for the ironclad *Arkansas*, pride of the Confederate Fleet, which had already twice whipped the entire Union Navy despite the abysmal poverty of her engines. The

Southern naval designers were very nearly the world's
finest; but nobody in the South knew how to build a
decent steam engine. Afloat, that was always the Confederacy's fatal weakness: that she had neither an Eads
or an Ericsson among her engineers. So Van Dorn waited
for one of the best fighting craft ever built by either
side, while she lay in sight of Baton Rouge, rammed
into a mudbank, with her starboard engine a mass of
shattered junk. They burned her there, to prevent her
falling into Union hands. And the Yankee troops surged
back and reoccupied Baton Rouge.

In the confusion, Lauriel Doumier slipped from the
house in which Tennessee McGraw had had her locked,
climbed down a drainpipe, and mounted the horse he
had left behind, since he had gone down to New Orleans
by steamboat. She rode out of Baton Rouge, feeling the
already noticeable swelling of her pregnancy jolting
with every stride the beast took. She hoped fervently
that the jolting would bring about a miscarriage. For she
hated her unborn child with the same intensity that
she did the man who had fathered it by force. In this, she
had no luck. But she did succeed in escaping both the
Confederate and Union patrols. By the time Tyler had
reached the city, she was miles away from there, heading
back to New Orleans, into whose teeming streets she
disappeared as completely as though she had never been.

Tyler, after four days of fruitless search, came back to
New Orleans. He entered that city without a pass by
the simple expedient of debarking at René Doumier's

landing above the city. Then, after having swept the debris from the fat little Quadroon's grave, and laid a bunch of wild flowers upon it, he walked into the city, arriving just after nine o'clock at night. He moved into the St. Charles Section by a little used route, zigzagging through the streets to evade the Yankee patrols. By eleven, he was safely at the Drakes' residence.

He held Sue, clad in nightdress and wrapper, small and feather light as a young child, in his arms. Years of going without proper food because of the blockade, had made her very thin and pale; but when he told her he must go, that in sober fact, it might be years before he could see her again, the last pale hint of color left her cheeks. She clung to him and cried, and roused the servants to give him food and drink.

Later, long after midnight, they sat together on the sofa, with Sue's bright head cradled against his shoulder. They did not talk, but sat there listening to the Grandfather clock in the hall taking the minutes away from them with slow and measured sound.

"Ty," Sue whispered, "it's getting mighty late. . . ."

"And we can't afford talk," Tyler said angrily. "I know, Sue. There's one more thing I can't afford either, and that's the wear and tear on my nerves—the pure damn agony inside my guts that comes from sitting here night after night, talking to you like we were strangers. . . ."

"Ty—" Sue said.

"You don't rightly need fire to make a hell, Babydoll. Ice will do mighty damn fine. All it takes for me is the sight of you sitting there, so close to me, and yet so many million aching miles out of reach. With my arms itching to hold you, and my mouth burning to kiss yours, and my eyes fair blinded by the sight of you, and—"

"Ty," she implored him, "please!"

"The rest of me," he went on savagely, "just plain hurting from wanting you. . . ."

"You promised, Ty," Susan wept. "Oh, Ty, you promised!"

"I know. Which is why I'm going to obey Ben Butler's order and get out of New Orleans. No other reason—I've stood all I can. . . ."

He stood up, his mouth a crooked wound across his hawk-lean face.

" 'Bye, Babydoll," he said.

Sue got up very slowly. She looked at him, standing there, while the tears gathered like crystals in her eyes, and spilled very slowly over her lashes, making twin tracks down her face, and trembling like moonsilver on her quivering lip corners in the light of the candles. Then, very quietly, and with enormous dignity, she put out her hand.

"Goodbye, Tyler," she said.

CHAPTER NINE

ALL THINGS RAN TOGETHER FINALLY: WAVE LIFT AND SEA surge and grey mist, driving. And time and thought and belief and caring and man's hope. What was left was emptiness, impenetrable even to gull mew and tern whimper and the white and black spread of ominous albatross, crucified against the void of heaven; unbroken even by smoke plume or sail glint or land-dark lancing the rim of vision.

March third, 1864. The date itself was a nothingness. So many slate grey days, days thunderous with storm, blue bright days, until they, too, ran together in the flux of time and what was left, was apathy.

Tyler pushed his hand under his shirt, and rubbed the edges of the great, crescent-shaped scar that almost bisected his middle. He often did that; for when the weather was bad, his old wounds ached. He had twelve of them, all of them gotten the day that the Union Cruiser *Niphon* had laid a shrapnel burst clean on the bridge of the *Sea Witch* just outside New Inlet. His helmsman had been badly wounded; his Executive Officer, while unhurt, knocked unconscious by the concussion. So Tyler had taken the wheel and brought the *Sea Witch* in, with eleven hunks of Union steel in his hide, his belly ripped across by a shell splinter, not quite deep enough to cut through the muscles protecting his vitals; and he had spent the next three months in a Wilmington Hospital where the doctors came closer to killing him than the Yankees had. When the almost undamaged *Sea Witch* was readied for sea under another captain, the crew mutinied to a man, swearing they'd sail under nobody else than their beloved "Old Man" who always brought his ships in, come hell or high water.

And Tyler, looking like an emaciated ghost, had gotten out of bed, and sailed the *Sea Witch* back to Nassau finally, to find the *Captain Pat* waiting for him. She was a good craft, a great craft, a shade faster than the *Sea Witch*, and much, much stronger. He had run her in and out of the blockade for almost a year now, since the day he took command in April, 1863. His fame had spread, men fought to sail with him; even the blockading captains knew him not by name, but by the title Captain Rebel, which he flaunted like a banner across the sweep of seas, and the prize money offered for his capture was the highest on record.

All this should have been a source of pride. But he felt no pride. What he did feel was a weariness nearly mortal, an emptiness inside him as vast and echoing as the sea and sky. Lauriel was gone, vanished utterly from the world of men. And he had neither seen nor had one scribbled note from Susan since that August day in 1862 when he had quitted New Orleans, his great cotton raid come to naught, and all his bright plans of a world well gained for Sue, broken upon the rock of her fidelity.

He had been successful ever since. He did not know how much money he had. His salary alone had amounted to fifty five thousand dollars in those eleven months. To the credit of Meredith Associates be it said that they continued to pay him even while he was hospitalized. But he no longer bothered to count his mounting fortune; did not, because money was another thing that didn't matter any more.

He amused himself mightily while in port: there were in Nassau a yellow wench, and the young wives of two elderly British officials. In Wilmington there was the exceedingly pretty spouse of a blind and crippled Confederate Colonel, whom she nursed with matchless devotion, leaving him only when Tyler Meredith was in port. Then she would slip from the helpless side of her soldier husband, rendered by fate into something less than a man, and come to Tyler's lodgings, where she would weep and mourn and call herself a sluttish bitch and eternally damned, and proclaim her eternal love for her martyred mate while lying naked in her lover's arms.

Tyler had found this amusing at first. It fitted into his ironic concept of human falsity and frailty; but he was tired of it now. Death tired and belly sick of her and all such meaningless loves. The last three voyages before this one he had not seen her at all; but this time, she had come to his lodgings and made such a noise in the street that in self defense he had had to admit her. And she had wept and cursed herself and been as dementedly passionate as ever, so that watching her blood flecked mouth, bitten through with her own teeth, her insane writhings, even the counterfeit of passion died within him, leaving him cold and sick. Afterwards, she had been more reasonable. He had talked to her until nearly dawn, convincing her finally to take the money he offered her that would enable her to take her husband back to their Georgia home. She had taken the money; but whether or not she had truly gone he didn't know. He fervently hoped she had. . . .

He would sight Nassau within the hour. And waiting at his diggings would be the perfumed notes. And on the pier itself, the Quadroon wench. He shuddered, thinking about it.

He was exactly right, of course, about his prospects in Nassau. He dismissed the Quadroon with a smart slap on her bottom, saying he'd see her soon. The notes he tore, unread, into tiny pieces, and let them fall into the unlit fireplace. He sat there, thinking.

Vivian. I can talk to him. He'd understand. Funny. He and Ced are so different. Cedric's the hearty type, gay, and thoughtless, and—animal, sort of. But Vivian's quiet. And peaceful. No not peaceful—he *has* peace. Strange what a different thing that is. He sure Lord has done one damned fine job of managing the Nassau office. . . .

He got up with sudden decision and strode out of the room. Ten minutes later, he walked into the Nassau Branch Office of Meredith & Associates.

"I've had enough," he growled without ceremony. "Do I get time off to go to New Orleans, or do I quit outright?"

Vivian applied a fresh match to his pipe.

"Temperamental beast, aren't you?" he drawled. "Of course you get time off. Edgy as you are right now, you'd probably pile the *Captain Pat* into a wharf and sink her. Besides, I'm not your employer. You're a major stock holder and therefore self employed. What I don't understand, Ty, is the reason for all the heat. . . ."

"Sorry," Tyler said. "Reckon you called it. I am edgy. I've seen a few too many good men die for things that weren't worth dying for in the first place. . . ."

"Depends upon what you think is worth dying for," Vivian said. "By the way, old boy, I nearly forgot. The *Captain Pat II* is almost ready. In fact, she should be launched the first of July, which means you'll have her about the middle or the end of August."

"Me? Why? What's wrong with the *Captain Pat I?*"

"Nothing. Only the *Pat II* is one of the fastest, most maneuverable vessels ever built. She has twin screws, not paddles, Ty. You can put one propeller full ahead, and the other half astern, and turn her in her own length. And she's made of steel. She's the fourth craft in the world to use steel plate construction. Naturally, she cost a devil of a lot of money. . . ."

"So?" Tyler said.

"The stockholders, old boy. Some of the same ones who were howling for your blood two years ago, have voted that she be entrusted to no other captain. One out of three blockade runners is being captured these days— and you're one of the few skippers who have never lost a vessel. The only one, I believe, who has kept a perfect record over so long a time. . . ."

"I can take my crew with me?"

"Of course, Ty. They almost mutiny every time they have to sail with anyone else. Hargraves is the worst. He promptly comes down with a mysterious ailment, and takes sick leave 'til you're back."

"You know," Tyler said soberly, "It's plumb, downright frightening the faith the Chief has in me. Don't know why he should have. He's lived through a couple of close shaves due to errors of judgment on my part. . . ."

"He," Vivian said, "believes in your luck. But, beyond that, he believes your luck is based upon your integrity. And not even he could call that show of bringing the *Sea Witch* into Wilmington, after you'd been cut practically in half by a shell, luck. That was something else: pride and faith in yourself, in your knowledge, and your competence. And something more: from the amount of blood you were losing, you'd have been perfectly justified in lying down and submitting to capture, rather than bring your ship in at the accepted cost of your life. For you had accepted it, old boy, even if you had underestimated your basic toughness. . . ."

"Wasn't shot in half. That splinter had ripped all the way through, my guts would have fallen out like—"

"Yes?" Vivian said.

"Like Reed Clayton's," Tyler said bitterly. "And I didn't have any noble thoughts. It was just instinct, I reckon. Figured I was going to die, because I was losing too much blood. So wasn't it natural to prefer to die free on my own soil than on the deck of a Yankee vessel?"

"No," Vivian said. "The average man doesn't give a damn where he dies. He is too concerned with the fact that he is dying. You negate everything, Tyler; you belittle every fine thing you've done. To your credit it can only be said that you don't boast about the vile ones.

That's one of the most maddening things about you—
that you, a man who brought his ship in under fire, with
his life pumping out of him, his clothes so plastered to his
body with his own blood that they had to cut them off
of him, could seriously believe that anyone on earth
can diminish the meaning of—honor."

"I can," Tyler said flatly. "I have."

"You've tried. And your drunkenness and your wenching have been exactly as effective in reducing your essential decency, your incorruptibility, as the chains,
whips, and hairshirts of the medieval penitents were in
modifying the lusts of the flesh. . . ."

Tyler stared at his cousin.

"Goddamn you, Vivian!" he said. "Goddamn your
soul to hell!"

Then he turned on his heel and strode out of there.

A month later, he was in Galveston, Texas, having had
great difficulties in even getting that far. The blockade
off Mobile had become nearly impossible to run. The
Union cruisers were capturing as high as eighty per cent
of all the craft that tried it. Since it had become too
risky to ship aboard one of the Yankee coasting steamers
sailing out of Matamoros, Mexico, to New Orleans, so
well known had his name become, and because of the
danger that one of the dozens of Yankee spies from
Nassau might point him out, he was forced to take the
train North to Houston. By law, the trains of the Confederacy were forbidden to run faster than ten miles an
hour. The prohibition was needless as far as the Houston

train was concerned; eight miles an hour would have caused it to fall apart. At intervals, the engineer stopped it, and he and the fireman strolled off into the prairie to shoot quail. But they did get to Houston finally; and after two days, Tyler was able to buy a fairly respectable horse.

He set out to ride to Louisiana. On his way, he fought off a gang of bushwhackers, intent upon stripping him of his fine clothes and the gold they were sure he carried. Tyler was very good with a revolver, even from horse-back. The bushwhackers fled, two of them wounded. But at St. Martinsville, he gave way to his weakness, fatigue, and the effects of his old wounds. He was abed for three weeks, tenderly cared for by an Acadian family, who not only made no attempt to rob him of the money belt which they took off him and hid for safe-keeping while he tossed unconsciously in fever, but also refused to accept one penny for their services when they gave it back to him after he had recovered his faculties. Tyler, seeing their poverty, especially the miserable con-dition of their livestock, bought them a cow, a boar, and three brood sows, from a neighboring farmer. These they took. These were real. Money to them was mean-ingless and a symbol of corruption. They know, Tyler thought, what it takes a heap of so-called smart folks a lifetime to learn.

He reached New Orleans on May fifth, 1864. That was the day that the first battle of the Wilderness began. But he did not know that. His mind was intent upon other things. He rode, weary, travel-stained, unshaven, straight to George Drake's house.

Susan, herself, opened the door for him. Looking at her, he felt the pain moving in his heart. She had always been small; but now, her thinness hurt him to look at. He realized, suddenly, that everytime he had come home she had looked frailer than the time before.

If this damned war doesn't end soon, he mused . . . but then he stopped, unwilling to complete his own fearful thought.

She didn't say anything. She just stood there, looking at him, while the joy poured into her face like an illumination. Then, very slowly, she came to his waiting arms.

CHAPTER TEN

FATHER JOSEPH MEREDITH SAT IN THE SHADE OF A TREE
on a little knoll and looked down on the camp, on the
banks of the Rapidan. Not that you could tell it was a
camp to look at it. The only way you could do that
was by the smell. That smell was composed of many
things: the smudge of cooking fires, the acceptable odor
of beef being roasted, the stench of the latrines, and,
closer, the stink of unwashed bodies. There were no
tents. There hadn't been for a long time. Some of the
men had "flies," sheets of canvas with buttons and but-
ton-holes about the edges; three of them fastened together made a not too bad shelter. Like everything that
smacked of orderly manufacture, these had been captured from the enemy. Except guns and gunpowder, and
the fine ironclads with the bad engines, the Confederacy
produced nothing, while the things she had from before
the war, railroads and wagons for instance, were in the
last stages of wearing out.

Besides the captured "flies," some of the men had
built "she-bangs," which were a kind of leanto. They
made them by driving two forked sticks into the ground,
laying a pole in the crotch of the forks, angling two
more poles down from that into the direction that the

wind came from, and piling brush on the angled poles.
But most of them didn't even bother to do that. They lay
on the ground, wrapped in the tattered shreds of blankets. They were so hardened by three years of war that
they dropped instantly into slumber, feeling neither the
cold nor the damp, nor the lice that devoured them.

They had been in camp for some time. You could tell
that because most of the men were clean shaven. By
some unwritten law, beards were mostly reserved for
officers. In the haste of marching and counter marching,
in the press of battle, beards sprouted on every face.
But in camp, men shaved them off because they made
one more nesting place for the lice.

The men lolled about. A dozen poker and dice games
went on at the same time. Two intellectuals bent over
a game of chess. Some of the younger men, their youth
as yet unforgotten, knuckled down, playing marbles.
Aggies and peewees and flints were prized. In battle, the
larger ones made fair substitutes for minié balls when a
man had shot away his last. Others played ball, making
weird and wonderful games of their own invention. A
few wrote letters.

Father Joseph looked down upon the men of his regiment. What was it called now? Oh, yes, Howell's regiment. The Louisiana Rifles didn't exist any longer. Of
the men who had marched away to war under that
proud name, only he and George Drake were left. The
others were dead, or so badly wounded that they had
been invalided out. A few had deserted. It was strange
how few. Many of the men weren't even from Louisiana
now. They had been shifted from the West, to Central

Tennessee, and after that to Virginia. The Rifles had been dissolved for lack of effectiveness, and after that Smith's Regiment had been formed of their remnants, and Boswell's Regiment out of the shreds and tatters of Smith's, and Thompson's out of Boswell's and—God! Was there no end to it?

His boys. His and God's. His lips moved forming words.

But there was a coldness at the core of his heart and he ceased to pray.

After Shiloh, he had, by an effort of will, put down his doubts; but they rose again to plague him. Some of them were doubts no longer; they had crystallized into certainties. The Confederacy had won many more battles than the Union; but even in winning them, the South had lost the war. Already. Perhaps even before now; maybe even the day that old Edmund Ruffin had yanked the lanyard of the cannon which sent the first shot screaming upon Fort Sumter. There had been brilliant feats of arms, masterly cavalry maneuvers, generalship on the part of the South's leaders nigh onto genius. But—

But the North's victories stayed won. The South's didn't. There was the grinding necessity of fighting them over and over again until all the world was drowned in blood. No major city captured by the Union: New Orleans, Baton Rouge, Natchez, Vicksburg, Nashville— ever again fell permanently into Confederate hands. They had slaughtered Yankees by the tens of thousands, while losing by the thousands themselves. The only trouble was that the North could afford the tens of thousands, while now, in May, 1864, the South was down to her irreplaceables; near the time when a General must refuse a battle he was certain of winning, because he couldn't even afford the men it would cost him to win.

What ate at Father Joseph's heart was the impossibility of stopping the slaughter. The war, which he and many other men knew was lost, must go on. He could not accustom himself to the violent, unlovely dying; and it was far worse now, knowing that it served for naught. On the other side, there were men, as good Christians as he, praying for victory to the same God, to Whom he prayed. Which of them would God listen to—if—

He stiffened against the pine, the sickness of death inside his vitals. That thought again. I must not, he cried inside his heart; this is sinful and wicked and— But the thought moved resistlessly across his consciousness, shaping itself in letters as bright as the campfire: If there is a God. . . .

He was about to fall to his knees and say his prayers; but before the words could form upon his lips, he saw George Drake coming toward him. George had a steaming mug in his hand.

"Here, Padre," George said, "drink this. It's coffee. Real, honest to john coffee, not roasted peanut hulls. . . ."

"Where did you get this, George?" Father Joseph said.

"From the Yankee pickets," George said calmly. "Traded a pound of chewing tobacco for a pound of coffee. Rightly decent boys, those Yanks. . . ."

Father Joseph sat there, considering the thought. Was it more or less terrible that men who no longer hated each other should continue to kill? He didn't know. Yes, the Yankees were rightly decent boys, and so were the Southerners, and so were most men everywhere. The sentries of the two armies exchanged things, swam in the river together when their officers weren't looking; talked across the barriers about home and the girls they'd left behind them with the same sick longing. Brothers. They were brothers, men, often, of the same faiths; and still it must go on until only the greybeards and children were left and the world was wrecked beyond hope of repairing.

He sipped the scalding coffee. Now, in May, it was still a little cool for swimming; but the soldiers exchanged their surpluses for the other's lacks by floating them across the Rapidan on tiny rafts. In the stillness he looked at George Drake.

George was a sight to see. The seat of his butternut trousers were patched in the shape of a heart pierced by an arrow. Such designs were all the rage in the Army of Northern Virginia. Some fanciful wag, last fall, had started the fashion. Now nobody had the old round or oval or square patches. Red flannel was in great demand, because it made the designs stand out more clearly. There were bleeding hearts and hearts entwined, pierced hearts—and diamonds, spades, and clubs—anything and everything the longing or the ribald heart of a soldier could imagine. On his feet, George wore rope sandals with wooden soles. He was lucky. Many of the men were barefooted.

But it was his face that held Father Joseph most of all. Thin from too little food, and most of that bad, and covered with the stubble of a beard, George Drake's face, nevertheless, was one of the most peaceful in the world. Far more peaceful than mine, Father Joseph thought bitterly. For George Drake was that rare thing, a natural soldier. He was alive after three years of war because he was. He dug himself a little hollow with his bayonet or his hands each time he stopped, no matter how tired he was. He fired with great care, aiming well, and squeezing the trigger instead of jerking it. He was often afraid; but always dominated the fear. When he had to run, he ran carefully, in zigzags, taking advantage of every piece of natural cover the terrain afforded. He could go to sleep anywhere, even standing up. He could eat anything without getting sick. He was impervious to heat or cold. And above all, he didn't think too much.

He had not seen his wife since the war began. In the first year of the war he had been too far away from New Orleans, and too busy, to get a furlough, though he often asked for one. In the second, there was no longer any home to get a furlough to. He didn't worry about it any more than was absolutely necessary. He knew that the Yankees were rightly decent boys, and that rape was not one of their failings. He suspected that Sue, in a captured city, was suffering less than the women in the cities still in Confederate hands. New Orleans, belonging once more to the Union, was no longer blockaded. And neutral ships could bring in the supplies that the rest of the South was slowly dying for the lack of. He had an unshakable belief in his wife's virtue. Other women could and did err, driven by loneliness, after years of separation from their men. But not Sue. He was sure of that. He did not think her perfect. He was aware that she had a lingering fondness for Tyler Meredith. But Tyler was not in New Orleans. He was running the blockade on the high seas. He was not there, and he could not possibly enter the city. On that score, George's mind was at ease.

George was a good Christian in a solid, unimaginative way. He did not get his entrails tangled over his own failures. When he was furloughed to Richmond or St. Petersburg, he occasionally consorted with whores. He knew that it was a sin, but he did not attach too much importance to it. He came back, prayed over his failings until his mind was at ease; and the next time he was in Richmond, either abstained from loose women or consorted with them again according to how he felt. He drank a great deal. He was fully and clearly aware that a man in hourly danger of dying had a very nearly perfect right to get drunk and to appease his sexual hungers. The teachings of his religion were against it, so he appeased them, too, by use of the wise and tolerant techniques set up by the church itself. He sinned, prayed until he found a sort of peace; and sinned again, repeating the pattern as often as was necessary. But he did not torment himself with guilt, and trouble himself with subtleties. He was not a subtle man.

Not the least of his achievements was the fact that now, after three years of war, he was still a high private. He had been wounded twice, and decorated for bravery three times. But each of the acts for which he had been decorated had been accidental, resulting from doing the right thing under the circumstances he found himself in.

Nothing he ever did had that dash that earns a man a promotion on the field.

He had known a great many officers and men with great dash, elan, courage. And all of them were dead now. It was very beautiful and inspiring and brave to charge across an open field waving a sabre and bellowing the Rebel yell. But a minié ball didn't know the difference. It simply went into your guts with a soft plop, and tore all hell out of your insides. It was a great deal less beautiful and inspiring and brave to wiggle forward across that field on your belly, using every stone, brush, stump and hollow as cover. But like that you often got there and killed the enemy. And if you didn't, it was simply bad luck. A man could accept bad luck; but it robbed death of all comfort when you lay there gutshot or lungshot, strangling in your own blood and reflecting that you'd been a damned fool.

Something in Father Joe's face caught his attention. Ever since Shiloh, he had seen that sadness in the Padre's eyes. But now it was worse, far worse. It was more than a bad sadness, a very bad sadness; it was the death of hope. That shocked him. A man could lose hope. He had, himself, many times. But always in battle. Afterwards, safe in camp, hope came back again. He had never permitted himself to lose it before a battle. That was the worst thing of all. It was as truly suicidal as real panic. Fear was a lifesaver; it made a man alert, conscious, quick. But panic paralyzed you, pinned you down in the open under fire, made you do the wrong things at the wrong times. And to go into battle without hope was as bad—no, worse. What shocked him was that a minister with a true vocation should have it. That was really bad.

He, and all the other men in the Regiment, regarded Father Joseph as a sort of a talisman. The Padre was in the thick of every fight, yet he never got hit. Part of this, George knew, was due to the reluctance of the troops on either side to shoot a Chaplain. But in the heat of battle it was easy to make mistakes. And neither shrapnel nor grape shot had any nice sense of discrimination. Got to cheer him up, George thought; got to —like this he's no good. Doesn't look like he could even manage a prayer. . . .

"Look, Padre," he said. "New issue of the *Rapid Ann*. Got a new lesson in tactics in it. Reckon I'll send it on to Sue. . . ."

He handed the dirty, smudged copy of the camp newspaper to Father Joseph. It was written by hand in pencil on every kind of paper they could find. For the most part, Father Joseph rarely saw the paper. Some of the jokes in the *Rapid Ann* were hardly calculated to meet the approval of a Padre.

He took it without looking at it. Instead he looked at George Drake.

"Ever hear from her?" he said.

"No," George said sadly. "Hardly possible, now, Padre. She used to get a pass from the Feds to cross the lines, and mail me letters from any place still in our hands. But now that means travelling all the way past Alexandria. As I said, most Yankees is rightly decent boys; but bushwackers, Reb, or Yank—ain't. Lots of

wild niggers wandering about, too. Then I found out
about that business of searching—"

"Searching?" Father Joseph said.

"Yep. Lots of women were smuggling stuff out of
New Orleans to their relatives and the Army. Stuff like
salt and quinine. They can get medicines and such like
in New Orleans now. So they started searching 'em. . . ."

Father Joseph stiffened; his face white with anger.

"They searched—women?" he said.

"Not them. Not the soldiers. They brought in women
to do it. Lot of Unionist sentiment in the upper parts
of the State, you know. Those women are mostly Southern, with a few horsefaced Yankee women thrown in
for good measure. And they're rough. They make our
women go into a room and strip mothernaked. 'Course
the blinds are closed; but those Yanks always manage
to peek. And after they've searched their clothes,
they—"

"Yes, George," Father Joseph said, "go on."

"Don't reckon I ought to, seeing as how you're a
Padre. Heck, you're a man and a soldier. They search
their hair, and their bodies; they even look into the most
intimate places to see whether our girls have got tubes
of quinine—"

He was watching Father Joseph's face. The hopelessness was gone. Anger had replaced it. George sighed
with pure relief. It was going to be all right, now.

"One of the bad things about being a Parson," Father
Joseph said, "is that you're forbidden to swear!"

"Don't worry about it, Padre," George grinned.
"Reckon I can take care of that chore for both of us.

So—I had to forbid her to try it anymore. Gets right pert lonesome without her letters. But I'll be seeing her after this cruel war is over. . . ."

"You're sure of that, aren't you?" Father Joseph said.

"Yep. I'm the best damn—forgive me, Padre—entrencher, cover finder, and retreater in this man's Army. Don't reckon I'm a coward, though. That's no good either. Man shot for cowardice is just as dead as one killed in battle. Besides, cowards get themselves killed mighty near as often as heroes. They pause, stand up, and run for cover. Bullet that hits you from the back while you're running scrambles your guts just like one hitting you from the front while you're charging. Got it figured out: know just how brave to be without being a dead damnfool—again, Padre—of a hero; and just how scairt to keep my hide unperforated without panicking and doing something fatal. Don't want no more medals. Mighty little comfort in medals. Mostly your widow hangs them on the wall and throws 'em up at the fat pig of a profiteer she ups and marries after you're gone, and she's mad at him. Never volunteer. Never show the faintest sign of intelligence—brains gets you promoted; and in this here war, the Yankee sharpshooters do purely love a cornfed officer. Eat all you can, and sleep every chance you get. Stay out of the sight of sergeants. Disappear every time a lieutenant comes within half a mile of where you're at. Captains, majors, colonels and on up, is all right. Beneath their dignity to notice you. By the time their orders for a detail of men to do something rightly unpleasant, like burying corpses which have lain in the sun for four days, filters down to you, you can be three miles from there. Details is always formed of men on the spot. . . ."

Father Joseph threw back his head and laughed aloud.

"Drake's Tactics!" he chuckled. "George, I think you make a lot more sense than old Hardee ever did. . . ."

"Think so, too," George said complacently. "But, speaking of tactics, look what the *Rapid Ann* has to say on that subject. . . ."

He pointed a grimy finger at the smudged pencil scrawl.

"Tactics of kissing," Father Joseph read. "Recruit is placed in front of the piece. First motion—Bend the right knee; straighten the left; bring the head on a level with the face of the piece; at the same time, extend the arms and clasp the cheeks of the piece firmly in both hands. Second motion—Bend the body slightly forward; pucker the mouth, and apply the lips smartly to the muzzle mouldings. Third motion—Break off promptly, on both legs, to escape jarring or injury should the piece recoil."

"Very good!" Father Joseph laughed. He was feeling much better now. George had done that for him. George had the knack. Still, it was a little shameful to accept comfort from another, when, actually, it was his job to provide comfort.

"George," he said, "Think they'll attack?"

"Know they will. You know who's commanding 'em, Padre?"

"Yes," Father Joseph said, his voice very low, "Grant. . . ."

There was a silence between them. A long silence.

Down below, a soldier began singing "I'll Take You Home Again, Kathleen." It was a very beautiful song, haunting and sad, and sweet. It had been written that winter by a man named Crouch, a bugler in one of the other regiments. The soldier was Irish, and had a fine tenor voice. It soared on the silence, the notes silvery and sad.

"Well," George Drake said. "It had to happen sometime. . . ."

Father Joseph looked at him.

"What had to happen?" he said.

"That they'd give the command to one of those Western Generals: Thomas or Sherman or—Grant. . . ."

"I'll take you home again, Kathleen," the soldier sang. "Across the ocean wild and wide, to where your heart has ever been. . . ."

"You think—he can beat Lee?" Father Joseph whispered.

"Nope," George spat, "but then he don't need to—"

"And when the fields are fresh—" the tenor soared up.

"Why not?" Father Joseph said.

"Nobody ever needed to beat Marse Robert," George said. "All they needed to do was not to run from him. . . ."

"—And green—" the tenor quavered.

"You mean that even taking a hiding, they'll—?"

"Lick us in the end. They've always had more men. Heaps more. All they had to do was attack and get beat, then attack and get beat again. And again. 'Cause—"

"I'll take you to your home again," the soldier finished.

"They've always got replacements. We're robbing

Peter already to pay Paul even to stay up to strength
in any one sector. And every time they attack, they
weaken us. So we'll lick them and lick them and lick
them until we're too weak to lick them any more. Then
they'll attack one more time—and the war will be
over. . . ."

"George," Joseph Meredith said, "You should have
been a General."

"If I was, the war'd be over right now. I'd surrender
so blame fast it'd make your head swim. It's foolish
to go on. Our women and old folks and children are
suffering something awful. We can't win this war.
Reckon we never could have, only we thought so. I
thought so—up 'til Shiloh. Then I knew we couldn't.
We only could of won it if what we believed before
had been true: that the Yankees couldn't or wouldn't
fight. But anybody thinks Grant or Thomas or Phil
Sheridan or Sherman won't fight, is crazy. Them, or
the men under them. Had them licked at Shiloh the
first day. Any ordinary self-respecting Union General
would of retreated. But not Grant. Ever hear tell of
Ulysses retreating?"

"No," Father Joseph said.

"Nope. He gets licked and keeps on coming. Ain't
a man they got can out think Marse Robert. So don't
try it. Just roll over him and mash him flat. Don't play
tactics and maneuvering with him. That's his game.
Just hit him and hit him 'gain knowing you can afford
to get hurt, and he can't—not any more. In a way,
I'm glad."

"Glad?" Father Joseph said.

"Yep. Reckon we'll get home pretty soon, now. . . ."

On May fourth, 1864, they pulled back into the Wilderness, before Grant could advance to join battle with them. They marched along through the little green leaves just beginning to open, amid great masses of purple violets. They filed along the cowpaths between the oaktopped ridges, amid a suffocation of underbrush. If anything more was needed to prove what a master tactician Lee was, this was it. In this rank jungle, numbers counted for nothing. One man, with plenty of ammunition lying out of sight in this brush was truly the equal of ten charging to attack him. A squad, a platoon, with some of its numbers lying on the firing line, and others behind them to reload and pass them the muskets as fast as they needed them, could stand off a regiment. A regiment could stand off a division. A division could murder an army.

"Oh, this cover!" George Drake grinned. "This lovely, beautiful cover!"

Father Joseph said nothing. He was praying.

They drew up their lines that night along the Orange Turnpike. They dug in. And at seven thirty the next morning, having crossed Germania Ford, the enemy found them.

Afterwards, there was nothing much about it that either Father Joseph or George Drake could remember. The things that came to mind, recalling it, were chaotic: the feeling of surprise that this perfect terrain for defense was negated at first by the human element: by Yanks that attacked like no Yanks had ever attacked before, swarming amid the trees in a blue clad horde, rolling

Ewell's center up, breaking the first line in minutes,
the second in more minutes, and hurling them back upon
the third. But Confederate Ewell, one of Lee's finest
lieutenants, flanked them, finally, cutting Union General
Griffin's division to rags, to ribbons, driving them back;
then flanking to the left, Ewell caught Wadsworth's
Division flatfooted, and drove them back almost to
Wilderness Tavern. But there the Yankees had both
open ground and artillery, their best arm, the one thing
they understood with the love and precision and care
that the South lavished upon Cavalry; and they fought
the yelling, creeping, dodging grey and butternut boys
to a stand. To come out into the open was a mistake.
The mounds of Confederate dead before Warren's guns
proved that.

So they retreated, leading the Union troops back into
the Wilderness. And the battle settled down to a murderous rifle duel from cover, with a hundred men killed
every minute, and every man, North or South, trying,
in the intervals between the volleys to burrow straight
through to China. It went on like that all day and all
night, with the rifle flashes spitting the darkness under
the trees; even J. E. B. Stuart, the Bayard of the Confederacy, having met his match, his horsemen dismounted, fighting like infantry against the equally un-
horsed cavalry of Phil Sheridan. The fight went on all
the next day, and then it happened: the last straw, the
one, last, almost absolutely unacceptable thing, that
came as near to breaking Father Joseph Meredith as anything ever could. . . .

It hadn't rained in a long time, and the leaves under-

foot were as dry as tinder. Here and there in a dozen
places, then in a hundred, the rifle flashes set them afire.
Just out between the lines lay the dead—and the
wounded, half hidden in the brush, Union and Confederate alike. There were many more blueclad dead
and wounded than grey; but it didn't make any difference; by May, 1864, nobody had enough hate left in
his heart to exult over what happened to them.

The brush fires crackled forward, jumping from knoll
to knoll. The rifle fire died down, the men coughing and
crying from the smoke smudge that was strangling them.
And in the silence between the scattered bursts, the
first of the wounded began to scream.

Father Joe stood up; but George Drake tackled him
about the knees and brought him down heavily into the
brush. The young Chaplain hammered at George with
his fist, grating:

"Let me go, George! Don't you see, I've got to go!"

"No, Father," George said. "And please stop hitting
me. You're mighty damn' strong. . . ."

"Sorry," Father Joe whispered, "but for God's love,
man, listen to them!"

George could hear them all right. What was worse,
now that the wind had shifted, he could smell them, too.
The Confederate wounded were closer; you could see
them writhing in the fire. Then the paper cartridges in
their gunbelts began to explode from the heat. When
they went, a burst of smoke would balloon out from
the man's middle, and the man would jerk, his mouth
tearing open; the ugly, strangling, animal screams ripping
out. And afterwards you could see the little flames

licking about the black, curling holes torn in the uniforms, and under that—

"God!" Joseph Meredith wept, "God, God, God!"

George had four muskets he had taken off of dead
men. In a brush cover fight, extra muskets counted.
You got buddies, even slightly wounded men to reload
for you and pass them up as fast as you fired.

"Father," George said solemnly, "Will you reload
for me?"

And looking at him, Father Joe understood what he
meant.

"No!" he got out. "No, George, no!"

But twenty yards in front of them, a wounded man
screamed again. Father Joe bent and picked up a musket.
He bit the corner of a paper cartridge off, poured the
powder down the barrel, patched and rammed home
the ball, lifted the hammer, placed the cap in the little
hollow of the percussion lock. George lifted the Enfield,
sighted carefully. It slammed against his shoulder and
the screaming stopped. Father Joseph passed him up
another. George fired again and again and the anguished
crying in the smoke dark, flame-shot forest lessened.

Lessened, but did not cease. There were too many of
them, and most of them were too far away. All night
long they could hear them screaming, until one by one
the screams stopped. The silence was a mercy. A benediction. Even knowing that there was nothing left alive
between the lines. Death, when it came, however it
came, was always peaceful.

There was no answering fire from the Union lines.
Joseph Meredith walked out from their hiding place
and looked at the dead. After a moment, George Drake

followed him, and stood there looking at them too. They weren't pretty.

George saw the young Chaplain's hands come up, clawing at the insignia of the Cross he wore upon his uniform. He tore it loose, hurled it into the charred cinders underfoot, lifted his booted foot to grind it in; but George was too quick for him. He slammed into Father Joseph with his shoulder, knocking him aside. Then he bent down and picked up the insignia, the symbol of his Faith, brushed it off, and handed it back to Joseph.

"No, Padre," he said gently. "If you do this, what's to become of the rest of us?"

Joseph Meredith stood there, staring woodenly at his friend. The tears came down his face now, pencilling lines through the smoke grime.

Then, very slowly, he put out his hand, and took the Cross again, for the second time in his life.

And one thing more: As the beaten Union troops filed out of the Wilderness, leaving seventeen thousand dead and wounded behind, they came to the fork in front of Chancellorville House. The road to the left led back across the Rappahannock, back to the Potomac; back to good camps, food, even some comfort, back to life. But the right fork went back into the Wilderness again; past the Rebel front, back into that smouldering hell where the wounded burned to death, and at every step an hundred men went down forever. They came, tired, beaten, sore, heads bent, slogging along, out of step, their rifles at ragged angles, cursing, saying: "Licked again, by cracky!"

But at the fork they stopped. For a dumpy little man

in an old blue coat sat on horseback at the crossroads. A dirty frump of a man with a crushed campaign hat on his head, and a stub of a cigar clenched between his teeth. He sat there, motionless, chewing on the cigar, while tobacco juice ran down into his scraggly beard.

Then he lifted his hand and pointed to the right. The men stared a moment longer, then the musket barrels snapped into the correct angle, and the long, slanting lines of steel moved down that road toward death, but not silently. For every man there opened his mouth, and ripped the murky, smoke stained heavens apart with his cheers.

For George Drake had been right: Under Ulysses Grant, they could never be whipped, and they knew it.

CHAPTER ELEVEN

T YLER HELPED S UE UP INTO THE LITTLE BUCKBOARD.
As he did so, he felt the bones of her arm, sharply
through the scant covering of her flesh. She was terribly
thin now, and on the last two occasions he had visited
her, he noticed that she was suppressing a dry, but
distinctly noticeable cough. He was a great deal more
worried about her than he cared to admit, even to himself. He hadn't mentioned her failing health to her, both
because he knew how valiantly she was trying to keep
him from becoming aware of it; and because he had
the helpless feeling that there wasn't anything he could
do about it anyway. His contempt for the medical
profession was even greater than that he held for humanity at large. He got in, himself, and took the reins.

"Well, Babydoll?" he said.

"Oh—anywhere, Ty," Sue said. "I—I just couldn't
stand the house any longer. Ty—"

"Yes, Suebaby?"

"Why—don't you get married? You're a very handsome man and there are lots of nice girls who'd—"

He looked at her a long time and very steadily. The
words died on her lips.

"Now that we've disposed of that subject," he said
dryly, "what'll be talk about, Sue?"

235

"Oh, I don't know. The War, maybe. Do you think it'll be over soon, Ty?"

"Yep," Tyler drawled. "It'll be over soon and I say to hell with it. The only war I'm interested in right now is the battle I'm having with you, trying to make you see the light of reason. Funny—in a way, I'm fighting for my own salvation. The only decent emotion I've had in my whole blamed life is loving you—and look where that gets me. . . ."

"Is it," Sue said gravely, "really a decent emotion, Ty, when it leads you to make love to another man's wife?"

"Yep. It is. If you loved George, it would'nt be. I'd be an intruder, then—a kind of a thief. But all I'm trying to do is to repossess what was rightfully mine in the first place. . . ."

"I won't listen to this," Sue said. "I won't listen to you. You make things too hard for me, Ty. Every time I get my mind half way at ease, you bring up a new line of argument so straight that it takes me weeks to see what's wrong with it—mostly, I reckon, because I don't really want to see. Please, Ty—"

"No," he said. "I've got to have my say, Sue. Every time I try to talk sense to you, you put me off with your ideas about what's right, and what's wrong. . . ."

"According to you," Sue said tartly, "there aren't any such things."

"There are right and wrong, Sue," Tyler said quietly; "but they aren't as simple as folks try to make them. What I mean, I reckon, is that most rules and laws are plain nonsense, because they try to make a thing always right or wrong without taking the circumstances into consideration. . . ."

"We have to have laws, Ty—"

"I know, I know. But what we don't have to have is the law's rigidity. It's a crime to kill, steal, commit adultery. But I can give you a dozen examples offhand of times when it was eminently right to do any of those things. . . ."

"Right to kill, Ty?"

"Yep. For instance, down in Nassau, my cousin Vivian had a nigger houseboy named Hiram. Nice little fellow, reminded me a lot of Cato, except he was younger. He was a little odd, but we thought that was funny. Didn't interfere with his work. He was always hearing voices and the Spirit was always telling him to do things. Well, one day, the Spirit told him to kill all the white folks in Nassau. So he took a machete and started out to do it. Vivian, thank God, wasn't home. Hiram started down the street and met a German trader. Cut him damn near in half. Mr. Smithers, the storekeeper, was spry and fast. He only lost his right arm. Saw him running down the street with it dangling by a shred, with Hiram behind him swinging that machete. Just then, Mrs. Willoughby came out of the house with her five-year-old daughter Candace. We called her Candy. Prettiest little tyke you ever did see—"

"Tyler, for God's love—"

"I'm getting there, Baby. Hiram saw them, and stopped. He started walking toward them like a cat. His eyes were absolutely wild. Rolling in his head. That was when I shot him. And I shot to kill, Babydoll. Mind you, I liked Hiram. If he could have been captured and brought to trial, I'd have testified in his behalf on the score that a lunatic isn't responsible for his actions. But he had killed one man, half killed another, and the lives of a woman and a child were at stake. I've never felt the slightest guilt over killing him. . . ."

"I can see that," Sue said slowly. "Reckon if I asked you, you'd come up with an example justifying breaking every law there is. But, Ty, we have to have something to measure by—we have to!"

"We have. Human intelligence and the power to think. Take our case—"

"Oh, no! Please, Tyler, you mustn't. I—"

"You're married," Tyler went on calmly, "and in our society, there's only one thing that justifies that—a complete and abiding love for the person whose life you've decided to share. You don't love George Drake; you never did. You married him in anger against me, not in love. All right, it was understandable under the circumstances, and mostly my fault. You made a mistake. I'll accept that. What I won't accept is the idea that you have to spend the rest of your life paying for that mistake, that the woman must suffer for the error of the school girl. The church frowns on divorce, and adultery is a sin. I solemnly submit, Doll, that either of them is less of a sin than the obscenity of wifely relations with a man you don't love. . . ."

"Tyler, please! It's not the Church, not the laws of men. Our Lord, Himself, forbade divorce in His own words. . . ."

"Our Lord forbade a lot of things. And He lived nineteen hundred years ago. What He said was: "Whom

God hath joined together, let no man put asunder . . ."
But you're assuming one heck of a lot, if you think that
a loveless marriage is one joined by God. Reckon He'd
consider it a deceit, entered under false pretenses, in-
valid, and a sin. Besides, by the record, He wasn't rigid.
He could think; He took things into consideration.
Remember what He said to the woman taken in adultery? 'Neither do I condemn Thee. Go and sin no
more. . . .'"

"He forgave sins, Ty," Sue said gently. "He didn't
encourage people to commit them. . . ."

"Oh, hell!" Tyler said. "What's the use?" He jerked
at the reins, turning the horse's head.

"Don't take me home yet," Susan said. "I know you're
angry. But please have patience with me, Ty. I did so
want to go for a nice long ride—sort of clear away the
cobwebs or something like that. I can't help the way I
think. You can't change the habits of a lifetime. . . ."

"I'm not taking you home," Tyler said. "Just remembered I'd better stop by the British Consulate. Told
Viv he could write me in care of the Consul. Safer that
way. Don't want any military censor poking into my
mail. . . ."

Sue sat in the buckboard and waited for him. He came
out of the Consulate holding the open letter. He walked
very slowly, gazing at the ground; but when he was
very close, he raised his head, and she saw his face.

"Ty—" she breathed.

He didn't answer her. He climbed into the buckboard
and took the reins. They moved off, winding through
the narrow streets of the city.

"Ty," she said. "Ty, you've got to tell me!"

He looked at her, and his eyes were ice.

"Why?" he said. "By your own decision, you've declined to share my life, Sue. You want nothing from me—neither my joys, nor my sorrows . . ."

She put her hand on his arm.

"I can't share your joys," she said slowly. "That's forbidden me. But nothing I know of, no law, no canon, no dogma says I can't take your sorrows upon myself, and try to comfort you. Tell me, Ty—please—"

He looked at her a long time, and she could see the pain moving in his eyes.

"All right," he said. "The *Captain Pat* went down in a gale off the Georgia coast—with nearly all hands. She was Nassau bound, and had run out of Wilmington through the blockade. They were already manning the pumps when the gale came up. The Yankees had holed her hull in five places, and her gunwales were already nearly awash. Didn't have a chance. Sea swamped the fires, and without steam the pumps went out. The hand pumps were useless in such a gale. Another steamer picked up three survivors. Just three, Sue, out of all those men aboard. I knew them all. They were my crew, my friends—"

"Oh, I am so sorry, Ty," She whispered.

"Sorry!" he grated. "Hell of a lot of good that does me. Those boys trusted me. Twice before they've threatened to mutiny before they'd sail with somebody else in command. And I left them—to come to see you. Because I had to see you. Damn it, Sue, if I'd been there, they'd been alive today, or—"

"Or you'd have gone down with them," Sue said

flatly, "and condemned me. So now, on top of making
you unhappy by refusing to divorce my husband or
become your mistress, I'm to blame for the loss of your
ship. . . ."

Tyler looked at her. Then he smiled a little.

"Sorry, Babydoll," he said. "That was rotten of me,
wasn't it? Not your fault. You didn't want me to come.
You haven't written me a line; you would have been a
heck of a lot better off if I had stayed put where I was,
and—"

She caught both of his hands in hers, suddenly.

"Tyler," she whispered; "Oh, Ty—love, if you hadn't
come, I think I would have died!"

He sat there, staring at her.

"You would have died if I hadn't come," he said
slowly; "and now that I'm here, what good is it, Sue?
What good at all?"

"It is good!" She sobbed. "Just seeing you—just
having you here! I wake up in the morning, and I say
to myself: In a few hours he'll come for me—and I live
all day upon that. When I do see you, I'm so wonderfully, deliriously happy. And at night, I go to bed
thinking: tomorrow I'll see him again. Sometimes I can't
sleep; but when I do, I dream about you—always, Ty.
You don't know what a comfort it is to have you here,
you don't—"

"A comfort," he said. "For you it's a comfort. Reckon
women are made different from men—closer to angels,
maybe. For me, it's—torture. Actual, physical torture.
I'm just not pure and ethereal, Babydoll. I love you,
and I want you; and for me they're the same thing. I

could make verses about your eyes being bluer than the sky; but that wouldn't stop me from wanting to put my arms around you, or keep my mouth from aching to kiss yours, or—"

"Tyler, for God's love!"

"Have any effect upon my wanting to hold you all night, naked in my arms, and get sons from you, and to live out my days at your side in peace and quietude. It's better when I don't see you. I can kind of dull my mind with drink, or work myself into a stupor. Sometimes I even forget you for as long as five minutes at a time. But this—this is no good. You buy your comfort out of my anguish, Doll. . . ."

"Tyler," she whispered, "haven't you any pity in your heart?"

"Not a damned bit. Come on, I'll take you home, now."

"No. Not home. Take me to the Church, Ty."

"The Church? Why, Sue?"

"I want to say a prayer—for the *Captain Pat*, and for the souls of the men who drowned. Only that, Ty—and maybe another little prayer to God to give me back the strength you've taken away from me. Will you, Ty?"

"All right," he said; "Anything you say, Babydoll."

He stood a little behind her, watching her as she knelt at the altar rail in prayer. He didn't kneel. He stood there, stony-eyed, and watched her.

He had prayed before, in his hour of need, and his prayers had not been answered. He had prayed unselfishly, not for himself, but in behalf of others; and his

appeals had been ignored. He would not humble himself
again; he would not negate the cold precision of his
intellect. What he was now, was a proud thing: a man
without hope, refusing to bow to incertitude. He had
seen good men go down to death, and the wicked
saved. He had seen heroes die, and cowards live. And,
he had seen the exact reverse of those things; but in
neither was there any discernible pattern.

Chance, blind accidentality, superior force, stronger
intellect, determined the order of the world. And these,
the chance, the accidentality, the force, the intellect,
were sometimes combined with virtue, goodness, humility, sweetness of heart, and sometimes not; as far as he
could see, they were just as effective when coupled with
guile, deceit, vileness, dishonesty—or perhaps even a
little more effective, he could not tell. Human behavior,
good or ill, was a complete irrelevancy to man's fate.
Man was at best a sport and a plaything for—

Blind Cosmos? Or the ancient, ribald gods?

The Greeks, he thought mockingly, were smarter
than we. They made their head god a drunken old
lecher; and created Prometheus chained to his rock,
vulture-devoured; Tantalus in his pool that receded
when he bent to drink, with fruits overhead that blew
just beyond his fingertips when he reached for them;
Orestes, pursued the world over by the furies as symbols
of man's fate. Their gods were capricious, doing things
without rhyme or reason, and damned if that doesn't fit.
Fight a war, and one set of deities can help out Priam
and Hector, while another set urge on Achilles and
Odysseus. That would be kind of useful, right now.

Instead we have to compete for the favor of the same God. . . .

Only thing they were wrong about though, was that somehow or another they managed to leave man his dignity and his self respect. Life isn't like that. Life is a hurricane roaring along blowing down outhouses and catching mankind with his trousers at half mast. . . .

Sue stood up slowly, and turned to him, her face once more serene.

Tyler looked at her in mockery and contempt, and wonder and awe and envy at her certainty. But he didn't say anything. She took his hand.

"All right, Tyler," she said gently. "You can take me home now. . . ."

The summer of 1864 wore itself out. Cold Harbor had been fought. Petersburg was under siege. And Sherman was loose in Georgia, scorching the earth until a crow flying across the track of ruin he'd left behind would have to carry his own rations. Off Cherbourg, France, the *Keararge* had sunk the *Alabama*. Submarines and aerial reconnaissance by observation balloons had been used in warfare for the first time in the history of the world. And Farragut had damned the torpedoes in Mobile bay. Hood was dug in before Atlanta; would he hold? Could he? And Lee was whipping Grant every time they met, covering the ground with piles of Union dead, which stubborn Grant, "Butcher" Grant to the Northern newspapers now, would ask no truce from Marse Robert even to bury, leaving his own wounded

to die as he pounded on: attack, defeat, attack, no quarter asked or given, no prisoners exchanged, while blue
clad boys starved to death or died of scurvy, of tuberculosis, of filth in Andersonville prison because the
South no longer had food or blankets or medicines to
give them, having in his glacial heart the courage to
ignore the cries against him, knowing his monstrous
policy was actually a kindness, because they, the
wounded left to die, the men littering the slopes of every
Southern breastworks, the prisoners dying by agonizing
inches in Rebel prisons were as nothing compared to the
men who would have to die if the war went on another
year. The summer of Sixty four ground on while the
American States drowned in blood, in a fratricidal con-
test between butchers, in the worst fought, worst
planned, most costly war in terms of lives lost that
Americans had ever fought, and perhaps ever were
to. . . .

Tyler spent those days with Sue. Since, in December
1862, General Butler had been recalled from the civic
administration he did so very well—as a result of his
famous woman's order—and sent back to the military
operations he did so very badly, Tyler was not troubled
by the Occupation Authorities. Nor by his own lack of
participation in the great adventure. Knowing that he
would not be recalled to Nassau until the *Captain Pat II*
was ready, he moved out of the St. Louis Hotel, and
took an apartment in the Vieux Carré, with Cato and
Bessie to work for him. He scrupulously paid them
wages, which Cato used to get drunk upon, causing
Bessie to crown his efforts with any available heavy

implement. Thereafter Tyler paid the wages to Bessie, and peace reigned in the household.

On August twenty ninth, he called upon Susan Drake. He had a letter from Vivian in his pocket. He found her in the sewing room, trying to salvage garments worn out by four long years, during which they had been irreplaceable. Ruth was with her.

"Sue," Tyler began. Ruth bit off a thread between her teeth, and stood up. Tyler looked at her. "Don't go, Kitten," he said. "This is going to be a mighty brief call. . . ."

Ruth sat down again.

"The *Captain Pat Second* is ready," Tyler said without ceremony. "I'll be leaving soon, Doll. . . ."

Sue did not move, or speak.

"How soon, Ty?" Ruth said.

"In about two weeks, maybe sooner. I should, actually, go tomorrow. But I reckon I'll hang around a bit more . . ." He moved toward the hall. "Just thought I'd let you all know," he said.

Sue got up then, and came to him.

"I—I'll walk you to the door," she said. "Excuse me, Ruth?"

Ruth did not answer her. She went on sewing.

Sue took Tyler's arm and walked down the hall with him.

"Ty—" she whispered. "Oh, Ty—"

"Yes, Babydoll?" he said gruffly.

"You'll come back soon, won't you, Ty? It won't be so long, like before, will it, Love? Tell me you'll come back soon!"

He stood there, looking at her.

"No," he said quietly. "I won't come back soon, Doll."

She stared at him, making no effort to hide her tears.

"But—after the war," she said, her voice high, taut, strangling. "It'll be over soon now. You said yourself, it—"

Her words slid down a long incline into silence.

"Ty!" she got out. "Oh, Ty, no! You couldn't! You'd never—"

His gaze swept over her like the lash of a whip.

"New Orleans isn't big enough for both of us, Sue," he said quietly. "And it sure Lord won't hold you, me, and George Drake. You asked me to respect your marriage. Well, I'm going to, the only way I know how. When I go, it'll be goodbye, Sue. For keeps."

She stood there, looking at him, and the tears were no longer droplets now, but a flood, an inundation. She stood there and she did not move or speak. She did not, because she couldn't.

Tyler grinned at her, his wide mouth twisted in mockery.

" 'Bye, bye, Babydoll," he said. "Be seeing you. . . ."

He lay awake, long after midnight, smoking a cigar and reading scattered snatches from his pocket edition of Shakespeare. He often did that. He knew whole scenes from the plays by heart. But always he seemed to find a new quotation that suited exactly his mood. Tonight, however, he was aware that little of what he read reached his mind. It was a hot night, and Tyler

was not given to sleeping in nightshirts or anything else.
His finger tips strayed over the ridges of scar tissue
on his muscular belly. He was not conscious of the gesture.

" 'Macbeth hath murdered sleep,' " he read.

Tyler Meredith hath murdered sleep, he mocked himself. Murdered it by his folly, and his pride . . . And it
was then, at that precise instant, before he could even
complete his thought, that he heard the knocking at
the door. The sound came, not from the entrance to his
bedchamber but from below, at the street level.

He thought about ringing for Cato; but dismissed the
thought. Even on the pittance that Bessie doled out to
him, Cato could afford his little nip. If the bellcord
had been attached to the lanyard of a thirty-two
pounder, it would have been difficult to awaken Cato.
And Bessie slept as soundly.

Tyler swore under his breath, and swung his long
legs from the bed. The knocking sounded again, louder
now. He slipped on his robe, and went out on the
gallery.

"Who's there?" he called.

She took a backward step from under the gallery, and
the moonlight fell upon her pitiful, grief-ravished face.
He stood there through a moment that stretched out to
the crack of doom and beyond. Then:

"Wait, Sue. I'll be right down," he said.

CHAPTER TWELVE

TYLER STOOD ON THE BRIDGE OF THE *Captain Pat II*, watching the shoreline move backward. It was pure comfort to see how fast any particular landmark dropped astern. The second *Captain Pat* could do a full nineteen knots, and cruise effortlessly for days on end at fifteen. She was three knots faster than any cruiser in the Union Service, and her powers of maneuver were all but incredible. He was sure the Federals would never be able to touch her; he would serve the war out in command.

The crew was shaping up well. Most of them were experienced blockade runners anyhow, lured to the *Pat Second* by high pay, and Tyler's fame. It was a good thought that the three survivors of the *Captain Pat I* had willingly, even eagerly signed aboard with the remark: "Cap'n Rebel don't get a body sunk. He brings his ships in, even if he has to half kill hisself to do it . . ." And Hargraves once more lorded it over the engine room, and the black gangs. Hargraves was not a survivor of the sinking. He had flatly and profanely refused to sail when Tyler was not skipper in command.

It was good, all of it: the backward speeding shoreline, the trim, off-white ship, the fine crew. That—and his memories of his last two weeks in New Orleans. He frowned a little, thinking about that. Of course it had been a joy and a glory; still—

Sue's reaction had startled him. He had been prepared for the worst: tears, recriminations, condemnation of herself, of him. But not for calm acceptance, awe, wonder, joy. Not for . . . her voice speaking, muffled, tired lips brushing the hollow of his throat:

"I didn't know it could be like this, Love. I simply didn't know. Even after being married, I—"

"Yes, Sue? he had said gently. "Yes, Babydoll?"

"I—thought it was—something a wife owed to her husband. A duty, Ty—and to get children. Ty! You don't reckon that I—that we—?"

"No, Dollbaby," he had said, his voice calm, reassuring, thinking: Wish I were sure; but you can't be. No good to scare her, though.

"Ty—it's strange. Thought I'd die of shame if ever I did such a terrible thing. But you know what, Ty?"

"No, what?" he had said.

"I—I'm not ashamed . . . I'm not, I'm not! I feel like a bird that's been let out of a cage. I feel like singing— like dancing. Only—" her voice dropped a languid octave, "I'm much too tired to dance. So tired . . . So wonderfully, deliciously tired. . . ."

And looking down at her, cradled in the crook of his arm, he had seen that she was already asleep.

He had awakened her just before dawn, and taken her back home, the knot of worry tight in his throat. If Ruth had awakened—Lord, God! Sister or not, her viperish tongue would be the ruination of them both. But Ruth had slept on, unaware of her sister's absence. And every night, he had had the same anxiety, taking the fine edge off his joy. He had known from past experience how reckless an aroused woman could be. But Sue proceeded to surpass them all: she came earlier and earlier to his lodgings—once even before Cato and Bessie had gone to bed. He had had to make a great pretense of going for a drive, returning hours later to tiptoe with elaborate caution up the stairs. She had, on two occasions, impulsively kissed him in public; he had found it necessary to warn her of the danger that her imprudence caused.

He hated it: the lying, the sneaking, the pretense. It cheapened their new found wonder, dulled their joy. With other women, that hadn't mattered. But this was not other women; this was—Sue. The way he felt was a thing he wanted to shout to the housetops; he wanted the world to know, to share his great pride in this wonder, this miracle, this feeling that now, for the first time since the dawn of history a man and a woman truly loved. Coldly and clearly, he knew that other men and other women had felt the same awe, magic, wonder, ecstasy; but he didn't really believe it; it was as if they, the two of them, had invented love.

But now, ploughing northward toward Wilmington, the little knot of muscle holding his forehead in the hard lines of frowning ached. He felt the contraction, the tightening in his chest, shutting off his breath. It was as though a mailed fist gripped his heart and lungs. He knew that feeling well by now. The name of it was fear.

This wonder, this joy, this miracle of love could not

last. It was doomed by too many things: his own long absences from New Orleans; by the fact the war was now, truly, drawing to a close and George Drake must come home again; by Sue's sense of duty; by her honor, slumbering now, but not dead.

He had left New Orleans the first week in September, long after he should have; but even so, Sue had already had time to think, to feel remorse, perhaps even to confess and say her prayers. It was now the last week of the month; but three weeks, he thought miserably, were more than time enough. He could not stretch his imagination to conjure up how it would be to once more live without her. He could only remember the boredom, the emptiness, the meaningless loves—if you could even call them loves—of his past with a revulsion that was almost physical. No matter what happened, he could not travel those roads again.

He had given Sue five thousand dollars in gold, the day before they parted—a fortune, actually, in those days of depreciated currency. He had been prepared to argue, to insist that she take it; for she and Ruth lived in actual want; but to his astonishment she had accepted it very simply with a murmured thanks as though it did not matter—which, in fact, it did not. Thinking about it, now, he realized that Sue had not even looked at the money; that she was beyond and above the implications he had feared she might have placed upon his gift; beyond and above even considering, at the moment of parting, anything at all except himself.

He turned at last and went down to his cabin. Better get some rest. Get love and Sue and all such personal considerations out of his mind. They hampered a man. Tonight he must not be tied by anything except the job at hand: driving the *Captain Pat* through the Yankee fleet. But he could not sleep. Every time he closed his eyes, Sue's face haunted him. He could see her lips moving, saying tender, wordless things. Finally, he swung himself down from his bunk, and getting out his small chart, began to plot his tactics. Unconsciously, he allowed his restlessness, his malaise to influence him.

The safest way into the Cape Fear River was to sail past the entrance to the North; and putting about, creep along the shoreline past Federal Point, turning to starboard into New Inlet, then making a dash straight up the river until the guns of Fort Fisher provided cover. In fact, that was the only way to do it as long as the cruisers of the Yankee Fleet were as fast or faster than the blockade runners. There were several Union cruisers, he well knew, which could outfoot either the *Sea Witch* or the *Captain Pat I*. But the Yankees didn't have a craft that the *Pat II* couldn't show her wake to. By now, moreover, the blockading captains knew the trick, and rode ever closer inshore, kept from closing New Inlet altogether by the fact that Colonel Lamb's guns outranged theirs, and, having solid masonry instead of a rolling deck to fire from, were far more accurate.

Smith's Inlet to the South, was much less closely guarded, on the sound assumption that a man had to be a fool to take the much greater risk.

But there's another factor now, Tyler thought grimly, our speed. Be a hell of a stunt to burst in amongst 'em, full ahead, going like blazes. Reckon they'd be too startled to get in a shot. Damn it; I'm going to try it!

He went down to the chartroom and gave the necessary orders to the Navigator, ordering him to keep his
mouth shut. No need to alarm the crew ahead of time.
Then he sought out Hargraves, and told the Chief his
plans. Hargraves shrugged. The Old Man, he was sure,
could sail a ship into and out of Hell itself. He said as
much, profanely. Tyler went back to the bridge. He
looked at his watch. As he suspected, the *Captain Pat II*
was so fast that they were already far North of where
they should have been in order to make the dash through
the Union Fleet in darkness. He ordered her speed
reduced and continued his pacing.

The helmsman leaned over and whispered to the
Executive Officer: "Lord God, Loot; the Old Man's
sure got a flea up his tail for fair!"

Lieutenant Meadow, the new Exec, was English, and
very correct.

"I," he snapped, "should like to have you and a half
dozen of you chaps serve under me on a British vessel.
By the time you'd tasted a bit of the cat, and been keel-
hauled once or twice, you'd learn proper respect for
your officers!"

"Well," the helmsman said cheerfully, "you ain't got
us; and the last time you tried a little plain and fancy
impressing to get yourselves some decent seamen for
a change, you got the pants licked off of you. . . ."

"Smithers," Tyler said quietly, "shut up! And, Mister
Meadows, it appears to me that discipline is hardly
served by indulging in arguments with the crew. Will

you please go aft and have them pay out the log line?
I think we're still moving too fast. . . ."

"Aye, aye, sir," Meadows said, and moved away, his
face several shades redder than usual.

The *Captain Pat* was moving too fast. There was
nothing to do but to resort to the dangerous expedient
of heaving to in the dusk, waiting for night to fall.
Tyler continued his restless pacing. All over the ship,
the tension ran from man to man like a galvanic current.
Hargraves kept the steam up just below the point that
would necessitate his blowing off the boilers. They'd
be able to move off smartly enough if a Union cruiser
sighted them; but every man aboard knew that the fastest
craft afloat getting under weigh can be overtaken by
a much slower vessel before she has had a chance to get
up to speed.

Never, since Joshua commanded the sun to stand
still, did night take so long to fall. But when it did fall
it was a lovely night, a perfect night, with no moon, and
clouds hanging so low they could not even see the stars.
Tyler crept her in until the spars of the Yankee cruisers
stood black against the ghostly swirl of the mist. Then
he picked up the speaking tube.

"Full speed ahead, Hargraves," he said. "We're going
to give these Johnnies a show."

Down below, men felt the hammering surge of the
engines, and rolled from their bunks, wild-eyed. The
helmsman aimed for the gap between two of the cruisers
and they swept through, throwing up a bow swell that
rocked even those tall ships, trailing a wake as white
as milk behind them. Aboard the Union craft, men were

tossed from their bunks by the sudden wash of water
striking the cruisers abeam. The *Captain Pat* had the
bone in her teeth and was ploughing through. Behind
them, the Yankee cruisers came alive; they could see
the gunflashes now, hear the whistling crack of shells
passing overhead.

"Hard aport!" Tyler said. He was laughing now, filled
with the pure delight that a race always awoke within
him. Smithers put the wheel over, and the *Pat Two*
responded like a living thing. They saw the shell bursts
pluming the night close to where they should have been.
By 1864, the Yankee gunners could almost call their
shots.

"Sta'board, Cap'n?" Smithers said.

"Not yet," Tyler grinned; then: "Now, Smithers!
Now!"

The *Captain Pat* heeled over hard, and they were back
on a starboard tack, the geysers thrown up by the
shells only twenty yards off their port bow. There were
other cruisers ahead, waiting; the last, the innermost
line. They were so close to them now that the ones
astern ceased their fire, for fear of hitting their own
ships. But Tyler rode her in, knowing that her knife-
like prow, headed directly for the inshore fleet, made
the poorest kind of a target, knowing that her off
white color blended so perfectly with the fog that she
would be in among them before they could see her.

And so it was. The *Captain Pat II* knifed in between
two frigates like a fencer, heeled over hard to port to
avoid ramming a gunboat, skidded dizzily back to starboard and raced on, laughing at the salvos they launched

against her, seeing the shell bursts raising their columns of white hundreds of yards away; then the great Whitsworth guns in Fort Fisher began to tune up, and they were free.

Of all things but human error. They came up to quarantine station, crawling along, it seemed to Tyler. Actually, his senses had not accustomed themselves to her speed. The long dash deceived him; she was moving at least twice as fast as she should have been. The fog complicated matters further. He could not see the rate that the shoreline was swirling backward. Then, at the last moment, he saw the quay ballooning up before him. He snatched up the tube.

"Hard astern!" he roared. "Both screws, Hargraves!"

Hargraves threw the engines into reverse. The lever was new and stiff; for several seconds it resisted his efforts. Then it gave, and white water foamed under the stern. Too late—not even those mighty engines could stop her in that distance. That and one thing more: she was propeller-driven, with none of the drag of the cumbersome paddle wheels. Smithers threw her over hard, but she ploughed into the quay slantwise, demolishing it for twenty yards, and rolling up the steel plates on one side of her bow as though with a can opener.

Picking himself up from the deck where he and every man aboard had been thrown, Tyler surveyed the damage as best he could in the darkness. Slowly, and with great feeling, he cursed himself for forty seven different kinds of a fool. He had just performed one of the most glorious feats in the annals of blockade running; then topped it off with one of the most stupid. Life, he thought savagely, has a way of making mincemeat of a man's pride.

There was nothing to do now but get the lines out, and wait for morning. They were in no danger of sinking; the hole ripped in the prow was far above the waterline. In the morning Chief Engineer Hargraves stood before the port authorities and lied blandly and cheerfully and completely about the impossibility of reversing the engines as the gear was stuck. He did it so well that he almost convinced Tyler, until Tyler remembered distinctly the shudder and roar as the engines had gone into reverse. Lloyds of London would pay for the damages, Tyler pointed out; but to expedite things, he'd write a draft for the estimated cost of repairs to the quay at once. It cost him twenty thousand dollars, but the authorities were appeased. He was allowed to proceed to the dock to unload.

As the crates of arms and ammunition were being slung over the side, Hargraves came up and saluted.

"Thanks, Chief," Tyler said, "but it really wasn't necessary to lie like that. I can take the blame for my mistakes. Fool trick to run a craft I wasn't familiar with in that fast. . . ."

"You didn't know how fast she was going, Cap'n," Hargraves said. " 'Sides, that lever was a mite stiff. Took me one hell of a time to get it over. And I'm getting too old to lick all the johnnies I'd have to if it got out that we just plumb ups and rams a dock. But that ain't what I came for. Cap'n, you got to give me leave to go up to Richmond to that there Tredegar Iron works and the

Belona Foundry. And I'm going to need an open letter of credit for any amount o' money they feel like asking —that is, if they have any iron plate to sell at all. Steel ships is rightly modern and fine, but right now I'd swap this one for the old *Pelican.* . . ."

Tyler stared at him. This aspect had never occurred to him. In her whole history the South had never produced enough iron to supply her peacetime needs; at war, the practice of moving railroad tracks from one section of the country to another as the military needs became more or less pressing, was common. Many of her ironclads were armored with rusted rails, scraps and bits of iron salvaged from anywhere it could be found. In Alabama, iron was plentiful, but by the fall of Sixty four, the Confederacy's woefully inadequate system of transportation was on its last legs, so that most of the Alabama production never reached the front.

That Hargraves could talk the authorities into letting him have the metal, now quite beyond price, was more than doubtful. And should he be able to perform this miracle, how he would be able to get the several tons of plate from Richmond to Wilmington was far more than Tyler was able to see. The accident was far graver than he had realized; before it had seemed merely annoying; now it was becoming tragic. Even if he tried to run the *Captain Pat* home to Nassau empty, he risked floundering her in a gale; and this was the season of gales. A wooden patch would not hold to steel, he knew.

Hargraves stood there, waiting. Nothing to do but let him go. Else they would sit out the war in Wilmington, or go down in the open sea.

"Let's go below, Chief," he said. They went down to his cabin. Tyler wrote the necessary letters, and gave them to Hargraves. He also gave the Chief five hundred dollars in gold to expedite matters. A judiciously placed bribe often worked wonders, and by September Sixty four, there were many men whose patriotism had worn extremely thin.

He shook hands with the Chief at the gangway, and wished him luck. Hargraves would need luck. In fact, he would need a fulldress miracle. He stood there, watching the stocky little man marching along the dock. Hargraves passed a woman, said something he shouldn't have to her, to judge from the angry way she tossed her head, and moved on. Tyler turned back to the gangway. Then he froze. The way she tossed her head! Nobody on earth—no one at all except—He whirled, already running. A minute later, she was in his arms.

She was crying and kissing his mouth. Her lips were salt with the taste of tears.

"It was so hard," she whispered. "I thought I'd never get here! Everybody asked so many questions. I—I told them my husband was wounded and in the hospital here. When I got here, I had to pretend to look for him. But it's all right now. I've found lodgings, and I'm helping out at the hospital . . . And—you're here. That's all that matters, Ty-Love; that's all that matters at all. . . ."

"What," Tyler said, "did you tell Ruth, Doll?"

"Nothing. I slipped my valises out of the house and had a colored boy watch them for me at the station. Then, when it was close to train time, I just strolled off, as cool as you please without even a fare-thee-well. You

aren't angry with me, are you, Ty? I had to come. I
had to—I was going out of my mind!"

"No," Tyler said. "I'm not angry, Sue. Come aboard
and wait for me. I'll have my things ready in a jiffy. . . ."

"I heard about your accident," Sue said. "Will it
keep you in port long?"

"Months," Tyler groaned, and she clapped her hands
delightedly, like a child.

They walked off the dock together, Tyler carrying
his seabag.

"Reckon I can find another place," he said, "big
enough for the two of us. . . ."

Sue stopped dead.

"No, Ty," she said. "I—I gave my real name and
everybody knows you here. We can't stay together. It'll
have to be like New Orleans. I'll come to you. We'll
have to be extremely careful . . . Ty, you must understand. The war'll be over soon and we have so little
time. We mustn't risk spoiling things. . . ."

He looked at her. Women! he thought; but he didn't
say anything. He had long since learned the absolute
uselessness of logical arguments when confronted with
the feminine mind.

She lay in his arms in the first light of dawn. She was
not looking at him. Instead she stared out of the window
a long, long time.

"Ty—" she said.

Something in her tone startled him. He pushed himself up on one elbow, so that he could see her face.

"I'm going to write George," she said. "I can quite easily from here. I'll ask him to divorce me. It may mean giving up the Church, I reckon. Ty, do you think that God cares? What else can I do? I thought I could give you up. But I can't, Love. I know that now. I couldn't live out the rest of my life in lies and deceit. It wouldn't even be fair to George. Tell me, Ty; do you think that if I should become a good sincere member of another church, God could forgive me?"

God, Tyler thought, Is there a God? But he didn't say that. All he said was: "Of course, Babydoll. Never could really believe that God was so small as to leave only one road open to His grace. But I don't know about this business about writing to George. Hell of a thing to upset a man who is going into battle. . . ."

She put her lips against his throat, so that moving, they brushed his flesh.

"I have to, Ty," she said. . . .

She addressed the letter to Boswell's Regiment, not knowing that the name had twice been changed since then. But one of the reasons for the high morale that the Army of Northern Virginia maintained to the end was the relative efficiency of the military postal service. Letters might be weeks late in coming; but in the end, they always came.

When she returned from posting it, her landlady stopped her. Susan stiffened, waiting for the inevitable question about where she had spent the night. She need not have worried; in this war, as in all other wars in human history, irregular behavior had become a commonplace. Mrs. Murphy, her landlady, had not the

slightest intention of annoying a lodger able to pay in
gold instead of the now all but worthless paper currency.

"There's a lady waiting to see you, Mrs. Meredith,"
she said cheerfully. "Pretty young lady who looks a
mighty heap like you. Your sister, maybe?"

Sue didn't answer her. God, she thought, Oh God, Oh
God, Oh God . . . She moved past her landlady into the
parlor. She closed the door firmly behind her. Ruth
stood up, staring at her.

"Don't worry, Susie-dear," she said quietly. "I don't
aim to interfere. Just had to convince myself, that's
all. Wasn't hard. 'Anybody here know Captain Meredith?—the one they call Captain Rebel?' 'Why sure,
Lady! Greatest blockade runner of them all . . .' 'Where
does he live?' 'I'd be delighted to show you, Ma'am. . . .'"

"Ruth—Oh Ruth—please!"

"He wasn't in, so I waited. Long enough to see him
come driving up with—his woman on his arm. His
mistress. His kept woman. The adulterous wife of a
brave soldier. My sister, upon whose basic decency, I'd
have staked my life. . . ."

"You don't understand," Sue said dully. "You can't
understand. You've never been confronted with the
choice between all the things you were taught and—
your life, Ruth. I'd die without him. I couldn't live
another hour. . . ."

"Yet," Ruth said, "you can live a great many hours
without thinking about your husband, out there in the
cold and the wet, lying in the bottom of a muddy trench,
unable to raise his head because of the Yankee fire. That

comes easy to you, doesn't it? Anything comes easy to you except honor and decency, and keeping your pledged word. . . ."

Sue took a step towards her. Even her knuckles were white.

"Get out of here!" she whispered. "Get out of here, Ruth! I've sins enough on my soul. Don't make me add another!"

Ruth stared at her.

"Why, she said, "you would! You really would, wouldn't you? Reckon you're right. I don't understand. Don't want to. As far as I'm concerned the emotions of a Gallatin Street girl are incomprehensible and I'd prefer letting them—"

Sue's hand, moving, was a whitish blur in the gloom. It exploded against her sister's face with a noise like a pistol shot. Then she stood there, staring at the wide spread marks of her fingers on Ruth's face. They were white at first; then they began to redden.

Ruth did not say anything, did not lift her hand to defend herself. She just stood there while the clocktick and the rasp of Susan's breathing filled up the room. Then she moved very slowly toward the door.

"Ruth!" Sue wept, "Oh, I am sorry! Ruth, Ruth, please!"

Ruth did not answer her. She moved to the door and put her hand on the knob. Then, suddenly, violently, she jerked it open, allowing Mrs. Murphy's fat bulk to fall into the room. The landlady's ear had been pressed so hard against the keyhole that it was fiery red. They could see that as she scrambled to her feet.

Ruth smiled at her sister.

"Nothing's unmixed in life, is it, Sue?" she said. "Always a mite of comedy tangled up in the grief. Anyhow, in the presence of this most excellent witness, I'd like to say one thing: I haven't a sister any longer. As far as I'm concerned, she's dead. . . ."

Then, very quietly, she turned and walked through the door.

But she did not leave Wilmington. Sue ran into her many times in the streets, always alone. At first, Sue tried to speak to her, but Ruth looked through her older sister as though she were not there, and passed on. To make it worse, she took work in the hospital, where Sue was forced to see her daily. Sue cried over it every night, her tears running heavy and salt against Tyler Meredith's face.

By the seventeenth of October, Sue was beginning to believe her letter to her husband lost. She was entirely wrong. It would have been much better for her if it had been.

Northwest of Washington, the Potomac narrows, swinging in a series of loops north by west, winding its way through the craggy foothills of the Alleghenies. It is terrible country: ravines and defiles, the high sweep of the Massanutton Mountains, North Mountain, Fisher's Hill. Streams cut it up into irregular blocks: Cacapon River, Tumbling Run, North Fork, Cedar Creek, the

Shenandoah. A great country for defense, providing
cover, too broken for cavalry—

For any cavalry not led by Wilson and Custer, and
any attacking infantry not under Phil Sheridan's command.

George Drake was worried. The rules weren't working any more. On the tenth of September, he had seen
his General, Early, fortify a defile where the Berryville
Road crosses Opequon Creek. It was beautiful terrain,
the best, better than the Wilderness even, because you
could see the enemy coming from afar off and slaughter
him from cover. But Wilson, the Union Cavalry Leader,
was ignorant of the facts of war; he didn't know you
weren't supposed to use cavalry in such terrain. So he
swarmed over the defile in a cloud of horsemen, riding
with utter disregard of life and limb; jumping ditches,
pounding on, hell for leather, firing revolvers and a new
kind of carbine that fired and fired like a pistol without
ever having to be reloaded. The impregnable defile
lasted minutes. The Union Infantry came up, bogged
down with ambulances and baggage wagons. Early
gathered his men, attacked, hurled the Yankees back; and
it was like the old days, the Army of Northern Virginia
was itself again, driving the Yankees before them like
sheep, until Phil Sheridan got there, standing up in the
stirrups, roaring:

"Get those damned wagons into the ditch!"

Too late. Early had Rodes' division in, slashing through
Wright's brigades, the Rebel Yell echoing above the
gun fire. But there was a battery of artillery from Maine,
standing at the end of the field, firing with the cool

precision of men at target practice; and Rodes' division melted into a broken rubble of running men, and piles of bodies on the ground looking like nothing human. Then Wilson, again on the right, with a thunderstorm, a hurricane of horsemen, more numerous than the Tartar hordes. Early stripped himself of cavalry, sending his last horse to meet Wilson, sure that here was every Yankee rider in the whole billy-be-damned world. But from the left, another blueclad mounted horde, just as many, charged home, led by a boy with flying yellow curls: Custer. Then an avalanche of infantry, Wright's, Crook's, Emory's, smashed through the center; and the Army of Northern Virginia ran from the field in headlong rout—for the first time in its long and glorious history.

The rules no longer applied: "Them Yanks got guns they load on Sunday, and shoot all week!" The Spencer and Henry repeating rifles. One Johnny Reb was worth three Yankees, most of the time—or so he believed. But one Yankee inventor was worth three Southern Armies with generals thrown in. What became of the rules when one Yankee now had the firepower of four Confederates?

George was no longer sure that the rule that Southern generals were superior strategists applied either, now. There was, a day or two later, the battle of Fisher's Hill. Early fortified the Hill, stating he could hold it against Napoleon himself. Only, George Drake mused, he ain't fighting Napoleon; he's fighting Phil Sheridan. Yet, he had to admit, Early had chosen well: North Mountain protected his left wing, the tall Massanuttons, his right; in front of him was a ravine not even goats could cross, let alone horses. He couldn't be carried by a frontal assault; and he couldn't be flanked, not unless Phil Sheridan had men who could walk across the face of cliffs with their heads sticking out at a ninety degree angle and their feet clinging to the rock wall like flies.

Which, it proved, he had. Crook's VIII Corps, their rifles wrapped in blankets so as not to clang, climbing indian file in the dark, not, of course, the rock faces, but the crest of North Mountain, a feat that would have given pause to a mountain goat. They fell upon Early's rear, and the cry went up: "We're flanked! Flanked, by God!" And the grey clad troops began at once to give. Ricket's VI Corps came moving up; the XIX Corps were already scrambling up the face of that hill, where, but for Crook's diversionary flanking attack, more mountaineering than warfare, they would have been slaughtered; and Phil Sheridan down below, roaring:

"Forward, forward everything!" And everything going forward, up and over; and one more impregnable position, one more masterfully chosen, absolutely perfect defense was taken by the man who hadn't been informed that perfect defenses existed.

Why don't we just quit? George Drake thought. He looked at Father Joe. The Padre was bad. He had that sadness that was death to a soldier. The kind you saw in men who nearly always got killed the next day. That bothered George. He was very fond of Father Joe. And he couldn't get out of his head the idea that a Padre should have been proof against that kind of a sadness. And this was the wrong time to feel that way.

Because tomorrow would be the end of it, one way or another. Lee had sent them Longstreet's entire corps with orders to crush Phil Sheridan or else. Mighty tall order. Marse Robert had only been fighting Grant, a clumsy bear who pawed, got hurt, and pawed again, as though getting hurt just woke him up a mite. But they had to contend with Phil Sheridan who had a mind like a rapier blade and nerves to match. Put a hard nut in front of that Yankee and he ain't happy 'til he cracks it. We always licked 'em before, because they was half licked before they started, knowing their generals was going to make one damnfool mistake after another. Yankees are as brave as any other breed of cuss, but they had the same kind of sadness in them that Father Joe's got now, from having to fight both us and their generals' muddled heads. But ol' Phil don't make mistakes; and his boys come in happy and sure—and that's what makes the difference. . . .

He chewed his hardtack and dried beef, cold because they were forbidden campfires. Tomorrow, October 19th, 1864, Phil Sheridan or us. And I don't much care one way or another. . . .

He heard the crash of hooves among the pine branches and the sentry's challenge. There was a flurry of talk, and the word "Mail" came over to him. He started to get up, then sat back down again. There wouldn't, he realized sadly, be any mail for him.

It was, as always, a near riot; but a captain appeared, ordered them into files, and taking the mail sack, began to call out names by the light of pineknot. There were many letters that drifted into piles atop a stump, because the men who bore those names lay mouldering in nameless graves across half Virginia. Then, astonishingly, George heard his own name called. He hadn't even joined the line of waiting men. But he got up now, and ran forward. He took his letter, moved apart from the others, and lit a fat pine knot to read it by. The officers knew too well the powerful effect of mail from home on a soldier's morale to forbid this breach of security. Besides, the forbidding of campfires had been an exaggerated precaution on Early's part, anyhow, born of his hard learned respect for Phil Sheridan. They weren't that close to the Yankee lines.

So George Drake read his letter. There are many kinds of death; but of them all, this one is the worst: when a man stands stock still under an icy sky and dies inside his heart, living still.

He thought about taking his letter to Father Joe. Then he remembered that sadness, that bad sadness, that very bad sadness, the worst, in the Padre's eyes. You don't get help from a cripple, he thought grimly, or leadership from the blind. . . .

He sat in the shadows alone. He could hear the other men laughing, exchanging news, giving thanks—even worrying aloud, some of them, because there was sickness at home, hardship, want; but not one of them had what he had, this aloneness, this sudden loss of joy and light and even hope. He hoped they would stay away from him. He didn't want to talk to them. He didn't want to answer questions.

Then, very suddenly and coldly and clearly, he knew what he must do. The postrider would be going back before morning, his sack bulging with the men's re-

plies. George dragged out a stub of pencil. From Father
Joe, he got paper, and an envelope. He was glad Father
Joe didn't look at him; he could not at that moment have
faced a Chaplain. He went back to his hiding place, and
tried to write. But it was too dark. Then he saw that the
Captain had allowed the men to build sheltered fires,
with brush piled around them to hide their glow. Besides them, the men wrote, men unaccustomed to words,
pouring out their hearts in awkward phrases. There was
nothing for him to do but to join one of the groups. He
sat with his paper held against a slab of wood and wrote
slowly, painfully, truly. He was unaware that the tears
were pencilling the grime on his face, red as blood drops
in the firelight. But the others saw it.

"George?" they said gruffly. "Trouble? Your Missus
sick?"

"She's in N'Awleans, ain't she? If them Gawddamned
Yankees—"

"Come on, George, speak up. No call to hold it in. A
man feels better, talking. . . ."

He looked at them, seeing the concern in their eyes,
the real sympathy, even the tenderness of strong men
welded into more than brothers by spilt blood, by
weary marches, by hardships shared. They were men,
and brothers. They had bled together, shared their tattered rags of blankets, their last bit of jerked beef and
imitation coffee. Brothers. And he needed to talk to
somebody. Father Joe was no longer there for that.
Father Joe was finished as Parson, maybe even as a
man. He looked at them a long, slow time, with the tears
trickling into his scraggly beard. Then he told them.

And in that hour, Susan Drake ruined the morale of an

entire company, perhaps, even effected to some extent the outcome of a major battle. Men in the ranks are very close. The laughter died. And each man there put himself instantly and thoroughly in George Drake's place. That letter from Becky, now—was it just a cover up? That yellow polecat Rad Waters had managed to get himself exempted from the draft. Mary Ann was gone down to Greensboro to visit her sister. And she was brought up in Greensboro, and how could a body know just who—

Lord God! We get our guts shot out and the blockade running pimps and the fat profiteers and the conscription dodging bastids—Lord God. . . .

One of them stood up.

"Goddamnit!" he said. "Goddamnit all to hell!"

They fell upon Phil Sheridan's men like a thunderbolt. They smashed his camp, catching the VII Corps still in bed. They rolled up the XIX Corps before it had a chance to form. The Yankees flew down the road, leaving fifteen hundred prisoners and twenty two guns in Early's hands. But fate would not let them go. Half starved for months, they found the Union's good beef and white bread and real coffee. They gave up the chase, and sat down to gorge themselves. Their officers could do nothing with them.

Far in the rear, Sheridan heard the ominous rumble of the quarreling guns. He was in the saddle upon that instant, galloping toward the battle. He met his own fleeing troops, stood tall in the saddle, and shouted:

"Turn around, boys! We're going back!"

The men stopped, stared at him goggle-eyed. Then some one ripped out a cheer.

"Turn, you bastids! Turn! It's Phil! Get moving! We'll see those Johnny Rebs in hell yet!"

So, they surged back, a sea of blue, crested with a steely foam of bayonets. And they found Wright with the Sixth Corps, standing like heroes, muzzles of his thirty-pounders level, firing at point blank range into the yelling, charging greyclad mass. They brought the cavalry up, Custer on the right, Merrit on the left. Phil Sheridan kept them champing on the bit for an hour before sounding the charge that loosed them on their prey.

Early's men were spread too thin. That was one thing. Another was the fact that he had placed Merton's Regiment, as the group George Drake and Father Joseph Meredith now served in was called, to hold the vital right flank. And they were done, firing blindly, thinking: Up here gitting myself kilt, while some fat swine of a profiteer is likely warming my own bed this minute!

George Custer in his velvet cloak, his yellow curls aflying, thundering down upon them: the Colt revolvers and the Spencer repeating carbines crackling like a bush fire that could not be put out. It is a hard thing to face cavalry in the open. The ironshod hooves are terrible enough. But when a man has to shoot, then stand up, bite the edge of paper cartridge through, pour the powder down the barrel, lay a patch of cloth over the muzzel, place a minié ball on the patch, ram the patched ball home, raise the hammer, slip a percussion cap into

the priming lock, and cock the musket before he can
fire again, and this while being charged by horsemen
armed with Colt Dragoon revolvers firing six times
before they had to reload, and Spencer Carbines with
a magazine in their stocks holding seven copper-jacketed
bullets and a lever attached to the trigger guard which
pumped a new one into the breech chamber as fast as the
old one fired, that man must have a heart as high as
heaven and utter disregard of fear to stand before the
flying horsemen pounding down on him.

Merton's regiment stood it for three minutes. Then
they threw away their muskets and ran like sheep. All
of them but two: George Drake, walking slowly toward
the Union horse, firing a revolver he'd taken off a dead
officer, and Father Joseph Meredith scrambling after
him to pull him back.

George shot a trooper out of the saddle, and a dozen
carbines rested upon him and crashed. He halted as
though his body were still under his mind's command,
and Father Joseph saw the patches of cloth fly from his
back as the fifty-caliber conical Spencer bullets tore
through. Then he went down, loosening into death, becoming boneless, and Father Joe, crawling to reach his
side, to say one last prayer for him, was hit by a shrapnel burst that all but tore his right arm off at the shoulder.

At that, he was lucky. He rolled into the brush and
bandaged the wound with his scarf. He lay there three
days before the Union medical corpsmen found him.
And in this consisted his luck, that the maggots got into
the wound and ate away the festered flesh, so that the
great gash was cleansed. He did not, therefore, get

gangrene; and even the bonesaw loving butchers who served the Union Army as surgeons had no excuse to amputate his arm.

But his luck was not unmixed. Lying there, feeling the terrible, slimy things crawling in his flesh, with George Drake's unburied corpse swelling three yards away, he had too much time in his own Gethsemane. When they found him, he was unconscious, his left hand balled into a fist. They pried his fingers open, and found a crumpled ball of cloth. Spread out, it was the insignia of the cross which had been sewn upon his uniform.

CHAPTER THIRTEEN

RUTH FORRESTER TOOK UP THE BASIN OF WATER SHE HAD used to cleanse the soldier's wounds and moved down the aisle between the beds. She was conscious, as she did so, of the drumming of the rain on the roof of the hospital. It had been raining everyday for two weeks now; and outside the windows the streets were a sea of mud and water. Twice already that morning, she had had to move a soldier's bed because the water pouring through the holes in the ceiling was all but drowning him.

She was careful not to look into the basin, for, although she had confidence in the state of her stomach, there had been times lately that it had betrayed her. In her first week of service at the hospital in Wilmington, she had twice reached the open air just in time to keep from fainting. She wouldn't faint, no matter what; but even to give way to the racking nausea that seized her every day, would have disgraced her in her own eyes.

It was so hard. There was the smell. A body never got used to the smell of flesh rotting from the bones of living men . . . Blood was hard to face at first; but you got accustomed to it. Blood was a natural thing, and clean; but the discharge from suppurating wounds was something almost impossible to bear. That and the flies that swarmed over the helpless men. And having to watch men die. Washing the wounded men and changing bedpans were less bad. But there was one thing that was absolutely beyond her, so much so that she had learned to avoid it entirely by getting the matron to warn her the day before so that she could stay home: that was the days when the surgeons had to operate.

The operations were mostly amputations. The surgeons had all but given up operating upon body wounds, particularly deep abdominal ones. A gutshot man so rarely survived as to not make it worth the bother. But, not infrequently, lopping off a gangrenous limb saved a man's life. It was these operations which accounted for the two times she had almost fainted. The second had been worse than the first, because she knew by then what to expect:

The surgeon, his smock crusted with old bloodstains, so that he looked like the head man of an abattoir, his finger nails black with dried blood, walked into the operating room. Then they would roll the patient in— dead drunk from all the whiskey they had given him, which was usually the only way they had to dull his agony, for, even with all the women of Wilmington growing poppies in their front yards, there was never opium enough—and strap him to the table. There would be a few minutes of silence, then the screaming would start, because the whiskey, or even the opium on the rare occasions that they had any opium, wasn't any good against that. There was a pattern to the screaming: low at first, then higher and higher until it was woman-shrill; and between the shrieks, as the man dragged air

into his open mouth to scream again, the grating of the
bone saw. It was absolutely and finally the most unbearable sound in the world. Then the grating stopped;
and you heard the harsh hiss, and smelled the burning
flesh as the hot irons were applied; then the one great
scream ripping into your very entrails when you heard
it; then blessedly, mercifully the silence.

The silence that three times out of five meant the man
was dead of shock. But the other two times made it
worth it. Still she couldn't bear it. There were limits to
anybody's strength.

She hated the surgeons with cold ferocity. There were
good reasons for this hatred. Southern men, even doctors, could not get over their distaste at having gently
bred women changing bedpans, and washing even the
most intimate parts of a man's body. They had tried,
successfully at first, to keep women out of the hospitals.
Then, as the need had grown too great, they had tried
to limit the work to elderly ladies, and especially married
women. In this, too, they had been successful for a long
time, were, in fact, still successful in the overwhelming
majority of the hospitals. But in the few, like the Wilmington Hospital, forced by hard necessity to accept
any girl they could get, the lot of the unmarried vol-
untary nurse was far from easy.

The surgeons treated them with brusque, studied contempt. The townspeople assumed, with lifted eyebrows,
that a girl who would perform such intimate services
for young men, must be a creature without morals. And
the terrible part about it, Ruth thought bitterly, is how
often they're right!

The women who came only to be near their husbands or lovers. The ill favored women who came seeking husbands among the helpless, trading upon simple human gratitude to accomplish what they had not been able to achieve otherwise; the women, who seemed moved by simple hysteria, who came to work drunk, and drank all day long until the surgeons were forced to have them removed from the premises. The well meaning women who stubbornly disobeyed orders, and killed men with their infallible home remedies. The flirts. The ones, thank God very rare, who set convalescence back by weeks by offering comfort of a kind that the men were not sufficiently recovered to undertake without harm.

Then the good ones. The fine, brave ones like her sister, Sue, down to skin and bones now, from overwork and bad food, and not enough of that. And with that racking cough from being constantly soaked by the rain coming to, and going from work—and to Tyler Meredith's lodgings in the storm whipped night. Sue, who had found an interior strength that belied her frail body, and who defied the surgeons and stood wiping a boy's face in the slaughterhouse, as the operating room was called, because he had asked her to be there. But even they, the good ones, suffered from the not so subtle ostracism of the townspeople, and the contempt of the surgeons. But they went on, held fast, endured.

I, Ruth thought, couldn't do it. I'd faint. But Sue can. She is the finest and the bravest and the best. I'm not fit to tie her shoes, and I scorn her because she is living in sin with the man I love. The man I'd do anything for—even worse than what Sue's doing. I have

no right to scorn her. I'm not as good as she is. I'm not—
I'm not—

She dumped the unspeakable contents of the basin on
the ground, and turned back into that charnel house.
I'll go to her, she thought. I'll go to her today and beg
her pardon. I've been a bad sister to her. I've been a
jealous female and a bad sister. The Good Book says
we mustn't judge—

She sat down beside the dying soldier and picked up
the fly whisk. When they were this weak, you had to
fan them constantly, or the flies would get into their
open mouths, their ears, their nostrils, and their eyes.
She swung the whisk, and the blue flies rose in a singing
cloud. God, she prayed: "Oh, dear kind God. Our
Father Which art in heaven—"

Then, suddenly, she saw Sue coming toward her. She
came very slowly, and her face was white. There was
something in her hand. Two things, two pieces of paper.

Ruth got up, and stood there, facing her.

"Sue," she said; "Oh, Sue, darling, I—"

Sue's hand came up with the jerky motion of a mario-
nette.

"Read them," she said harshly, "read them both. . . ."

Ruth took the papers from her sister's hand. One of
them was in pencil, and badly smudged. The words were
covered with something like dried rain drops. She had
a hard time making them out:

"So, my darling, for you remain that in spite of all
you've done, there is no need to ask me to divorce you.
It is against our Faith, and a sin. Yet, you shall be free.
Tomorrow we attack General Sheridan's forces. I shall

not survive that battle. It is so simple, dearest. A man doesn't have to do anything not to live. All he needs to do is to neglect a few small things: to walk upright instead of to crawl, to fail to dig in, not to try too hard to find cover. I hope you shall be happy. I doubt it. I don't think Tyler Meredith is worthy of you. I don't think I was, or that any man is. Only, I loved you so. Oh, Sue, Sue—"

There was no more; not even a signature. The other letter was shorter. It was written in ink upon official stationery, and it came from the War Department. It stated that Colonel—name completely illegible—begged regretfully to inform Mrs. George Drake on behalf of the Department, that her husband, Private George Drake, was missing in action under such circumstances that his death must be presumed.

Ruth's eyes came up inch by slow inch to her sister's face. She tried to speak, but she could not. Her tongue was as dry as dust. It cleaved to the roof of her mouth. Then, seeing Sue bent half over with a terrible spasm of coughing, she threw out her arms, and drew her sister to her. She could feel the rattling paroxysms tearing through the thin form. They stopped finally, and Sue lifted her head; but even then she did not cry.

"What—what are you going to do?" Ruth got out.

"Work," Sue said, "all day, as usual. Some of my boys would die, if I left them before my replacement comes. Then, tonight, I'm going to see Tyler—also as usual—"

She felt Ruth stiffen; but she went on, imperturbably:

"I have two things to tell him. First—that I am going to bear his child and—"

"Sue!" Ruth whispered. "Oh, Sue, you poor darling, I—"

"Secondly, that he shall never see either of us, me, or the child, again as long as he lives . . ."

"It," Ruth said furiously, "will serve him right! Oh, the beast! And to think—"

"That you loved him. You must not stop, Ruth. He'll need you. And he is not a scoundrel. None of this is his fault."

"Now, really, Sue—"

"None," Sue repeated firmly. "He told me he was leaving New Orleans forever because he couldn't face living in the same town with me—and my husband. That night, for the first time, I went to his lodgings. Of my own free will. He did not ask me to come. I followed him to Wilmington. He didn't know I was coming here. He didn't even know I was here until I sought him out. So go on loving him, child, if you can. He'll need you. . . ."

"But you, Sue—you! What on earth will you do?"

"Go away. Find work. I'll say the child is my husband's, born after his death—not to spare myself, Ruth, but for my baby's sake. It isn't fair to make him suffer for what he wasn't responsible for. Devote the rest of my life to bringing him up in decency and honor and the fear of God. . . ."

"Oh, Sue, I am so sorry! I don't know how—"

"There are flies on your soldier's face. Fan them off, child."

Then, very quietly, Sue turned and walked back to her post.

Tyler Meredith lay propped up against the pillows, a bottle of bourbon on the night table at his side. He could see the rain silvering the window glass, hear its incessant pounding on the roof over his head.

Damn it all, he thought. I sure wish it would stop. Hope Sue won't try to come tonight. She's sick enough already. Besides, I want to think. . . .

He was not drunk. He had had only two fairly stiff drinks, because he was occupied with his plans. The letter had come from Hargraves that day. Steel plate was not to be had—nowhere in the Confederacy. Tyler lay there, calculating the chances. A wooden patch braced inside the hull with tansverse beams might hold if the weather were not too bad. No cargo, or almost none. Just enough to serve as ballast. A skeleton crew to reduce the loss of life in case she floundered. Extra provisions and water for the lifeboats. Every precaution taken. The moment that he saw the water was gaining on the pumps, he'd order them to abandon ship. He had enough on his conscience now.

Sue—that was bad. He hoped George would give her the divorce. No matter how you looked at it, it was an ugly thing. George Drake was a good man and a fine soldier. A man ought to be able to defend his country without some stinking polecat—

Only, I can't give her up. Right or wrong, I can't. This is ugly. This is puking rotten; but I can't—

He heard the door open very quietly. He never locked it now; and he had given Sue a key to the street entrance. He straightened up, and put out his arms to her.

She came to him, trailing pools of water from her sodden clothing. He saw that she had two pieces of paper in her outstretched hand.

"Read these," she began, but a gale of coughing stopped her speech.

He took them from her and laid them on the night table without even glancing at them. Then he poured her half a glass of the bourbon.

"Here," he said. "Drink this. Ought to help. . . ."

She almost strangled getting it down, but it did stop the coughing.

"Tyler," she said; "Please read those letters. . . ."

"Later," he said carelessly. "First you get out of those wet things. You look like a drowned cat. Then get in here with me so I can warm you. . . ."

"No," she said, her voice strangling again. "No, Ty—the—the—let—" She could not finish the word. She hadn't the breath.

A frown creased his forehead. He lunged out suddenly and dragged her forward into his arms.

"No!" she said. "No, Tyler. No! Geo—"

But he stopped her words with his mouth. He kissed her a long time. Expertly—no, better than expertly, honestly. With the love and longing and tenderness and desire he really felt. With that true, fine passion that is born of love, that fleshly desire that exalts the beloved body, worshipping it as the temple of the long sought spirit; and which has nothing of lust in it, being love's very self and its purest expression.

She brought up her hands to break his embrace. But, suddenly, inexplicably, they would not work like that. Instead, they stole upward, and locked behind his head, the fingers straying ceaselessly through his thickly silvered hair.

"Oh Ty," she whispered, her words muffled against his mouth, "We can't we mustn't, not now oh Ty—"

Later, lying in that wonderful lethargy of afterlove, that bone deep, soul deep, warm tide of contentment akin to sleep, he became aware that she was no longer beside him. A sound came over to him. He turned and saw her bent over from the terrible spasms of her coughing, her handkerchief thrust into her mouth to deaden the sound. She was fully dressed again; but her clothing was little dryer than before.

"Sue," he growled, "You can't go out in this weather. You've damned near caught your death already. Stay here a while and I'll drive you home."

"In what?" she said quietly. "You haven't a buggy, Ty. And certainly you won't find a livery stable open this time of night. . . ."

"Then I'll take the umbrella and walk you to your place," he said, and started to throw back the covers. But she came to him, then, and laid a hand on his arm.

"No, Ty. Even late as it is, somebody might see us together. We've been lucky, before; but our luck's all played out. Not that it matters—now. Not that anything matters any more. Besides, I want to walk home alone. There's something I want to think about quietly—all by myself. Please, Tyler—stay where you are—like that —it's the way I want to remember you . . ." She bent to kiss his mouth. He held her away from him.

"Damn it, Sue!" he said angrily, "if you think I'm going to let you go home at this hour of the night alone —in this kind of weather—you're crazy!"

She stared at him, her eyes bleak.

"Perhaps I am," she said. "That would be one explanation for what I've done. . . ."

"Don't talk nonsense, Doll," he said. "I've let you come here alone because it was always the early part of the night and fairly safe. But I've never let you go home alone through the streets of this thug infested town, and I don't intend to start now."

"I've that little pistol you gave me," Sue whispered.

"Oh, for God's sake!" Tyler said. "Turn your back, Sue, while I get dressed. . . ."

He walked her home through the rain lashed streets, holding the umbrella over her. It didn't do very much good. Both of them were soaked by the time they reached her lodgings. She coughed fearfully at intervals all the way.

At the door, when he bent to kiss her, she turned aside her face.

"Now what's wrong, Sue?" he growled.

"Don't kiss me, Ty," she whispered. "I wouldn't want you to catch—"

"Oh, to hell with that," he said and kissed her. Then he stood back, peering through the darkness, trying to see her face. Her lips had been like ice, without any response upon them at all. He stared at her, thoroughly discomforted.

"Goodnight, Babydoll," he said.

She did not answer at once. He was aware that she

was fighting for breath. When she did speak, what she said was strange. He was halfway home before the nature of that strangeness came to him: it was not "Good night," or "See you tomorrow," but "Goodbye," that Susan Drake had said.

In his room, Tyler undressed in the dark, not bothering to relight the lamp. He scattered his wet clothing on the floor, and leaped into bed, seeking warmth. Then he put out his hand and felt for the bottle of bourbon. He drank half the whiskey that remained in one long pull, and set the bottle down again.

"Women!" he said morosely, and turned over. But it was a long time before he slept.

He came awake in the first light of morning. It was still raining, a slow, sullen drizzle, whispering against the windowpane. He lay there a quarter of an hour listening to it, while something cold and still probed at the very edge of his consciousness, pushing in, twisting, tugging at his mind.

Then he was sitting bolt upright in his bed. He put up his hand and felt the icy sweat upon his forehead. And her last kiss was still upon his mouth, called back by memory to put a seal upon his sudden terror. That last brief kiss that had not had the warm moist, slack lipped languor of after love; but the salt of tears, and the chill of—

George, he thought slowly; she started to say something about George and I—

He turned slowly toward the night table. The papers were still there. He sat there, staring at them, while the pounding of his heart filled up the silence in the room.

He stared at them a long, long time before putting out his hand to take them up.

When he reached the house where Sue lived, he could not breathe or speak. He had run all the way, not having had time to get a horse, not even remembering that he could not, in any case, have rented a mount at that hour of the morning. He hung there before the door, shaking all over like a palsied man. Then he knocked upon the door, lightly at first; then harder and harder until he was hammering upon it in a frenzied crescendo of sound.

The landlady, appearing at last in curlpapers and a shapeless wrapper, was not pleased.

"She's not here," she snapped. "Left before dawn this morning, and took her valise with her."

"Did she," Tyler croaked, "say where she was going?"

"No," the landlady said. "Now git along with you, Mister! This ain't a fitting hour to drag a body out of bed to answer fool questions about some flighty woman. You hear me, git!"

Slowly, Tyler turned away from the door.

I'll go to Ruth, he thought; maybe she knows. . . .

Moving down the aisle of the rickety train that ran between Wilmington and Richmond, Sue could feel the weariness right down to the marrow of her bones. She had to fight hard to keep from coughing; for so great was the fear of consumption, as Southerners called tuberculosis, that she risked being put off the train if she

gave way to the wracking in her lungs. She didn't mean
to be put off because she had had to bribe the conductor
twenty-five dollars in gold from the money that Tyler
had given her even to be allowed aboard at all. The
trains were all crowded to the bursting point and many
a conductor had taken it upon himself to refuse passage
to an unescorted female.

She glanced timidly at the male passengers as she
passed, hoping one of them would offer her his seat. But
they would not even look at her. She understood their
attitude. Chivalry towards women was a casualty of the
war. In Wilmington, even with the blockade runners
bringing in supplies, people were all but starving; and
suffering, contrary to the writers of romances, always
debases public manners and morals, never ennobles them.

In Richmond, Sue knew well, people actually were
starving. Yet, she had to go there—at least as a start to
moving on to somewhere else.

"Women," a man growled, intentionally loud enough
for her to hear it, "got no damn business traipsing off
about the country during wartime. Let 'em stand up, I
say. You so damn polite, you give her your seat!"

She didn't wait to hear his seatmate's reply. She moved
on through the car, and came out on the little platform
between it and the next. The icy rain bit into her face.
She put her valise down, and let the tearing, racking
paroxyms of coughing out. When the seizure had passed,
she was so dizzy she had to sit down on the valise until
her head cleared. As cold as it was on the platform, she
felt hot. She sought and found her own pulse, and sat

there counting it. She had worked in the hospital too long not to recognize her own symptoms.

La Grippe, she thought; maybe pneumonia. Not consumption, 'cause there's no blood—yet . . . Wasn't for the baby, I wouldn't care. But his coming is not his fault. He's got to have his chance—he's got to. Maybe—if I got to some place where it was sort of dry and warm and rested for a spell . . . maybe. . . .

She got up wearily and moved on through the cars. They were all packed with unwashed humanity, whose stench was made barely bearable by the cold. She was about to give it up, retreat to one of the open platforms between the cars and take her chances with the rain and the cold, when she pushed open the door to the last coach.

This one had nearly all of the windows broken, so that the rain came in without let or hindrance. It was less crowded than the others, and a moment later she saw the reason: the occupants of it were nearly all wounded soldiers, discharged from the hospital to go home, except for one lone woman who was sitting with her arms around a sleeping soldier, and a drunken civilian who snored noisily in his seat.

The wounded men stared at her listlessly, though they, some of them, must have recognized her. They were too hurt, sick, broken and dispirited to care. Many of them were in their shirt sleeves despite the cold, displaying ghastly unbandaged wounds.

A few months ago, she thought, I'd have fainted at far less than this. Now it doesn't matter; it doesn't matter at all.

She saw that the two seats across the aisle from the woman and the sleeping soldier were vacant, although some of the wounded soldiers were standing up at the end of the car. She was too grateful for her good luck to even inquire into the strangeness of it. But, as she walked toward the seats, she saw one of the soldiers bathing his infected, hideously malodorous arm in the bucket containing the coach's drinking water. Feeling the fever raging within her, and the parching thirst in her throat, she almost wept. But she was too tired even for tears.

She dropped wearily into one of the two vacant seats. Across the aisle, the woman was talking ceaselessly to the sleeping soldier, crooning to him tenderly like a mother with her child. But he slumped against her without answering her. Sue stared at the woman, and, at that moment, a gust of rain filled air brought the smell full into her nostrils.

The soldier was dead. He had been dead a good, long time. And the woman's eyes, meeting hers across the aisle, were finally and completely mad.

Sue wondered how the woman had got the dead man aboard. Bribed the conductor, she guessed. But she was past caring even about that. She lay back against the seat and closed her eyes. She ached all over in every joint and muscle. The jolting of the train over the uneven rails was torture to her. Nevertheless, she slept.

She dreamed that she was in Tyler's room and he was kissing her; but not tenderly, as he usually did. He was hurting her mouth, and he hadn't shaved very well. His whiskers scratched her face. Besides, he had a powerful sight too much whiskey on his breath. She pushed him away angrily, and came awake to find the face of the drunken civilian inches away from her own.

She opened her mouth to scream; but, instead, the minute the cold air struck her lungs, she started coughing. It went on and on, worse than ever, until everything inside of her seemed to tear loose. The drunk reeled away from her, his grimy, unshaven face paling.

"What's the matter, gal?" he whispered. "What kind of a sickness you got?"

Sue sat there, staring at her handkerchief. Then she balled it up and threw it through the broken window. One corner of it struck against the glass as it went through. The drunk had followed the motion. He hung there, staring at the thick splotch of red on the broken pane. The dark droplets crawled downward from it, slowly, slowly.

"And I kissed you!" the man croaked. "Lord God, lemme out of here!"

He fled down the aisle and out of the coach. The walking wounded stared after him. Across the aisle, the mad woman crooned tenderly to the corpse. Sue closed her eyes and slept again.

She slept all the way to Richmond—except for the five times an hour that the train jerked to a stop, almost throwing her from the seat as the brakes were applied. Usually that meant that something had broken, so that they had to sit there and wait until the engineer found the damage and repaired it. But twice they had to get out and walk through the rain: once because the ancient, wheezy engine lacked the power to haul their weight up a steep grade; and once because the engineer, a humane man, didn't want to risk their lives on a bridge the train had to cross.

Even the acute misery she had grown accustomed to in Wilmington had not prepared her for the conditions in Richmond. The city was crowded with refugees, many of them women, seeking some news of male relatives missing in action, or there to petition the Government for aid in relieving their appalling distress. Every hotel, every boarding house was filled. There were people living in tents and packing boxes in the vacant lots.

She trudged the streets for three days, sleeping in the open lots at night, with the small pistol Tyler had given her beside her under her coat. She alternately burned with fever, and shook with chills. She had thrown away every handkerchief she had. In a store, she bought two yards of coarse cloth and ripped it into squares. By forcing herself not to cough until she absolutely had to, she calculated these would last her a week.

The third night it rained, and the next morning, soaked to the skin, she made the rounds again. Of course, having the money Tyler had given her, she had been able to eat; but the food, even in the best places, was all but nauseating. She forced it down, realizing that was the only way she could stay alive.

But even so, she knew that if she had to spend another night in the open, she would die before morning. She had to find lodgings that day and she knew it.

She was filled with a great, all consuming love for her unborn child; and it was this that drove her on even after the last of her strength was gone.

"Make it like him, God," she prayed. "Dear God, make it just like him. . . ."

She came at nightfall to a broken-down wreck of a hotel. She crept up the stairs, dragging her valise with her. She was aware that she was filthy and looked like nothing human; but from the odors which met her when she pushed open the door, she reckoned that these people would not care.

She was right. They didn't. The ancient witch at the desk glared at her with one baleful eye and snapped:

"Yep, we got a room. You'll have to share it with three other women, though. It'll be five dollars a day. Meals extra. . . ."

The other women stared at her as she came in. But they didn't move or speak. They were no cleaner, and only a little healthier than she was. Looking around the room, Sue would have cried, if she had had any tears left. It had one narrow bed in it, a table balanced uncertainly on its three remaining legs, a broken mirror, pallets of unbelievable filthiness upon the floor, a washstand and commode combination containing a nightjar, which, if her nose was any judge, hadn't been emptied in weeks.

She sat down on the bed and started to cough. The three women stared at her. Then, without saying anything, they got up and left the room. They came back with the one-eyed harridan.

"You'll have to git out," the old witch spat. "Can't have no comsumptives in my place. Give th' hotel a bad name . . ."

"But I can't! I'll die if——"

"You'll die anyhow. Don't want no corpses on my hands and trouble with the authorities. . . ."

"Give her her money back, Miz Jane," one of the women said.

"Humph! Reckon I'll have to," the landlady said. "Ought to keep it though, to learn her a lesson. Coming here like this, spreading infection. . . ."

Sue opened her mouth to protest, to beg; but the coughing seized her again. The old witch clamped her bony hand down on her shoulder, and propelled her, still coughing, through the door. One of the other women came out and handed her the valise.

She stumbled blindly down the street, dragging the valise. She couldn't see for the crying and the spasms of coughing that ripped her body like so many knives. She was burning alive despite the cold. Her mind was no longer quite clear. At times it seemed to her that George Drake strode along beside her, looking at her with terrible, accusing eyes.

"Yes," she wept. "Yes, George, I know I'm bad. I'm bad and damned because of what I did. I killed you—and knowing that—knowing you were dead I—"

But it wasn't George beside her any longer.

"Tyler!" she whispered. "Oh, Ty, my darling, my love, I—" She stretched out her arms to him; but he retreated from her, going away now, thinning out, becoming transparent, a part of the rain and the mist.

"Tyler!" she screamed, her voice, edged and shrill, slashing the night apart. "Ty! Don't leave me! Oh, Ty, Ty don't ever leave me. . . ."

Her voice trailed off into a broken jumble of sobs.

She took three more steps before she fell. She forced
herself up to her knees and started to crawl. She had
almost reached the vacant lot where the tents were when
she knew she wasn't going to make it. She lay in the
mud, crying. She cried a long, long time before the
woman in the nearest tent decided that the sound was
not a part of the rain and the wind.

The woman came out of the tent and stood there,
looking at her. Then she turned:

"Joe!" she called. "Come here and give me a hand!"

The man came. Between the two of them they managed to get Susan Drake into the tent.

And it was there, two days later, that Ruth Forrester
and Tyler Meredith found her. She had been dead
exactly one hour when they got there.

Ruth lifted her face, tear streaked in the lantern light,
and looked at Tyler.

"How does it feel to be a murderer?" she said, speaking with that flat toned, perfect calm of pure hysteria.
"Tell me, Tyler, how does it feel?"

He didn't answer her. He couldn't.

"You'd better go get a wagon or something to take her
away in—if you please, Mister Meredith," Ruth Forrester said.

CHAPTER FOURTEEN

"D'YOU THINK HE EVEN HEARS WHAT YOU SAY TO HIM?"
Lieutenant Meadows said.

Hargraves looked at the Executive Officer.

"Damned if I know," he said. "I keep stealing his
whiskey; but he always manages to get another bottle
somewheres. . . ."

"It's not the whiskey," Meadows said.

"I know, I know," Hargraves growled. "Damn women
anyhow! If there's anything worse than a finger reef
on a howlin' night with the bilge pumps out and the sea
a-gaining, it's a woman!"

"Oh come now, Hargraves," the young Englishman
said. "It seems to me that you don't exactly scorn their
society . . ."

"Don't get myself warped in. One night's shore leave,
and I shove off again. But that there filly's dying up there
in Richmond sure Lord got to him. Best damn skipper
I ever had—now look at him. Plumb ruint!"

"Do you," Meadows hesitated, "think his—his
mind—?"

"Nope. When he comes out of that there stupor, he
talks as clear as a bell. Gave me them directions for plug-
ging the rip in the bow. It ain't perfect, but it'll come

as nigh to holding as anything will. He give you loading orders?"

"Sent them to me in writing. That's what seems curious to me. He completely overruled Matthews, the Supercargo. What's even stranger, he's leaving Matthews behind. Ordered him ashore in a rather highhanded fashion. Matt's a bit put out. Can't say I blame him. And the Old Man has beached more than half the crew. Not to mention ordering me not to put anything aboard except a few hogsheads of tobacco and scarcely enough cotton to fill the aft hold. . . ."

"Lieut," Hargraves said flatly, "You got anything 'twixt your ears?"

"I should hope so," Meadows smiled. "Why?" He had become much less stiff during the last two months.

"Just wondered. Here you are, more than half accusing the Old Man of being off course 'cause he ups and gives you the most sensible set of orders that any skipper could under the circumstances. . . ."

"Sensible? Oh I say, Hargraves!"

"Look, Lieut—just you set back and listen to me real careful like. The cargo—that's sense. You load the *Cap'n Pat* till she draws any water a-tall, and we'll flounder in the first fresh breeze. That rip's fairly high above the waterline. Load her lightly, and it'll stay there. Barring heavy seas breaking over the bow, we'll be as safe as if we was in church. Leaving the Supercargo and half the crew—likewise. Don't need a Super if you ain't got no cargo, right? And the Old Man always had a reputation for taking care of his men. Since we're putting out to sea in an already damaged vessel, ain't no more than decent to cut down the number of men that'll have to risk their hides. Catch on, Lieut?"

"I see," Meadows said. "Yes, come to think of it, the orders do make sense. Better to lose our profits than the vessel. We're still set to sail on the twenty third?"

"Far as I know. I was looking forward to Christmas ashore; but after all, he's the skipper. . . ."

Meadows opened his mouth to say something, but the knocking on the door interrupted him. He crossed the cabin and opened it.

A young Confederate lieutenant stood there. He saluted smartly.

"Lieutenant Brooke," he said, "presents Colonel Lamb's compliments, Sir. The Colonel would like to see Captain Meredith at once down at the Fort. It's highly important. The Colonel even sent a mount for the Captain. . . ."

Meadows looked at Hargraves. Slowly the Chief Engineer shook his head. Meadows cleared his throat.

"Sorry, Lieutenant," he said, "but Captain Meredith is rather seriously ill. However, I'm Executive Officer aboard, and fully empowered to act in his place. I should be delighted to accompany the Lieutenant and to relay whatever suggestions or orders Colonel Lamb may have to Captain Meredith."

"Well—" Lieutenant Brooke said, "He did tell me to bring the Captain. But I reckon under the circumstances—"

"I'll be with you in a minute, Lieutenant," Meadows said. . . .

An hour and a half later, Lieutenant Meadows sat with Colonel Lamb in his quarters at Fort Fisher.

"I'm sorry to learn of Captain Meredith's illness," Colonel Lamb said gravely. "He's a fine skipper. I wish he could have come. I wanted to warn him about something, and also to request a service. . . ."

"Yes, Sir?" Meadows said.

"We've information that the naval squadrons off Cape Fear have been heavily reenforced. That may indicate an attack. Naturally, too, it greatly increases the danger of running the blockade which is what I wanted to warn him about. The other thing is: Could you find space to ship aboard five or six of our men? I want an accurate count of the Union fleet, and some knowledge of their disposition. Once you're free of the blockade, you could put my men ashore somewhere South of here, and they could return to me with the intelligence I require. . . ."

Lieutenant Meadows did not hesitate. Like most upper class Englishmen, he was a rabid supporter of the Confederacy.

"We'd be delighted, Sir!" he said. "We're sailing light and short handed anyway to minimize the dangers resulting from our—unfortunate accident. And I have Captain Meredith's permission to consent to any request you might make of us. . . ."

"Good!" Colonel Lamb said; "You sail the twenty third?"

"Yes, Sir. Day after tomorrow."

"I'll have the men aboard tomorrow night," Colonel Lamb said.

At half past ten o'clock on the night of December twenty third, 1864, the *Captain Pat Second* shipped anchor and got under weigh. She made the sixteen miles from Wilmington to Federal Point in little more than an hour. Executive Officer Meadows was in a state of high nervous tension. For the first time in his life he was taking a ship out under his own command.

Chief Engineer Hargraves was even more nervous. Of course, Captain Meredith was aboard, but what difference did that make when he was in his cabin blind drunk as usual, leaving his vessel in the young Englishman's inexperienced hands? And that business of those Marines aboard to count the Yankee fleet! Blast and damn the Yankee fleet! It was their business to stay the clinking ding dang blazes as far away from Union cruisers as possible, not to go looking for them!

Still, the Exec seemed to know what he was doing. He had got the *Captain Pat* under weigh smartly, in real seamanlike fashion. The English were good sailors; you had to give them that . . . If only the Old Man would get a hold of himself. Every thing else might be in short supply in the Confederacy, but young, good looking fillies sure Lord weren't. To grieve and drink himself to death because one damnfool woman had up and died, just wasn't smart. Never could see why some men put such a high and mighty valuation on women-folks; commonest commodity there was, Hargraves reckoned. . . .

He looked at the pressure gauges. Everything was shipshape and doing fine. Ought to be raising New Inlet by now. Another hour, and they'd sight the Yankee fleet. . . .

He heard the speaking tube squawking furiously. He

picked it up, and Meadows' voice came over to him, wildly:

"Full speed ahead! Full ahead, Chief! We're already among them!"

Then, before he could put down the tube, he heard the sickening crash of the first shot.

In his cabin, Tyler Meredith had picked up the bottle to pour himself another drink when the shell hit. The bottle crashed to the floor.

Waste of damn' fine whiskey, he thought woodenly. Somebody's going to pay for this. . . .

He lurched to his feet, opened the door. He was bleary-eyed, unshaven, his uniform unbuttoned. He swayed down the corridor to the deck. Then he saw it. They had boiled out of New Inlet; and there, in sight of the breakers, the Union fleet stood. The fleet that should have been miles off shore for fear of the guns in Fort Fisher and on Smith's Island. The swaying of his body stopped; he dashed for the ladder, mounted to the bridge in two long bounds. He tore the door open.

"What the hell's going on here?" he roared.

"Sir—" Meadows began but Tyler had the speaking tube, barking orders:

"Give me more steam, Chief! Yes, goddammit, tie 'em down if you have to! Full ahead! Too late to go back now. . . ."

He whirled to the helmsman.

"Keep her pointing. Don't tack! We can't afford to

lose speed zig zagging. Lord God, where did all those gunboats come from?"

"The Union fleet's been reenforced, Sir," Meadows said. "They plan an attack—"

"And you took her out, knowing that? Goddamnit, Meadows, why in ruddy hellsfire didn't you consult me?"

"Colonel Lamb requested, Sir, that we get some information about their intentions. We've some of his men aboard and—"

"Information!" Tyler exploded. "This is a private vessel under British registry, Meadows! Not a twice-befouled Rebel picket boat! I was aboard! Why in the name of everything unholy you didn't request my permission before embarking on this idiocy is more than I can see!"

The Executive Officer drew himself up to full attention.

"Begging the Captain's pardon," he said icily, "I tried to consult the Captain. . . ."

Tyler's wrath died. He felt cold suddenly—cold and sick.

"You're right, Lieutenant," he said. "My humblest apologies. . . ."

The shell geysers stood up all around them. The *Captain Pat* was heeled over hard, running like a greyhound, closing the gap between them and the Union gunboats, most of them ironclads, with every second. There was no question of Navy trained gunners missing at that point blank range. The funnel went. Both masts. The boats were kindling, the air alive with whining splinters. They pounded down upon the nearest gun-

boat, their broken funnels trailing a banner of flame,
not smoke. The gunboat skipper lost his nerve, gave
water. They foamed past, ten yards off his stern.

The crew ripped out a cheer. Too soon—for beyond
the line of gun boats and ironclads were the fast sloops
of war and the cruisers. More of them than Tyler had
ever seen before, filling up the moonsilvered night with
ominous spars. He saw the starshaped splash of flame
from a bowchaser aboard a cruiser. Then one by one
they opened up, their black hulls lighted by the gun
bursts, firing in salvos, raising pillars of white all around
the *Captain Pat*, ringing her with the silver geysers of
sudden death, finding the range now, slamming solid
shot into her steel hull until she reeled like a drunkard,
sweeping her decks with shrapnel and grape until all
the scuppers ran with blood.

There was not a glass left in the bridge enclosure.
Every man there, Meadows, the helmsman, Tyler, was
already slightly wounded by the flying glass and bits of
steel. Still they raced on, miraculously afloat.

"We're afire, Sir," Lieutenant Meadows said. His
voice was beautifully controlled. They've got salt water
in their veins, Tyler thought admiringly; salt water and
ice. Damn it, you've got to respect 'em—greatest race
of seafarers that ever lived. . . .

He turned and saw the flameshot smoke pluming from
the engine room. He felt as though he were watching
a well loved friend die.

"Order the men to abandon ship, Lieutenant," he
said quietly. "We've done our best. No time for heroics
now. . . ."

"Aye, aye, Sir," Meadows said. "But, Sir—the boats—"

"See that every man who can't swim is lashed to a spar or a plank. There's enough rubble from the boats and the decks to provide for that. The Yankees will pick them up. Then report back to me—if we're still afloat. . . ."

"Yes, Sir!" Meadows said.

Tyler saw the helmsman's eyes rolling in fear.

"Give me the wheel, Smithers," he said. "Tell me, son —can you swim?"

"Nary a lick, Sir!" Smithers groaned.

Tyler looked about him. The door to the bridge enclosure was hanging by one hinge.

"Kick that door loose, boy," he said calmly. "Then tie yourself to it and get over the side. It'll hold you up. . . ."

Smithers tore the door loose with one mighty kick. Then, holding it, he turned back to his Captain.

"Good luck, Smithers," Tyler said.

"Thank you, Sir," the helmsman whispered. "But what about—you, Sir?"

"I'll be all right," Tyler said. "Get going, son!"

Yes. I'll be all right. For the first time since—Sue died. I won't have to think anymore. They say it's quick, and relatively painless. Never lost a vessel before. There's a first time for everything, I reckon—even for dying. Didn't have the guts to do it with a pistol. But this way's kind of fine. Those fools ashore will talk about the traditions of the sea, all that sort of muck. A pity. They'll spout solemn nonsense about the great Captain Rebel going down with his ship, declaiming noble words. Better like that. Better anything but the truth: that I took this way out because dying is easier than living, and I'll be at peace at last—at peace—

"Captain!" Meadows shouted, "The men are all off—except the dead. There was one boat—I got the wounded into that—"

"Sure everyone's off?" Tyler said.

"Except the black gang—and Hargraves, Sir. Couldn't get to them. The engine room's afire. Wait, Captain! There's no time! We're going down by the head!"

"Go over the side, Meadows," Tyler said. "You're a damned fine swimmer and you've time. . . ."

"But you, Sir! There'll be so much suction when she goes that—"

"I'll risk it," Tyler said. "I have to look after the Chief."

"Then I'm staying with you, Sir!" Meadows said. "As Exec, I have as much right—"

Tyler stopped, looking at the young man.

"You're pretty damned fine, aren't you, Meadows?" he said. "All right, over you go . . . Reckon that's an order, son."

The Executive Officer had tears in his eyes.

"Please, Sir, let me stay!" he got out. "I can help! I—"

Tyler's arm stiffened, propelling him to the rail with tremendous force.

"Get the goddamned hell over the side, Meadows!" he said.

"Aye, aye, Sir!" Meadows whispered, and dived free.

Tyler raced down the ladders. Down below, the heat was unbearable but he went on, wrapping his scarf over his mouth and his nose. The engine room was an inferno; a wall of flame stood between him and the bodies scattered on the floor. Then he saw his chance; water was pouring through a shell hole, drowning the flames near one bulkhead. He eased along the gap. His uniform singed, his brows and lashes went, strips of skin peeled from his forehead. But he fought clear and reached the Chief.

Hargraves was unconscious; but there was not a mark on him. His pulse beat strongly. Concussion, Tyler guessed, and picked him up. He glanced at the others. Most of them were dead. The shell burst that had started the fire had killed them instantly. The wounded were, mercifully, unconscious. Without realizing what he did, Tyler said a prayer for them, and started topside. It was easier now. The water was drowning the fire. He fought his way upward to the deck. There he lay Hargraves down, took the last splintered section of the mast in sight, and tied the unconscious engineer to it. He was aware, as he did so, that the Yankee ships were no longer firing. He lifted Hargraves up, and got to the rail with him, thinking: The cold water will revive him. Hope he drifts clear before—

But aboard the nearest Yankee cruiser, the gunnery officer put down his glass.

"They're all off," he said. "Give her a salvo. She's taking too damned long to sink, and holding up the attack."

Tyler, poised at the rail, with Hargraves in his arms saw the gun flashes. That was the last thing he saw in a long, long time. The rail disappeared in a burst of splinters; the deck beneath his feet dissolved into a roaring, flameshot emptiness, and he was falling, falling down into nothing, into nowhere, into the icy dark. . . .

Later, in the prison hospital in New York, they told him about it: How they had picked up Hargraves swimming strongly, revived, as Tyler had hoped, by the icy water, and dragging a man along behind him by the hair—a man who trailed bloody tendrils through the moonsilvered waters. But that was a long time after— four long months, in which he lay in coma or woke to delirium, crying out for Sue.

Four months. And this: Two days after he woke for the first time with clear eyes, his thoughts cool and sane, a bearded little man, frowzy and unkempt as usual, wearing a battle stained private's jacket with general's stars pinned ludicrously to the shoulders, sat and talked awkwardly to a tall and kingly man in a grey dress uniform of regal splendor. Then he picked up a pen and wrote briefly: Patrolled on your word of honor not to take up arms against the United States—keep your sidearms and your horses—you'll need them for the Spring ploughing . . . Or words to that effect.

And there was a stillness at the McLean residence near Appomatox Courthouse. The stillness of Appomatox. The silence of no more war.

CHAPTER FIFTEEN

On the twenty sixth of june, 1865, Tyler meredith stood on the steps of the Post Office in New Orleans. He had reached his native city only that morning, and so far, he had not had time to inquire after either his brother or Ruth Forrester. He hoped that both of them had come home; but he couldn't be sure of that. There wasn't anything any longer, he realized, to tie them to the place of their birth.

He opened the single letter that had come for him during his absence. The letter was from his cousin Vivian, and it had been posted in England. He read it carefully, then folded it again, and put it in his pocket. So Viv was back in England. That was a good thing. So was young Tom Meadows. It was characteristic of Meadows that Tyler hadn't even known his name was Tom. He had come aboard the first day with a crisp, "Meadows reporting, Sir!" and that had been that. But the surprising thing was that Hargraves had gone with them.

"Never did set horses with no Yankees," Vivian had quoted him as saying. "They going to run the country, I'll get out. 'Sides, don't rightly make much difference who I sail under now, seeing as how there ain't no more danger. . . ."

Good men, all of them. But Hargraves was the best. He'd miss them. Them—and—But he had trained himself to think about that as little as possible. He moved off, down the street.

Nothing about New Orleans had changed; and everything about it had changed. The narrow streets of the Vieux Carré were crowded from wall to wall with the surge and press of crowds. Tyler stood on the corner of Chartres and Iberville Streets and tried to decide what the difference was. The houses were the same, only a bit more shabby and dilapidated than they had been before the war, bearing their age well, for most of them had stood there since the days of Spanish rule; and four years more, added but the barest trifle to their patina of years. Stores were open again, under the shadow of the galleries; and the inhabitants of upper storey flats had resumed their old custom of letting down a bucket on a rope, with money in it and a list of their needs, which the green-grocers, bakers, and butchers promptly supplied, whereupon the apartment dwellers hauled up their buckets again, saving themselves a weary climb.

Nuns moved through the crowds, and Negro laundresses balanced bundles of wash upon their heads. Street vendors hawked their rice cake, *estomac du mulatre*, praline candies, toys. Newsboys cried the news in voices as hoarse and incomprehensible as ever. Drunks weaved and meandered, jostling sober citizens. . . .

That was one thing. There were more drunks than he had ever seen before. And more grog shops and barrelhouses. There was also, faint and subtle, almost indefinable, an air of letting down, or slackening, notice-

able even in a city with a nationwide reputation for
slackness. He saw a couple of women, obviously rouged
and powdered, ambling along among the predominately
male throngs, and regarding every man who passed with
bold stares. That was new. New Orleans had always
been generously supplied with harlots, but before the
war they had kept strictly to their districts. To see two
of them promenading on Chartres Street, was evidence
of—He didn't know what.

He was aware of the shabbiness of the crowds. Men
and women alike, in New Orleans, had prided themselves
upon being well-dressed. But there were visible patches
on the trousers of distinguished gentlemen, and women's
gowns were faded. New Orleans had suffered; not like
Atlanta, Richmond, Columbia, Charleston, Alexandria
and other cities only now beginning to rebuild the
gutted shells that were all the Yankee armies had left
them; but in subtler, less obvious ways.

He stopped a passerby.

"Pardon me," he said, "but could you tell me where
to find Miss Forrester's Female Academy?"

"Never heard of it," the man snapped, the nasal
Yankee accent sounding through his voice. "I'm a
stranger here myself, Mister. . . ."

"Sorry," Tyler murmured. That was still another
thing, another part of the strangeness. A goodly number
of the crowd had neither the bearing nor the appearance
of Southern men. Which was, when he stopped to think of
it, hardly strange: New Orleans had been in Yankee
hands since April, Sixty two, and a Northerner could
smell a dollar from forty miles away against the wind.

The next time he chose his informant with more care.
The man was lean and tall, with a tired, lined face, about
fifty, Tyler guessed. He was obviously a native Orleanais;
moreover, there was something familiar about him.

"Miss Forrester's Academy? Of course, Sir. It's just
around the corner on Conti Street. I'd be most happy to
accompany you. . . ."

Tyler felt a little glow of warmth. It wasn't all dead,
not all of it. Some of the old, level-eyed courtesy; the
almost inborn gentility of Southerners had managed to
survive.

"Thank you mighty kindly," he said, "but I wouldn't
want to inconvenience you, Sir. . . ."

"No inconvienence at all. You don't imagine that an
old unreconstructed rebel like me has anything to do
with his time? It's a pleasure to—Lord God!"

"What is it?" Tyler said.

"You're Meredith—Tyler Meredith! And to think I
didn't know you!"

"You've still got the better of me, Sir," Tyler said. "I
confess I don't—"

"No reason why you should. I'm Caldwell Vickers.
Apart from the fact that we frequented the same clubs,
our acquaintance was slight. Don't reckon we were
ever formally introduced. . . ."

"Then why do you remember me?" Tyler said.

"You're something of a legend. I managed the un-
paralleled stupidity of getting myself badly wounded
in a minor skirmish long before Shiloh, the day before
Fort Donelson fell, in fact. I was back in New Orleans
before the Federals captured the city. Even then your

fame as a blockade runner was widespread. The great
Captain Rebel everybody called you. And I saw you
being marched through the streets surrounded by Yankee soldiers on two occasions when that unspeakable
swine, Butler, seemed to be making you the butt of his
personal vindictiveness. It was seriously believed hereabouts that he was seeking an excuse to hang you as
a public example; though most folks were confident of
your ability to wiggle out of any danger—correctly so,
as events proved. Lord, how you've changed! You can't
be more than thirty and—"

"I look sixty-five. I know. I've been told that
before. . . ."

"Hardly that. I'd have guessed forty-ish. Never will
forget that speech you made at the Eakins Club about
getting the whole Yankee army drunk on bourbon and
capturing them without firing a shot. We should have
tried it. Might have worked. Certainly nothing else
did. . . ."

Now, finally, Tyler remembered the man. And the
feeling of sadness inside him increased with the recognition: Caldwell Vickers was a year or two younger than
he was. War did this to a man: even if it spared his life
it ended his youth.

They walked through the streets, Vickers chattering
away. He was, Tyler remembered now, Banker Randolph Vicker's son—and a graduate of Harvard, which
accounted for the slightly pedantic quality of his speech.

"Here we are," Vickers said. "It's one flight up. By
the way, before I leave you, I'd like to invite you to the
first meeting of a new club we're organizing. Our first
formal meeting is set for the fifteenth of next month. We

want to consider means of protecting the rights of Southern white people against Yankee-inspired Negro encroachment. We could use a man like you. . . ."

Tyler started to refuse, flatly; then he reconsidered. If he were going to live in New Orleans, he'd better be aware of what was going on. He could attend a meeting without overly committing himself.

"I'll come," he said. "Where will it be held?"

"The old Eakins Club—about eight o'clock. It has been mighty nice seeing you again, Mr. Meredith. Glad you're back. So many others—won't ever be. You knew about George Drake?"

"Yes," Tyler said harshly, "I knew. . . ."

"Strange about his wife though. Miss Forrester's been awfully closemouthed. All she would say was that her sister—died. . . ."

"That's right," Tyler said. "In Richmond. Thank you very kindly, Mr. Vickers. . . ."

The girls were dressed neatly, in faded pinafores. Ruth, sitting at the desk, had her hair brushed severely back, and caught into a tight bun on her neck. She wore steel rimmed spectacles. They made her look much older.

There was a moment of silence, then a ripple of school-girl tittering. Ruth looked up. She stared blankly; then she took off her spectacles. The moment she did so, her face changed.

"Class will come to order!" she said. "Mary Ann, I appoint you monitor to keep order while I talk to this gentleman. No foolishness now. I'll be only a moment. . . ."

They stood in the hallway, looking at each other.

"Well, Ruth?" Tyler said.

"I thought you were dead," Ruth said. "I'd hoped you were. But now that I see you're not, I'm glad."

"Thank you for that much," Tyler said. "Can't we go somewhere, and—"

"No. I've my class to attend to. Besides, I don't think we can have very much to say to each other, Tyler."

"I," Tyler said wearily, "have a great deal to say to you, Ruth." He was aware, speaking, that he no longer had the impulse to call her 'Kitten'. It did not fit her any more. That or any other pet name whatsoever. "Could I call for you tonight—at seven, say?"

"I," Ruth said, "have papers to correct. And my own studies. I confess I'm badly fitted to be a schoolmistress. I have to work to keep ahead of my brighter pupils. But there's the unfortunate necessity of keeping alive. . . ."

"Couldn't you make an exception this one evening?" he asked. "At heart, you were always fair—once you'd worked your temper off. Do you mean to condemn me without a hearing?"

She looked at him a long time, thinking: I'm a fool. You killed my sister and wrecked my life. And yet —I—I—

"All right," she said crisply. "Tonight. I have a little flat above the school. The house is being sold for taxes. I haven't the money to pay them. You'll find me living in genteel poverty, but I can offer you a glass of wine."

"I'll take you out to dinner," Tyler said.

"No, thank you. I have no suitable dress. And I'm not at all sure I want to be seen with you. You may visit me at home, and I'll receive you. I'll hear you out. That's all I can promise. Fair enough, Tyler?"

"Fair enough," Tyler said. " 'Till tonight, then. . . .'"

He sat that night, in the armchair, looking at her. She had not changed her dress nor the style of her hair. She looked at him defiantly from behind the glasses. But not even they could disguise, now, close at hand, her youth or her great beauty.

"Why," he said slowly, "do you hold me responsible for your sister's death, Child?"

"Because," she said evenly, "you drove her to her death. Of course, she did talk wildly about never seeing you again; but that was just woman's talk. The least you could have done under the circumstances was to offer to marry her, Tyler."

"But I did," Tyler said. "Hundreds of times. I pleaded with her to ask George for a divorce. She refused. The night—she left, I did not even know she was free. She didn't tell me of George's death. To tell the truth, I didn't give her a chance to. I—oh hell, let's skip that. The point is, I found out about it, only after she had gone, from the letters she left behind. . . ."

"And you," Ruth said, "do not blame yourself?"

Tyler looked at her. Seeing his face, his eyes, she recoiled slightly. Then she leaned forward, feeling the ache in her fingertips to reach out and stroke his cheek, hearing the words of comfort rising unbidden in her throat, her defenses down, melting before what she saw in his eyes. She stifled both impulses and sat there, waiting.

"Yes," he said. "I blame myself, Ruth. More than you, or anybody else possibly could. I'll never stop blaming myself until the day I die. Which is why, maybe, it's so important to me that you—think well of me. I've grief enough to suit even you. I need your good will, Ruth. . . ."

"She came to you," Ruth said slowly, "and you gave her no chance to speak. You took her in your arms and —made love. She let you, knowing her husband was dead. Funny, but I understand that. I—I even forgive it, which is a thing only another woman, knowing what women are like—could. That was it, wasn't it, Tyler?"

"Yes," Tyler said bleakly. "That was it—"

"Drink your wine, Tyler," Ruth said.

"But—"

"It doesn't matter now. You loved her, wanted to marry her. You didn't cause her death by rejecting her— which was what I thought—"

"My God!" Tyler said. "What kind of a bastard did you think I was, Ruth?"

"Enough of one to do that. But, no matter. You had it all planned. She'd ask George to divorce her, then you'd marry her. Simple. Only you reckoned without George's sensitivity. So did I, Tyler. I thought he was a clod. You reckoned without that. You didn't even consider that there were such things as fate—and even the Hand of God. All right, then, I do think well of you again. You were wicked, you and my sister both. Wicked and selfish and thoughtless, but hardly criminal. Satisfied?"

"Yes," Tyler said. "Thanks, Ruth." He put his hand in his breastpocket and came out with an envelope. "Here," he said; "this is for you, Child. . . ."

She took it, opened it, and began to read. She straightened up, staring at him, her face white and still.

"You thought you could bribe me?" she said.

"No. If I'd thought that, I'd have offered you this before we began to talk. It's not that. The house is rightfully yours. I wanted you to have it. . . ."

"So you bought it for me for back taxes, and made me a present of the deeds. Noble of you. I'm sorry, Tyler, but—no."

"Why not, Ruth? There're no strings attached to it."

"I know that. But I don't want it. I could never live in that house again. You live in it, Tyler. It's yours. Live in it—"

They were standing now; both of them facing each other.

"If you can. If you have the stomach to see every day the chairs she sat in, the bed she slept in—with the husband, Tyler that you, both of you, sent out to die, after you'd taken from him all he had to live for—the curtains she made, the dishes she ate from, the—"

"Ruth, for God's love!"

"Yes. Live in it. Don't change anything. Except that one small empty room, Tyler Meredith. Change that— fit it out as a nursery for your child—the child she carried with her when she went—"

He stood there, looking at her. Even his lips were white. There was no color in his face at all. He didn't say anything. He turned and crossed to the doorway, pushed the door open and went down the hall.

He heard, dully, the patter of her footsteps racing after him. She caught up with him, seized his arms, whirled in front of him.

"Oh, Ty!" she sobbed. "You didn't know! You didn't know! She had no chance to tell you—Of course! How could she have? Ty, Ty—I'm a bitch! A mean, vicious, cruel bitch!"

"It's all right, Child," he said gently.

She clung to him, crying. "Ty," she got out. "You can't! You mustn't!"

"No, Ruth," he said. "I can't and I won't, even if there isn't any sense to living now. I'm just not built that way, I reckon . . ."

"Oh, thank God!" she whispered. "Ty listen to me!"

"Yes, Child?"

"I thought I hated you; but I don't. When you came into the school this morning, I thought I was going to faint. But it wasn't hate—not for you, anyhow. For myself, maybe; because I still love you so!"

He looked at her a long, slow time.

"Thanks, Ruth," he said, "for telling me that. But you mustn't. I'm not fit—"

"You are! You are! And even if you weren't, I'd love you still—"

He freed himself gently from her clasp.

"Goodnight, Ruth," he said.

"I—I'll see you? You will come to see me, Ty?"

"Yes," he said; "I'll come. . . ."

He started back toward the hotel; but her words kept echoing through his brain. He thought about Cato and Bessie busy at the task he had set them of cleaning the Drake house. And then, suddenly, inexplicably, he knew

he had to go there. He didn't know why he had to go;
but he had to.

Fool! he cursed himself. What do you want? The
lash and the hairshirt of the penitents? That house will
be haunted for you, yet—

He had to go.

It was very still when he opened the door with one
of the keys the sheriff had given him. Upstairs in their
quarters, Cato and Bessie slumbered. The house held
no aura of death for them. No one had ever died in
George Drake's house. The Negroes were incapable
of thinking it haunted, though they would not have
entered a house in which a tragic death had actually
occurred.

But, for Tyler Meredith, the house was alive with
phantoms. He walked from room to room, the feeling
growing in him that if he were to stop now, suddenly
turn his head—He fought the impulse. It was nonsense
and worse, his mind told him. He did not believe in
ghosts; but these were not the spirits of chilling romance;
these were the resurrection of memories, falling on his
mind and heart like a ceaseless rain of blows. As terrible
as any disembodied shade, dragging the mouldering incre-
ments of a tomb could have been, these were more terrible, for these were living things: Her voice speaking,
a morning sky flash of laughing eyes; the shell pink
curve of lip, floating there just beyond him, just out
of sight and sound.

He could hear the funeral drumroll of his heart; the
dry rasp of breath like a desert storm, burning through
his throat; feel the sickness inside him that coiled around

each sliver of steel in him that the Yankee surgeons had
not dared remove or hadn't even found.

Sue, he shaped her name, feeling the tears of brine
and fire running molten through his heart. Sue—and my
child, unborn, unliving—God!

No! he raged. I won't give in. I will not come crawling
back. I'm me—a man, not the plaything of childish
superstitions. I know what I'll do—I'll get drunk and
go down the line on Gallatin Street! I'll wallow in the
mire like a hog, because I'm not afraid, not afraid of—

He knew, even as he shaped the thought, that he
was already a little mad. He stood apart from himself
and examined his madness. Drink had always been a
thing he could take or leave alone; and whores awoke
in him an almost physical distaste. He had never particularly enjoyed drinking. He had drunk himself into
insensibility only a few times in his life, when the going
had been too rough for him. And his relationship with
women had never been on the basis of outright purchase;
more, a half suppressed vein of puritanism had kept him
away from them for increasingly longer intervals in
recent years. What he proposed to do was a violation
of his own personality, for, as his cousin Vivian had
put it, the words coming sharply into his mind once
again:

"Your drunkenness and your wenching, have been
exactly as effective in reducing your essential decency,
your incorruptibility as the chains, whips, and hairshirts
of the medieval penitents were in mortifying the lusts
of the flesh. . . ."

"Incorruptibility!" he said. "Ha!"

Two hours later, he was sitting in the parlor of a

house in the Tenderloin. He was only a little drunk,
though he had downed countless glasses of the gut rotting poison they sold in the barrelhouses. It seemed to
have lost the power to affect him.

"You'll stay the night?" the blowsy madam asked.
"Good; I'll bring in the girls. . . ."

She paraded them before him. Looking at them, the
nausea rose to the very base of his throat. He was about
to tell her to forget it, throw down a sheaf of bills and
leave, when one more girl came in. Different from the
others: willow slim, with light chestnut hair like a cloud
about the pitiful face that still retained traces of her
former beauty.

She saw him, stopped; her two hands flew up to hide
her face; she whirled and ran wildly through the doorway.

"Goddammit!" the madam roared; "I won't have—"

"Call her back," Tyler said. "I'll take her. . . ."

The madam lumbered out. In a moment she was back,
pushing the girl before her, one arm twisted cruelly behind her back. The girl's head was bent, staring at the
floor; and at her feet Tyler could see the splatter of her
tears.

"Turn her loose, Ma'am," Tyler said. "It's all right,
Laurie—Don't you cry. . . ."

He took her arm. She would not look at him.

"You treat this gentleman nice, you hear me!" the
madam said; "or else I'll have your hide!"

She led the way to the room upstairs. She unlocked
the door, casting a shrewd glance at the quiet richness
of his attire.

"That'll be twenty dollars," she said.

Tyler paid her without a word.

"You let me know if she gives you any trouble, Sir," she said.

"Oh, for God's sake—get out of here!" Tyler said.

The madam waddled out in an elephantine counterfeit of grace. Tyler turned back to Lauriel.

She looked him straight in the eyes, the unchecked tears running freely down her face. Then very slowly, she caught at the hem of her dress, lifted it—

"No!" Tyler got out. "For God's sake, Laurie—no!"

Slowly she let the skirt fall. Her voice speaking, was cold with mockery.

"Why?" she said. "Doesn't the rich, white gentleman want what he's paid for?"

"From you, no," Tyler said. "I want nothing from you—except to beg your pardon, Laurie. . . ."

"To beg—my pardon? For what, Ty?"

"For—allowing this to happen. For not getting to Sans Souci before McGraw. For not looking for you hard enough. Maybe for not caring enough. . . ."

She came to him, put out her hand and touched his face.

"How could you?" she whispered. "There were worlds between us, Tyler. And you were always good to me. You still are. It isn't that. It was just that I was so ashamed. . . ."

He drew her to him, gently.

"Don't be, little Lauriel," he said. "There's no more need of that. Come, I'll take you out of here and—"

"No," she said. "Not now! They'd beat you to death if you tried to take me away! Stay here tonight, Ty. You were going to anyhow, if it hadn't been me. Stay and

talk to me. Tomorrow, I can leave. They let us spend
the day as we please. . . ."

"All right," he said. "Tomorrow I'll arrange things
for you, Laurie. You were always good with the needle
as I recall. How would you like a little dressmaking
establishment—or a millinery shop?"

"I was hoping you were going to set me up as your
placée in a cottage on Rampart Street. . . ."

He looked at her, and saw the gentle mockery in her
eyes.

"No," he said. "Not you, Lauriel. You couldn't ever
be stuck away on the backstreets of my life. Since,
Chickee, the only way I'd want you is the way that
neither the law and mighty heap of folks will cotton to—
I don't want anything from you. I just want to set you
free. . . ."

"Ty—" she said.

"Yes, Chickee?"

"Aren't you going to ask me what I'm doing in this
place?"

"No. Don't reckon it's my business, since I sure Lord
didn't do anything much to help you. But if you want
to tell me, Laurie. . . ."

"Yes. God, yes! Ty—I—I have a child. A little girl
going on three years old now. Tennessee McGraw's
child. . . ."

"I see," Tyler said drily.

"You don't! How can you? He—he took me by force.
He beat me, starved me—I had to give in, Ty—I had
to!"

"There, there, Baby," Tyler said. "Don't cry—"

"The dreadful part about it is—I love her so. I thought I'd hate her—that I could put her out for adoption; but I couldn't. She's so beautiful. Even as a tiny infant she was. She doesn't look anything like him. She's little and helpless and sweet. And there wasn't any work—you understand that, Ty? I couldn't watch her crying of hunger, and me without a penny to buy her milk . . . So I—I came here, Ty. For her, for my baby. You see how it was, Ty—you see?"

"Yes, Laurie," he said; "Yes, I see . . ."

"I named her Merry. I couldn't do anything with Tyler; it just wouldn't go into a girl's name. But Meredith was better. With an "e" it sounded fine. Meredithe Doumier. Merry for short. Only—I used to say to myself, Merry Meredith . . . over and over again, dreaming how it would be if she were your child, the way she ought to be. It was presumptuous, I know, but. . . ."

"It wasn't presumptuous, Laurie," Tyler said gravely. "I'm honored."

She stood away from him, looking up into his eyes.

"Why," she breathed, "you mean that! You actually mean it—Oh, Ty, you are the nicest, kindest, sweetest—"

"No, Laurie. None of those things. But I am honored, just the same. . . ."

They lay, fully clothed, across the shabby bed and talked. Before morning, they slept a little.

"You can go now, Ty," Lauriel said. "Wait for me about ten o'clock on Rampart Street. Nobody'll pay any attention to us there. They'll just think—"

"I," Tyler said, "don't give a damn what they think."

"Dear Ty. And Ty—"

"Yes, Laurie?"

"Would you please kiss me? I haven't a—a disease. I was to the doctor's yesterday. I go regularly, because I'm so afraid of that. Would you, Ty?"

"Of course, Laurie," Tyler said.

CHAPTER SIXTEEN

HE CAME BACK FROM THE DOCK, AFTER HAVING PUT Lauriel and little Merry aboard the coasting steamer bound for New York. Lauriel had insisted upon that.

"I can't stay in New Orleans, Ty," she said. "It has too many bad memories for me. And your being here makes it worse. I couldn't bear having to see you all the time, and not—please, Ty; you do understand?"

He had given her a letter of credit upon his New York bank. The funds he had there would keep her for years, even educate the child. The child—Lord God, but she was a beauty! Bright red hair and blue eyes and the most delicate smile in the world. He had held her in his arms all day long, up until the minute the boat sailed. He had held Tennessee McGraw's near-white child, and dreamed up impossible schemes for adopting her. But they all involved the necessity of taking her from Lauriel, and he couldn't do that.

He walked slowly through the streets. He felt strange. The baby's fat little fingers, curled trustfully around his own, had drawn something out of him. It was as though by living, by the simple fact of having her being, she had replaced one part of his loss. He tried to analyze this new thing he had, this new feeling, moving warm and soft within his heart. And then, suddenly, passing before Christ Church on Jackson Avenue, he knew what it was. He looked up and smiled.

"I'm home now, Lord," he said. "Back into the safe harbor You've been plotting my course toward all this time. I know what You want of me, and I'll do it. Yes, I'll do it now."

He turned, and went, not into the Church but into the Rectory. He remained there with Father Edmunds for an hour.

"Yes, Tyler," Father Edmunds said. "There are many things that need to be done in New Orleans. I think you're one of the men who can do them, especially since you've decided to devote your fortune to God's work. Don't worry about it's being tainted money. You've asked God's forgiveness for that; and He has forgiven much greater sins. Our cause was lost anyhow. Maybe your profiteering as a blockade runner did contribute to its failure, but to a much slighter extent than you seem to believe. And the good you can do with the funds you call dirty gold will more than make up for any harm you might have done."

"Thanks, Father," Tyler said.

"Thank God, Son," Father Edmunds said. "He brought you home after a long, long voyage. But speaking of good works, how would you like to begin right now?"

"Now?" Tyler said. "Of course, Father."

"I," Father Edmunds said, "have a delicate job for you, my boy. In fact," he paused, studying Tyler's face, "it's a task I'm taking a tremendous risk in entrusting to you. But I think that you could do it. If anybody could, it would be you."

"What is it, Father?"

"Your—brother. He's been back from that Illinois Prisoner of War Camp some months now. I've been keeping him with me here in the Rectory. . . ."

"Joe! Lord, Father, let me see—"

"Wait, son. I said I've been keeping him in the Rectory. He's a sick man, Tyler. Not physically. He's fully recovered from his wound. He's soul sick. He—it's a dreadful thing, my son; but your brother has lost his faith. . . ."

"Joe? Not Joe! He couldn't. Why he—"

"He has, nonetheless. You see, the war was too much for him. It's not uncommon nowadays."

"And you want me to—"

"Restore it. I freely confess, I tried—and failed. No argument would budge him. His disbelief is as strong as his former faith. But there's God's Hand in this— your coming to me in full contrition, today, of all days. If anything can move him, it will be this. Will you see him now?"

Tyler took a deep breath.

"Yes, Father—gladly," he said.

He was prepared to see his brother changed; but he was shocked at Joe's appearance. This was not the brother he remembered, grave, confident, sure; not this grey, trembling wreck of a man. He stood there, looking at him.

"Well, Padre?" he said.

"Not—Padre," Joe said harshly. "I'm no longer a minister. Father Edmunds must have told you that."

Tyler did not let the smile upon his lean face waver. He put out his hand.

"Will you pray with me, Joe?" he said.

"With you!" Joseph said angrily. "What kind of tom-foolery is this, Tyler?"

"No tomfoolery," Father Edmunds said. "Tyler has come back to us, Joseph. You can pray with him now, if you will."

"Look Ty," Joseph said huskily, "I don't understand. It was your arguments that convinced me. Lying there in that stinking camp, I went over them in my mind. You were right. On every count, you were right. No God would permit the suffering, the cruelty—"

"Wait," Tyler said calmly. "I said pray, not argue. I'm not going to argue with you, Padre. I don't know any arguments any more, or any answers. Faith isn't a thing you can argue. You have it; or you don't. And God's reasons are His Own. I don't know the answer to the suffering, the cruelty, the lonely dying. I only know— now, at long last, and very surely—that there are an-swers. I don't think that God is going to indulge His spoiled and limited children to the extent of sharing with them reasons they aren't even equipped to understand. Besides," he smiled slowly, "you were right, Padre, when you rebuked me about my intellectual pride. It's gone now. Apparently you've caught it from me, like some rare, unlovely disease. Are you going to force me to suffer that one more sin upon my conscience, or will you pray with me, Joe? Will you?"

Joseph stood there a long, long time. Then they both saw it: the trembling had stopped, and color was stealing back into his greyish face. Reverently Father Edmunds bowed his head.

"Yes, Ty," said Joseph. "Let's kneel here now—and pray. . . ."

Tyler went, on the fifteenth of August, to the Eakins Club as he had promised Caldwell Vickers. From what he had already heard, the men were planning to resort to terrorism to frighten the Negroes from the polls, to keep them in their place. He went, accepting the risks he knew his action would entail, to try to persuade them not to do it.

To his vast astonishment, Vickers stood up and made a speech—about Tyler Meredith. Since their last meeting, the banker's son had done some serious research. He had looked up the newspaper files about Tyler's career; he had talked to sailors who had been in Nassau during the war; he had even interviewed Ruth Forrester, though this Tyler did not learn until later. But he had the information at his fingertips, and he presented it beautifully. All of it: the race to save Collins' life; the skillful evasions of the Yankee cruisers, Tyler's wounds, and his sufferings at "Beast" Butler's hands. In conclusion, he said:

"I can think of no better man to head our worthy organization. If the chairman will entertain it, I hereby move that Captain Tyler Meredith be nominated President of the White Man's Protective Association of New Orleans!"

The man who rose to second the motion was completely drowned out by the roars of approval.

"Ol' Ty! Of course! Just the man!"

"Remember how hard old 'Silver Spoons' tried to get something on him so he could string him up?"

"And that there speech right here in the club. I was here. Remember how he kicked that nigger over the balcony? Broke his back. Saw the bastid the other day, propped up in his goat cart, selling candy. . . ."

"Speech! Speech from our new President!"

"Hell, he ain't been elected yet!"

"Aw to heck with the formalities. I say he's it!"

"So do I!"

"And me!"

"Me, too!"

The chairman stood up.

"The chair will entertain a voice vote," he cried. "All those in favor of Mr. Tyler Meredith as President, say Aye!"

"Aye!" the members roared to the man.

Tyler got up slowly. He felt sick. The Negro in the goat cart! No wonder the man's face had twisted with fear when he had tossed him that silver dollar. I'll have to find him, he thought. Cato will know. He knows every Negro in town. Maybe a good surgeon—

He walked forward, raising his arms for silence.

"Boys," he said, "I want to thank you for your confidence in me. But you're betting your money on the wrong horse. I'm not on your side—"

The silence at his opening words was more thunderous than sound.

"Did a mighty heap of things when I was a youngster that shames me to my soul to even think of, now. Downed

my share of rot-gut; passed more than my share of nights
on Rampart Street and Gallatin. Even went in for that
cowardly business of nigger hazing. Trouble is, somewhere along the line, reckon I sort of grew up. I see
things differently now. Wouldn't do what I did before.
Couldn't for the life of me.

"So I'm going to have to decline this nomination. It
makes me sick to the pit of my stomach to realize I
earned the reputation that made you offer it to me. Won't
hide the face God gave me under a mask; won't ride
in the dark to horse-whip some poor old nigger; won't
burn his shack. There are some things that are just a
mite too dirty. And I want to go to my God with hands
as clean as it's possible to wash them, 'twixt now and
the day I die. . . .

"And I want to ask you as men and brothers, not to
do this thing. I beg you not to disgrace the dead who
lost this battle like men, in the open, facing the foe. Do
you believe this cowardice, this knavery, is any substitute for the courage of men like our own George Drake
who flashed like swords and stood tall in thunder? What's
happened to you? I call upon you to stand up tall in
the honor that was yours. You can't turn back the clock,
boys; you can't go back. You cannot push our South-
land down into a barbarity it'll take your children, and
their children's children a hundred years to recover
from. . . ."

He paused, looking at them.

"Going to lay it on the line, boys," he said. "I'm against
this thing, against you if you're mule stubborn enough
to persist in it. I'll fight you every way I can: with the

press, the law, the pulpit of the Most High God—every way except violence. I've seen enough blood to last me ten lifetimes. You can call me nigger lover, if you want; but it's our white children I'm thinking of. If I had a son, I'd want to leave him a better legacy than hate; I'd rather see him dead than growing up to the nasty, stinking business of man-killing. Well boys, you have my word; you know exactly where I stand. So the only thing I can do right now is say goodnight to you all, and leave you to your work for good or ill. . . ."

He got down from the rostrum and walked very quietly from the hall. And not a hand was raised to stop him.

Finding Fred Peters, the Negro he had injured was surprisingly easy. Cato knew exactly where he lived. In fact, it was Bessie who made the cakes and praline candies that he sold, 'borrowing' the supplies from the kitchen of Tyler's house, as she had done for years. He, and Cato left the Drake House, now his own, for he could live there now in perfect peace, and went down to the Negro district. They found Fred Peters sitting propped up in a chair, poring over a big Bible. In the years since he had been a cripple, he had taught himself to read.

He looked with wonder and not a little fear from one of them to the other.

"It's all right, Fred," Cato said. "Mister Ty done come to help you out. . . ."

"Yes," Tyler said. "And to say I'm mighty sorry for

what I've done. I'm going to send a doctor down here
to look at your back, and—"

"It's too late, Marse Ty. Them army doctors done
looked at me. Said trying to straighten me out would
kill me sure. 'Sides," the Negro's smile was peaceful, "It
ain't so bad. I don't feel no pain a-tall. So don't worry
your head about me, Suh. I be all right. . . ."

Looking at him, seeing how cheerful he was, Tyler
felt sick. Lord God, he prayed, have You forgiven me
this, too?

Tell me, Fred," he said, "why didn't I know you that
night you came for me?"

" 'Cause I was new. Your Pa done bought me just a
couple of days before off'n Marse Henry Sutton who was
breaking up his place to go to the war. Didn't have no
Missus nor children, Marse Henry. So he sold his folks
off. Freed some of 'em what had trades and knowed how
to read'n write. An' after I—got hurt, some free colored
folks took me in. Couldn't come back to your house,
Suh, 'cause I was real bad off. Then Cato come and told
me that you'n Father Joe hadn't even missed me—and,
seeing as how I wouldn't be no good to youall anyhow,
I decided to lay low. . . ."

"Look, Fred," Tyler said, "there must be something
I can do. I'll have you a decent cottage built for one
thing, and see that you never want for anything as long
as you live. . . ."

"Thank you, Suh," the Negro said; "but I'm mighty
comfortable here. Wouldn't like to move away from
my friends. And I do right well with ol' Bess' candies—"

"Don't be a fool, Fred!" Tyler said sharply. "I *want* to do something to help you. . . ."

Fred's forehead crinkled in thought.

"Don't reckon there's much you can do, Marse Ty," he said. "But I do mightily 'ppreciate your offer. Tell you what, suh—if you really wants to do something that will gladden up my spirits right pert, you can put the money you was going to spend on me in that fund them Yankee white folks done started to build a school for the colored children. . . ."

"Where are their offices, Fred?" Tyler said.

"Down on Canal Street, Suh. Cato'll show you. You really going to do that, Marse Ty? Be mighty grateful. Ain't nothing my folks need worse than trades and book learning. . . ."

"I," Tyler said, "am going to give them the land to build it on, and pay for a brick building—on the condition that they name it the Fred Peters' School. That suit you Fred?"

He saw the sudden spurt of tears in the black man's eyes.

"God bless you, Suh," Fred Peters said. "This here is worth getting crippled up for! Yes Suh, it purely is!"

But this—and his donation of very nearly all that remained of the fortune he had amassed by blockade running, for the building of two orphanages, the first for the children of Confederate dead, with the express stipulation that the orphans of Union soldiers, if any, be not excluded; and one for Negro children, usually the victims of desertion by their parents in the great migrations following the war, when the ex-slaves had surrendered in droves to the impulse to try the dimensions of their freedom; and having, sadly, not yet learned a sense of responsibility, often left their children behind in the care of former masters, or even casual colored acquaintances—was to prove his undoing.

His one great mistake was to order them built exactly alike with scrupulously equal accommodations. As a native Southerner, he should have known better. Perhaps he had already flown too far from the world of men; perhaps, in the calm of his new found peace, he did not care. But at any event, the results were disastrous.

Ruth Forrester came riding to her former home to speak her mind to him. He had visited her often, taken her riding, talking always to her with grave kindliness. But she, being a woman, interpreted his kindness according to the dictates of her heart. She was already sure of him. Ruth was nothing if not practical: Love was fine; but she meant to live well, too.

But he was not at home, having gone to visit the sites of the orphanages, where, simultaneously, construction had already begun. Cato opened the door for her. She saw at once that the little Negro was quaking in terror.

"Miss Ruth!" he cried. "Lord God, Miss Ruth, you better go find him! Crowd of white menfolks been here to tell him to stop building that there colored school and orphan home. 'Lowed they'd kill him if he didn't quit. They left here 'bout two hours ago, looking for him!"

Oh, God! Ruth thought. Oh, why can't he act like other people? Now, this! Aloud, she said: "It's all right,

Cato. Just big talk, I reckon. Don't worry, I'll find him."
Then she started off, riding very fast.

At the site of the Confederate Orphanage, Tyler found
the work going very well. He watched it for a while,
and drove off to visit the Negro one. But nothing was
being done there; not a worker was in sight. He sat in
the buckboard, frowning. They've done it, he thought;
this is the work of Vickers' fine White Man's Protective
Association. Lord God, what kind of a people are we,
that we can even war on children?

He turned his horse's head toward the street where
the Fred Peters' School was being built. It was already
late, nearly dusk; but he hoped to get there before the
men knocked off work—if, indeed, there were any men.
And just before he reached it, he saw them, trudging
down the street, with their picks and shovels over their
shoulders. He pulled up the horse.

"What the matter?" he said. "Why aren't you working? It's more than an hour before quitting time. . . ."

"It's quitting time right now," a red faced Irishman
said; "and for good, Mister! Them fellows mean business
—and they've got guns. I don't aim to get myself kilt
over a passel of nigger brats. You want your nigger
school, you build it. I quit!"

Tyler drove on toward the school site, pausing only to
toss a silver dollar at Matt Pearson, the blind man. You
old fraud, he thought; you can see as well as I can—
Then he remembered that George Drake had told him, on
the day he had come home from Annapolis, that Matt

had less than two per cent of his sight. Poor Matt, Tyler
thought; he wanders all over New Orleans, even into
the Negro quarter. Reckon he's learned the hard way
that one man's money is as good as another's. . . .

Then, as the buckboard rounded the corner, Tyler
saw them: Caldwell Vickers and the others, coats off,
busily demolishing with sledgehammers, the work already
done. He felt the sick rage rise to his throat; but he
prayed to God against it and stood up in the buckboard.

"Boys," he began, "this is a mighty shameful piece of
work—" He got no further.

"It's him!" a voice rang out: "Ol' nigger-lover,
himself!"

"Let me at him! I'll learn the bastid!"

"Kill him! Kill the scalawagging son of a bitch!"

"Boys!" Vickers cried. "No killing! We can teach
him a lesson without that!"

"Now, wait a minute," Tyler began, but they were
upon him. They dragged him down from the buggy.
Fists smashed into his face, sending him down. They
picked him up again, hammered at him. He went down
into the dirt. They ringed him, kicking.

He did not say anything, or even cry out. Vickers
stopped it finally, more out of fear than pity, just one
second before it was too late. One more kick would
have killed him.

"Don't kill him, boys!" Vickers cried. "Leave him!
Let's get out of here! There's going to be hell to pay!"

Tyler heard, dimly, the sound of running feet diminishing, dying out of time and mind. And almost instantly,
it seemed to him, though it must have been much later,

considering the speed at which even the nearly blind must travel, he felt the hand on his shoulder.

"Can I help you, Sir?" Matt Pearson said. "Can't you hear me? I said, can I help you?"

"Lift me up, Matt," Tyler said, the words forced out from between set teeth. The pain was very bad. "Get me into the buckboard," he said.

"Can't you walk, Sir?" the blind man said. "I can't drive no buggy. Can't see well enough to—There, let me get your arm around my shoulder. . . ."

Matt Pearson was strong. He got Tyler to his feet, and half carried, half dragged him away from there. The pain was bad. He passed out four times in the first block. But always he came back again. Matt got him around the corner, out of the Negro quarter; and they came into a street filled with people. They stared at the blind man, dragging his broken, bloody burden, then they surged forward, and took Tyler away from him.

They brought Tyler Meredith home on the springbed of a wagon. Men ran for the nearest doctor; others sought his brother. Father Joseph got there before Ruth did, arriving just as Doctor Le Pierre was finishing his work.

"Well, Doctor?" Joseph Meredith said. The little Creole shook his head.

"I don't know," he said. "It depends upon him, Father. He's got three broken ribs, and how much damage those blackguards did to his insides, considering the amount of shrapnel he's carrying around in his body, I truly can't say. He can pull through—if he wants to. But until he regains consciousness, I can't decide whether or not he's fighting. . . ."

"Tyler's eyes came open slowly.

"Reckon you'd better pray for me, Padre," he said.

It was two hours later, that Ruth, still riding through the streets in search of him, heard the story. She flew to the house, her weariness forgotten. She found him a little stronger. Father Joseph, for the first time, permitted himself to hope.

She sat by his bed and talked to him.

"Why did you do it?" she wept. "It was so foolish, Ty! Even if they hadn't hurt you like this, I don't see what you expected us to live on. . . ."

Tyler looked at her peacefully from across the dark river of time. He felt wonderfully detached, and very tired.

"Doesn't look like I'm going to be around to live on anything, Child," he said quietly. "I'm sorry, Ruth, but that's the way it is. . . ."

She came up out of the chair in one wild rush, and knelt beside the bed.

"Oh, no, Ty!" she wept. "You can't die! You can't! I've waited for you so long, and now that you've learned to love me a little—Oh, Ty, Ty—you musn't—you can't!"

She laid her head next to his on the pillow.

"Please, Ty," she whispered.

He lifted his hand feebly and stroked her bright hair.

"It's just that I'm so tired, Ruth, he said, "of life, and everything connected with it. . . ."

"Ty," she said, her voice urgent, intense, "Listen to

me! Doctor Le Pierre said you could get well if you'd just fight. And you must, Love. Not only for me—though I know I'm not important to you yet. I can get to be, if you'll only give me the chance—I know that—"

"Why do you know it, Kitten?" he said. It was the first time he had called her that since he had come back to New Orleans.

"Because of the way I love you. Ty. Darling, no man who ever lived has been loved the way I'll love you if— if you'll stay with me. I have so much to make up for— all the lonely years, all the wanting you—even my mean-ness and hard words and vile temper. You must give me that chance, Ty. You can't leave me here with a lifetime to think and remember all the cruel things I said to you—and to Sue. Ty, Ty—I'll be so good to you! I don't care anymore that we'll be poor. I'll see that you're never unhappy again, but always warm, and safe, and comforted. . . ."

He smiled at her, tiredly.

"But it's not only for me," she went on. "It's for all the people you're helping, all the wonderful, kind things you're doing. Ty—you can't let them be lost! You can't let a gang of cowardly thugs stop your work. You can't, darling. There's nobody else to do it—nobody at all. . . ."

She saw, with dawning hope, the little spark that flared in his eyes.

"So," she said, "you've got to fight, Ty—you've simply got to. Will you try, darling? Please tell me you'll try. . . ."

He felt, somewhere deep inside of him, the ebbtide of his strength flowing back again. It was slight, almost imperceptible. He thought perhaps he had imagined it.

She's right, he thought; killing me isn't anything much, but killing those kids' chances is something else again. Damn Vickers and his League anyhow! If they think—"

He smiled suddenly, warmly. He knew it wasn't imagination now.

"You," he said, "have always known how to get next to me, haven't you, Kitten?"

"No," she said sadly, "I've never even known how to make you love me—and that was what I wanted more than anything else in the world. . . ."

Tyler touched her cheek gently, letting her tears trail down his long, bony fingers.

Love? he thought. What does the word mean? Can a man who's lived the life I have find it again?

He doubted it. But what he did feel for her was more than pity, better than compassion—a deep, slow running kindness, quiet and soft and warm, that moved out to meet her loneliness and her need. Not the fire and pain and passion of his youth, but a different kind of emotion, a finer feeling really—full blown and manly and complete.

He let his fingers follow the downward track of her tears until he found her chin. He lifted her face with a strength that surprised even him.

"Yes, Kitten, I'll try," he said.

The Martini Book

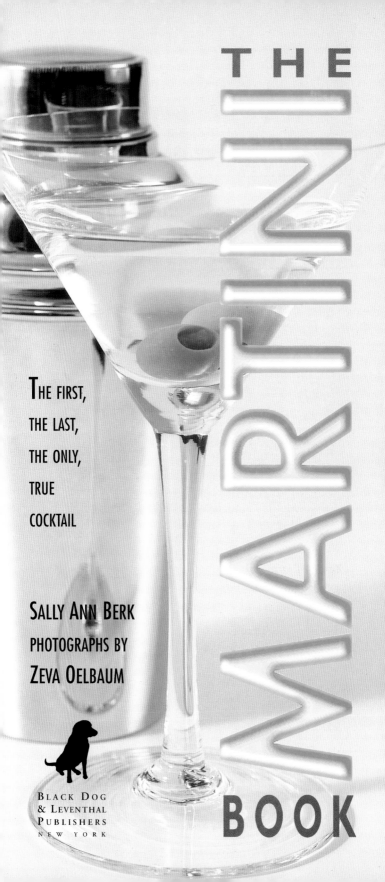

THE MARTINI

BOOK

THE FIRST,
THE LAST,
THE ONLY,
TRUE
COCKTAIL

SALLY ANN BERK
PHOTOGRAPHS BY
ZEVA OELBAUM

BLACK DOG
& LEVENTHAL
PUBLISHERS
NEW YORK

Published by
Black Dog & Leventhal Publishers, Inc.
151 West 19th Street
New York, NY 10011

Distributed by Workman Publishing Company
708 Broadway
New York, NY 10003

Hardcover ISBN-10: 1–884822–98–3
ISBN-13: 978–1–884822–98–8
w v u
Paperback ISBN-10: 1–57912–348–1
ISBN-13: 978–1–57912–348–2
j i h g f e d c b

Leather ISBN-10: 1–57912–188–8
ISBN-13: 978–1–57912–188–4
l k j i h

Acknowledgments

Many thanks to the following people
whose help was invaluable:
Zeva Oelbaum for her beautiful and creative photographs;
Joseph Teresa for his extraordinary food styling;
Karen Berman

Props from the collections of:
Ann Kerman and Bill Boyer
Jonette Jakobson
Steve and Dotty Malinchoc
Peter Malinchoc
Betsy Reid

Dedicated to James, my favorite martini maker

Book design by Jonette Jakobson

Printed in China

CONTENTS

"I know I'm not going to live forever,
and neither are you,
but until my furlough here on earth
is revoked, I should like to elbow aside
the established pieties and raise
my martini glass in salute to the
moral arts of pleasure."

Bob Shacochis
Award-winning novelist and
well-known hedonist

3

INTRODUCTION

THE MARTINI

The martini is the quintessential American cocktail. Born and bred in the United States, the martini has come to represent everything from sophistication to depravity, elegance to wild abandon. Sometimes called a "silver bullet", it's clean, it's cold, and it always hits the mark.

Presidents and movie stars, journalists and poets, fictional characters and their creators, have all looked to the martini for inspiration, release, love, humor. No other cocktail has such a complicated folklore. No other cocktail engenders the kind of passion true martini purists exhibit when mixing or discussing their unique ways of making a martini.

The origin of the martini has been the subject of much debate. It was discovered sometime during the latter part of the nineteenth century, but beyond that one probable fact, the stories of its origin diverge.

One of five theories places the martini in the San Francisco Bay Area after the Gold Rush. Another places it in Martinez, California, thus the name. Still another theory credits the bartender at the Hoffman House in New York around 1880. A fourth story attributes the martini to an Italian immigrant named Martini di Arma di Taggia, who tended bar at the Knickerbocker Hotel in New York in the early part of the twentieth century. Yet another story has the martini being created in the Netherlands.

There is no doubt that gin was developed in the Netherlands, but not the martini. Too much evidence points to America as its birthplace. New Yorkers usually adhere to the Hoffman House theory, while West Coasters prefer the San Francisco theory.

But why and how did this gin drink become a cultural icon? Why not the Rob Roy? The Rusty Nail? The Manhattan?

All of these drinks have their place among the pantheon of classic cocktails, but the martini captured the fancy and the taste of the people from the moment it was born, and except for a lapse during the 70s, it's remained the quintessential cocktail ever since.

Perhaps its simplicity is what gives the martini its staying power. Perhaps it's the iconic stature of the martini glass. Maybe it's the fact that all you need are the two essential ingredients of cold gin and vermouth to create something sublime. Creating a martini is almost alchemic—from two basic elements, one can create gold or the cocktail equivalent.

Whatever the reasons, the martini is here to stay. Many of us will usher in the next millennium with champagne. Some of us will toast the new age with our silver bullets.

THE
INGREDIENTS

G in or vodka, vermouth, and olives are all that are needed to create classic martinis. Before we look at other flourishes, let's explore these basic building blocks.

Gin comes to us from the Netherlands, where it was called *genievre*, which means "juniper." It is a clear liquor, distilled from grain, and flavored with juniper berries. Popular myth holds that it was first invented as a blood cleanser by a seventeenth century chemist.

Gin's popularity grew throughout Europe and spread to the Colonies. Dickens wrote about gin shops and Hogarth painted them. Henry Hudson brought it with him on his expeditions to the New World. Gin was easy to make because it required no aging. This is why gin became immensely popular during Prohibition, you could distill it anywhere.

There are three kinds of gin available today—Genever, Old Tom, and London Dry. Genever is the original Dutch formula. It is a highly flavored gin and is not usually used in martinis. Old Tom, a non-dry gin, is created when barley malt or sweetener is added to dry gin. It is not readily available, but its cousin, Pimm's Cup, is still served as a cocktail. It is widely believed that the original martini, the Martinez Cocktail, was created with Old Tom gin.

The gin most people know is London Dry. This is the gin served in bars and found in liquor stores the world over. All spirits are distilled once, but the craft of gin-making is exemplified during the second distillation. A gin-smith creates a fine dry gin in the redistillation of the liquor. During this second distillation flavorings are added. It is not unusual to find citrus peels, herbs, and spices added during the second distillation. Without them, a gin martini would not exist.

While one can use almost any kind of vodka to make a good vodka martini, the quality, taste, and smoothness of different gins can make or break the drink. With gin, you get what you pay for, and one should never go for the bargain basement gins. Start with Bombay, Bombay Sapphire, or Beefeater's. Try some others if you like, but keep in mind that because gin is so easy to manufacture, there are many gins that would do better as paint thinners. Since gin is arguably the key ingredient in a martini, it makes no sense to skimp.

The other key ingredient is vermouth. Even though a dry martini uses practically none, it needs to be there. Vermouth is a fortified wine that has been flavored with various herbs and spices. The word "vermouth" comes from the German word *wermut* which means "wormwood." Before wormwood was discovered to be poisonous, it was used in making vermouth (and its notorious relative, absinthe). The martini is made with white dry vermouth,

also known as French vermouth, a white liquid that can also be drunk as a cocktail. It should not be confused with bianco, an Italian version, which is also white but much sweeter. Sweet vermouth, or rosso, is a reddish vermouth used in Manhattans. Early recipes for martinis also used sweet vermouth.

Many purists consider the vodka martini a bastardization of a fine drink. Others consider it a legitimate variation and believe it has its rightful place in the martini pantheon. Even though vodka martinis did not become popular until the 1960s, we must consider vodka as an essential ingredient in this new generation of the drink.

Vodka is a Russian word meaning "little water." It has its

origins in Russia, but is made worldwide. It was originally made from distilling potatoes, but can, and is, made from any grain. It is a neutral spirit, which means it must be flavorless by law. It is not aged.

Many people will argue that more expensive vodka tastes better or is smoother. However, vodka shouldn't have a flavor to begin with, unless it is a flavored vodka. The only way to resolve this argument is to buy a bottle of bargain vodka and a bottle of premium vodka, remove the labels, and chill them to freezing. Sip one, then the other, and see if you can tell the difference. You can't. Of course, others will tell you that you can—that Ketel One is better than Stoli, and Absolut is the best. In the end, it's up to you.

What makes vodka interesting is not what's in the bottle, but what's on it. Since the collapse of the Soviet Union, we have access to vodka from such places as Georgia, Kazakhstan, the Ukraine, and other Russian republics. Vodka is also coming to us from Scandinavian countries, other European countries, and Japan. A good liquor store will carry Australian vodka. Absolut vodka has a following based on its advertising campaign, and Stolichnaya is expanding its offerings, selling vodkas flavored with everything from peaches to peppers to coffee. The culture of vodka becomes more intricate every day. We've come a long way since James Bond sipped his Smirnoff.

The quintessential garnish for a martini is an olive. Olives are a bitter fruit that originated in the Mediterranean. They require a multistep curing process to become edible. First they are soaked in an alkaline solution, then fermented in brine or salt to reduce bitterness and tenderize the flesh. After curing, some olives marinate in vinegars or herb mixtures to give them signature taste characteristics. They vary in color from an unripe pale green through pinkish-brown to fully ripened jet black, and come in a wide range of sizes and shapes. Ancient trees growing in the rocky soil of Italy, Spain, Greece, and Israel still bear fruit. Olive production is big business in California as well.

The most common olive used to garnish a martini is the Spanish olive. It is a small green olive, sometimes stuffed with a pimento. (The less commonly used black olive makes it a Buckeye Martini.)

Many different kinds of olives are widely available in delis, gourmet stores, and even supermarkets. To learn about olives and what you like, the best thing to do is taste them. You can invent your own variations on the martini by using different olives. Some dry martini aficionados like to replace the olive brine in a jar with vermouth. These vermouth-soaked olives make great garnishes for martinis, and make it unnecessary to use any vermouth in your drink.

SETTING UP
YOUR
MARTINI BAR

It is easy to set up your own martini bar in your home or office. You will need the ingredients (discussed in the previous section), of course, and certain equipment. This book contains recipes that go far beyond the basic martini. In order to make all the drinks in this book, and create some of your own, you will need more than vodka or gin, vermouth, and olives.

Be sure to have at least eight martini, or cocktail, glasses. These triangle-shaped glasses are the symbol of the drink. They are made of glass and can be found in good glassware or home furnishing stores. The finer the crystal, the greater the martini experience. Never use plastic! And you should also keep some crystal highball glasses handy for those who would drink their martinis on the rocks.

You will need a good stainless steel cocktail shaker. Stainless steel will chill a drink quickly and uniformly. For those who prefer their martini stirred, not shaken, a good mixing glass and a long stirring spoon are essential. Cocktail shakers and mixing glasses come in many designs and sizes. Anything from deco to modern or post-modern can be found if you look hard enough. Choose a shaker and mixing glass that complement your glassware. If you're ever stuck without a cocktail shaker, a tennis ball canister will do in a pinch.

There are several gadgets available to the martini mixer; they really aren't necessary, but they are fun. Eye droppers and misters for vermouth assure the very driest martini, and there's even something called a "martini tester" which allegedly checks the vermouth content of a martini.

There is much to explore beyond gin and vermouth. The modern martini mixer makes use of the flavored vodkas. Everything from coffee-flavored to pepper-flavored is on the shelves of your liquor store. You should include as many of them as possible when creating your martini bar. If you don't find a flavored vodka you need, you can always make your own. (The best pepper vodka is homemade.) Simply take the flavoring you desire—a hot pepper, a vanilla bean—and soak it in a bottle of plain vodka for at least a week. Taste it. If the vodka needs more flavor, soak it with the flavoring for a few more days. When the vodka is flavored the way you want it, strain it into a clean bottle.

Some distillers also make flavored gin, but this is not recommended—gin is flavorful enough on its own. A number of recipes in this book also call for scotch and rum, and any good home or office bar will include these other spirits on its shelves. Remember, quality counts. Be sure to buy the finest.

Also keep a good supply of cocktail olives on hand. Experiment with stuffed olives. They are delicious and can embolden many a martini. An almond-stuffed olive, a

15

jalapeño-stuffed olive, or a blue cheese-stuffed olive can change the character of a martini dramatically.

Garnishes for contemporary martinis go far beyond olives. Lemons, limes, and oranges should be part of your bar pantry, as well as cocktail onions. You will also have call for gumdrops, smoked oysters and clams, fresh berries in season, and pickled vegetables like asparagus and baby tomatoes. Read the recipes and see what you need. Explore the shelves of a gourmet store. There is no limit to what you can use as garnish. If you think it's a garnish, then it is.

Tools for making a martini are pretty basic. All you really need is a sharp paring knife for making citrus peel and zest. Citrus zesters are a nice labor saver and can be found in any kitchen store. Toothpicks are essential for creating elaborate garnishes.

Since temperature (cold!) is as important to a martini as gin, vodka, and vermouth are, all liquid ingredients should be stored in the freezer. They will not freeze. All garnishes also should be well-chilled in the refrigerator. An under-the-bar refrigerator/freezer is perfect for this purpose.

Finally, don't forget that the quality of the water used to make ice greatly affects the quality of a cocktail. Even if you are shaking and straining a drink, the ice should be made of pure spring or distilled water. Keep plenty on hand to make your ice.

SHAKERS

Decorative cocktail shakers and barware are stylish and useful additions to any martini bar. Ever since the birth of the cocktail, professional and home bartenders have used cocktail shakers not only to make drinks, but to make fashion statements. They add a touch of class.

Shakers have always reflected the design sensibilities of the era in which they're used. In many design museums you can find gorgeous Art Deco shakers from the 20s and 30s. These accoutrements served as conversation pieces as well as being utilitarian.

During the Great Depression of the 1930s, elegant bar-

ware was an affordable luxury for a "have-not" era. These gorgeous utensils not only made bartending an art, they deflected from the dingy realities of the 30s. Perhaps one could not travel to Paris, but one could recreate the elegant atmosphere of the Ritz with the right shaker and glass. And one could call to mind the elegance of a black tie evening with a novelty penguin cocktail shaker.

After World War II and into the 50s, as we entered the atomic age, barware began to look like rocket ships. Cocktail shakers were decorated with pictures of the atom and shaped like missiles.

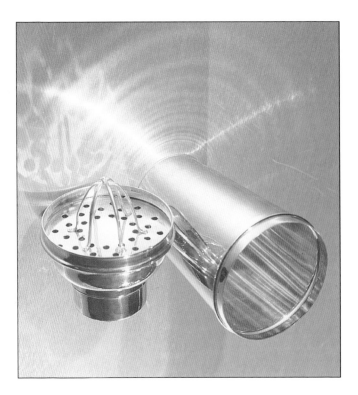

Early shakers were made of glass, silver plate, silver, Bakelite, and chromium. Glass is too fragile to be truly functional, but any metal shaker will do the job. Since the 1960s, most shakers have been made of stainless steel—a durable material that is excellent for completely chilling the cocktail.

Brand new shakers are available at houseware and department stores. High-end barware sets can be found at places like Tiffany's and Gump's. But if you're going to set up a martini bar in your home or office, we highly recommend a little antique hunting at flea markets and thrift shops. Almost every family before the late 70s had a full working bar at home, and the second-hand shops are full of these discarded treasures. Look for older, atomic-age silver shakers, or even older deco barware. You can start a collection for very little money, and have some usable art to display as you shake up martinis for your friends.

Martini—
The Drink of Presidents
and Publicists

Since its invention,
the martini has been the preferred cocktail
of presidents and heads-of-state.
FDR even carried a martini "kit"
on international summits, and Gerald Ford
thought the martini the exemplar of civilized life.
Prize-winning writers have sung its praise,
allowing themselves one (E.B. White)
or several (William Faulkner) for fortification
when facing the empty page.

Certainly not the sole territory of powerful men,
Dorothy Parker enjoyed martinis as did (and do)
many women journalists and authors.
As the three martini lunch comes back into favor,
look for the well-manicured and metallic-polished fingers
of book publicists and fashion editors
to be lifting their cocktail glasses at the Four Seasons,
a publishing haven,
whilst they toast the new millenium.

22

Famous Martini Drinkers

Robert Benchley

Humphrey Bogart

Luis Buñuel

Herb Caen

Raymond Chandler

Winston Churchill

William Faulkner

F. Scott and Zelda Fitzgerald

Gerald Ford

Robert Frost

Jackie Gleason

Ernest Hemingway

John F. Kennedy

Dorothy Lewis (Sinclair Lewis' wife)

H. L. Mencken

Dorothy Parker

Franklin Delano Roosevelt

E. B. White

Billy Wilder

P. G. Wodehouse

Alexander Woollcott

MARTINI RECIPES

Absolute Martini

5 parts vodka
1 part triple sec
2 parts fresh lemon juice
1 dash orange bitters

Combine all ingredients in a cocktail shaker with cracked ice and shake well. Strain into a chilled cocktail glass.

Allen Cocktail

4 parts gin
1 part maraschino liqueur
1/2 teaspoon fresh lemon juice
Lemon twist

Combine liquid ingredients in a cocktail shaker with cracked ice and shake well. Strain into a chilled cocktail glass and garnish with lemon twist.

Allen Cocktail

Ernest Hemingway was a correspondent during World War II and covered the liberation of Paris. He also personally saw to the "liberation" of the Ritz in the Place Vendome. After the Allies had liberated the city, Hemingway and a group of journalist friends went to the Ritz. The hotel was not damaged, but it was empty except for the manager, who welcomed them and put them into rooms. When asked what they needed, Hemingway ordered fifty martinis.

Allies Cocktail

3 parts gin
2 parts dry vermouth
1 teaspoon Jagermeister

Combine all ingredients in a cocktail shaker with cracked ice and stir. Strain into a chilled cocktail glass.

Alternatini

6 parts vodka
1/2 teaspoon sweet vermouth
1/2 teaspoon dry vermouth
1 teaspoon white crème de cacao
Sweetened cocoa powder
Hershey's® kiss

Rim a chilled cocktail glass with sweetened cocoa powder. Combine liquid ingredients in a cocktail shaker with cracked ice and shake well. Strain into cocktail glass and garnish with Hershey's® kiss.

Aperitivo

6 parts gin
3 parts white Sambuca
3 to 5 dashes orange bitters
Orange peel

Combine liquid ingredients in a mixing glass with ice cubes and stir. Strain into a chilled cocktail glass and garnish with orange peel.

Apple Pie Martini

6 parts vanilla flavored vodka
1 part Calvados
1 part dry vermouth
Apple slice

Combine liquid ingredients in a cocktail shaker with cracked ice and shake well. Strain into a chilled cocktail glass and garnish with a thin slice of apple.

Armada Martini

6 parts vodka
2 parts amontillado sherry
Orange twist

Combine liquid ingredients in a mixing glass with cracked ice and stir. Strain into a chilled cocktail glass and garnish with orange twist.

Artillery Cocktail

6 parts gin
2 parts sweet vermouth

Combine ingredients in a cocktail shaker with cracked ice and shake well. Strain into a chilled cocktail glass.

Babyface Martini

6 parts strawberry-flavored vodka
1 part dry vermouth
1/2 teaspoon maraschino liqueur
Fresh strawberry

Combine liquid ingredients in a cocktail shaker with
cracked ice and shake well. Strain into a chilled cocktail
glass and garnish with strawberry.

Barbed Wire

6 parts vodka
1 teaspoon sweet vermouth
1/2 teaspoon Pernod
1/2 teaspoon Chambord
Lemon twist

Combine liquid ingredients in a cocktail shaker with
cracked ice and shake well. Strain into a chilled cocktail
glass and garnish with lemon twist.

Barnum

6 parts gin
1 part apricot brandy
3 to 5 dashes Angostura bitters
3 to 5 dashes lemon juice

Combine all ingredients in a cocktail shaker with cracked
ice and shake well. Strain into a chilled cocktail glass.

Beadlestone

6 parts Scotch
3 parts dry vermouth

Combine ingredients in a mixing glass with ice cubes and
stir well. Strain into a chilled cocktail glass.

Bennett

6 parts gin
1/2 teaspoon bar sugar
3 to 5 dashes Angostura bitters

Combine all ingredients in a cocktail shaker with cracked ice and shake well. Strain into a chilled cocktail glass.

Berrytini

6 parts currant vodka
1 part raspberry eau-de-vie
Fresh raspberries

Combine vodka and eau-de-vie in a cocktail shaker with cracked ice and shake well. Strain into a chilled cocktail glass and garnish with raspberries.

Black & White Martini

6 parts vanilla vodka
2 parts crème de cacao
Black & white licorice candies

Combine liquid ingredients in a cocktail shaker with cracked ice and shake well. Strain into a chilled cocktail glass and garnish with black & white licorice candies.

Black & White Martini

"After four martinis,
my husband turns into
a disgusting beast.
And after the fifth,
I pass out altogether."

Anonymous

Black Dog

6 parts light rum
1 part dry vermouth
Pitted black olive

Combine liquid ingredients in mixing
glass with cracked ice and stir well.
Strain into a chilled cocktail glass and
garnish with olive.

Bloodhound

Bloodhound

6 parts gin
2 parts sweet vermouth
2 parts dry vermouth

3 fresh strawberries, hulled
Fresh strawberries for garnish

Combine all ingredients in a blender and mix until
well-blended. Pour into a chilled cocktail glass and
garnish with fresh strawberry.

Blue Moon Martini

6 parts gin
1 part blue curaçao
Lemon twist

Combine liquid ingredients in a mixing glass with ice cubes and stir well. Strain into a chilled cocktail glass and garnish with lemon twist.

Blue Moon
Martini

Blue-on-Blue Martini

6 parts vodka   **1 dash Angostura bitters**
1 part blue curaçao   **Cocktail olive**

Combine liquid ingredients in a cocktail shaker with cracked ice and shake well. Strain into a chilled cocktail glass and garnish with olive.

Boardwalk

6 parts vodka
2 parts dry vermouth
1/2 teaspoon maraschino liqueur
1 teaspoon fresh lemon juice
Lemon twist

Combine liquid ingredients in a
cocktail shaker with cracked ice
and shake well. Strain into a
chilled cocktail glass and garnish
with lemon twist.

Boomerang Martini

6 parts gin
1 dash Angostura bitters
2 parts dry vermouth
1 dash maraschino liqueur
Kiwi slice

Stir all liquid ingredients with ice
cubes in a mixing glass. Strain into
a chilled cocktail glass and garnish
with kiwi slice.

Broadway Martini

6 parts gin
1 part white crème de menthe
Fresh mint sprig

Combine liquid ingredients in a
cocktail shaker with cracked ice
and shake well. Strain into a
chilled cocktail glass and garnish
with mint sprig.

Boomerang Martini

The search—
some might say obsession—
for the driest martini continues.
One company sells
vermouth atomizers. Another sells
olives marinated in vermouth.
The driest martini is straight gin,
but even those have been
sent back to the bartender for
not being dry enough.

Bronx Terrace Cocktail

6 parts gin
2 parts fresh lime juice
1 part dry vermouth
Maraschino cherry

Combine liquid ingredients in a cocktail shaker with cracked ice and shake well. Strain into a chilled cocktail glass and garnish with cherry.

Brown Cocktail

4 parts gin
2 parts light rum
1 part dry vermouth
Kumquat

Stir all ingredients in a mixing glass with cracked ice. Strain into a chilled cocktail glass and garnish with kumquat.

Brown Cocktail

In the 1940s, John Lardner reported that the New York Yankees ball club had hired private detectives to keep track of their players. He noted that they "should have been easy to stalk because, belonging to a high-class ball club, they drank martinis and left a trail of olives."

Buckeye Martini

6 parts gin
1 part dry vermouth
Black olive

Combine liquid ingredients in a cocktail shaker with cracked ice and shake well. Strain into a chilled cocktail glass and garnish with black olive.

Cabaret Martini

6 parts gin
3 parts Dubonnet rouge
3 to 5 dashes Angostura bitters
3 to 5 dashes Pernod
Lime twist

Combine liquid ingredients in a cocktail shaker with cracked ice and shake well. Strain into a chilled cocktail glass and garnish with lime twist.

California Martini

6 parts vodka
1 part red wine
1 tablespoon dark rum
3 to 5 dashes orange bitters
Orange twist

Combine liquid ingredients in a cocktail shaker with cracked ice and shake well. Strain into a chilled cocktail glass and garnish with orange twist.

Cajun Martini

6 parts pepper vodka
1 dash of dry vermouth
Olive stuffed with pickled jalapeño pepper

Combine liquid ingredients in a mixing glass with cracked ice and stir. Strain into a chilled cocktail glass and garnish with olive.

Hot night on the Bayou. While others sipped their Sazeracs, Remy mixed me a Cajun Martini. When I bit into that vermouth-soaked olive stuffed with the jalapeño, a chill ran up and down my spine and my eyes opened wide. "Mmmm, good, honey! Now that's a martini!"

41

Campari Martini

6 parts vodka
1 part Campari
Lime twist

Combine liquid
ingredients in a
cocktail shaker
with cracked ice and
shake well. Strain
into a chilled
cocktail glass and
garnish with lime
twist.

She'd spent two months in Italy, touring and
looking for hidden Renaissance frescoes.
One evening in Florence, just after sunset, she
wandered into an American bar and ordered a
martini. The bartender winked at her and said,
"Cara, let me make you a martini `a la Italiano,"
and he served her a Campari Martini. To this day,
when she wants to remember Tuscany, no matter
where she is, all she needs to do is
make herself this Florentine specialty.

Caribou Martini

4 parts coffee-flavored vodka, chilled
Champagne or dry sparkling wine
Lemon twist
Coffee bean

Pour chilled vodka into a cocktail glass. Top off with champagne and stir gently. Garnish with lemon twist and drop in a coffee bean.

Caribou
Martini

A TRUE STORY: They were both fans of the television show "Northern Exposure". And the more they corresponded, the more they discovered how much they had in common—a love for science fiction, an appreciation of fine champagne and gourmet coffee, lacy underthings (he, to look; she, to wear), and, of course, martinis. Their first date was a seven-hour phone call. When they finally met in person, they were in love. They celebrated their first anniversary with the creation of the Caribou Martini.

Chocolate Martini

6 parts vodka
1 part chocolate liqueur
Chocolate curl

Combine vodka and liqueur in a mixing glass with ice cubes and stir. Strain into a chilled cocktail glass and garnish with chocolate curl.

Some families have eggnog recipes that have been passed down through generations. Others have a favorite wassail they share. No family is more sophisticated when it comes to Yuletide than the Fosters, who have celebrated Christmas since before Prohibition with their special Christmas Martini.

Christmas Martini

6 parts gin
1 part dry vermouth
1 teaspoon peppermint schnapps
Miniature candy cane

Combine liquid ingredients in a cocktail shaker with cracked ice and shake well. Strain into a chilled cocktail glass and garnish with candy cane.

Christmas Tini

6 parts vodka
1 teaspoon peppermint schnapps
1 part dry vermouth
Miniature candy cane

Combine liquid ingredients in a cocktail shaker with cracked ice and shake well. Strain into a chilled cocktail glass and garnish with candy cane.

Winston Churchill
was a martini aficionado.
Here is his recipe for a martini.
It is not unlike that of most fans of
the extremely dry martini.
Some people whisper,
"vermouth."
Others,
like Churchill,
look at the bottle.

Churchill's Martini

6 parts gin
Bottle of dry vermouth
Cocktail olive

Shake gin in a cocktail shaker with cracked ice. Strain into
a chilled cocktail glass and look at the bottle of vermouth.
Garnish glass with olive.

Church
Lady Martini

4 parts gin
2 parts dry vermouth
2 parts fresh orange juice
Lemon, lime, and orange wedges

Combine liquid ingredients in a cocktail shaker with
cracked ice and shake well. Strain into a chilled cocktail
glass. Garnish with fruit wedges.

Church
Lady
Martini

Citrus Martini

8 parts lemon-flavored vodka
1 teaspoon Grand Marnier or orange liqueur
1 teaspoon fresh lime juice
Lemon twist

Combine liquid ingredients in a cocktail shaker with cracked ice and shake well. Strain into a chilled cocktail glass and garnish with lemon twist.

Coffee Lover's Martini

6 parts coffee-flavored vodka
1 part dry vermouth
1 part Frangelico
Coffee beans

Combine liquid ingredients in a cocktail shaker with
cracked ice and shake well. Strain into a chilled cocktail
glass and garnish with a few coffee beans.

49

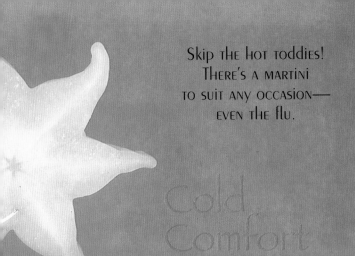

Skip the hot toddies!
There's a martini
to suit any occasion—
even the flu.

Cold Comfort Martini

4 parts lemon vodka
4 parts honey vodka
Lemon twist

Combine vodkas in a cocktail shaker with cracked ice and shake well. Strain into a chilled cocktail glass and garnish with lemon twist.

Colony Club Martini

6 parts gin
1 teaspoon Pernod
3 to 5 dashes orange bitters
Orange twist

Combine liquid ingredients in a cocktail shaker with cracked ice and shake well. Strain into a chilled cocktail glass and garnish with orange twist.

Cosmopolitan

4 parts vodka
2 parts triple sec
2 parts cranberry juice
1 part fresh lime juice

Combine ingredients in a cocktail shaker with cracked ice and shake well. Strain into a chilled cocktail glass.

Crantini

6 parts gin
1 part unsweetened cranberry juice
Lime or lemon twist

Pour gin into a chilled cocktail glass. Slowly add the cranberry juice. Garnish with lime or lemon twist.

Crantini

"Got a light?" He looked up
to see a beautiful woman holding an unlit Arturo
Fuente in her delicate fingers. "You shouldn't smoke.
It's bad for you," he said. "How about a drink?"
She paused, and put the cigar in her purse. She
smiled. "Better make it something healthy, buddy—
to rid my body of all this nasty, delicious, cigar smoke."
"But of course."

He ordered her a Crantini.

Crimson Martini

6 parts gin
1 part ruby port
2 teaspoons fresh lime juice
1 teaspoon grenadine
Lime twist

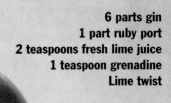

Combine liquid
ingredients in a
cocktail shaker
with cracked ice
and shake well.
Strain into a
chilled cocktail
glass and garnish
with lime twist.

54

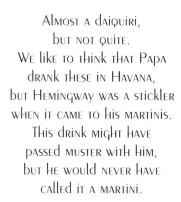

Almost a daiquiri, but not quite. We like to think that Papa drank these in Havana, but Hemingway was a stickler when it came to his martinis. This drink might have passed muster with him, but he would never have called it a martini.

Cuban Martini

6 parts light rum
1 part dry vermouth
Granulated sugar
Lime twist

Rim a chilled cocktail glass with sugar. Combine liquid ingredients in a cocktail shaker with cracked ice and shake well. Strain into cocktail glass and garnish with lime twist.

Danish Martini

6 parts aquavit
1 part dry vermouth
Cocktail olive

Combine liquid ingredients in a cocktail shaker with cracked ice and shake well. Strain into a chilled cocktail glass and garnish with olive.

Daydream Martini

6 parts citrus vodka
1 part triple sec
2 parts fresh orange juice
1/4 teaspoon bar sugar

Combine all ingredients in a mixing glass with cracked ice and stir well. Strain into a chilled cocktail glass.

Deep Sea Martini

6 parts gin
2 parts dry vermouth
1/2 teaspoon Pernod
1 dash orange bitters

Combine all ingredients in a mixing glass with cracked ice and stir well. Strain into a chilled cocktail glass.

Delicious Martini

6 parts coffee-flavored vodka
1 part Grand Marnier
Orange twist

Combine liquid ingredients in a cocktail shaker with cracked ice and shake well. Strain into a chilled cocktail glass and garnish with orange twist.

Desperate Martini

6 parts gin
1 part dry vermouth
1 part blackberry brandy
Fresh blackberries (optional)

Combine liquid ingredients in a cocktail shaker with cracked ice and shake well. Strain into a chilled cocktail glass and garnish with fresh blackberries.

It is said that
Jackie Gleason once ordered a martini
at a bar in a fashionable Miami Beach hotel.
When the bartender asked him
if he wanted a twist of lemon with it,
he exclaimed,
"When I want a goddam lemonade,
I'll ask for it!"

Dirty Martini

6 parts gin
2 parts dry vermouth
1 part olive brine
Cocktail olives

Combine liquid ingredients in a cocktail shaker with cracked ice and shake well. Strain into a chilled cocktail glass and garnish with one or two olives.

E. B. White
had a more conservative approach
to his favorite cocktail than most writers.
"Before I start to write,
I always treat myself to a nice dry martini.
Just one, to give me the courage
to get started.
After that, I am on my own."

Dirty Martini

Dirty Vodka Martini

6 parts vodka
2 parts dry vermouth
1 part olive brine
Cocktail olives

Combine liquid ingredients in a cocktail shaker with cracked ice and shake well. Strain into a chilled cocktail glass and garnish with one or two olives.

Double Fudge Martini

6 parts vodka
Chocolate cocktail straw
1 part chocolate liqueur
1 part coffee liqueur

Combine liquid ingredients in a mixing glass with cracked ice and stir well. Strain into a chilled cocktail glass and garnish with chocolate straw.

East Wing

6 parts vodka
1 part Campari
2 parts cherry brandy
Lemon twist

Combine liquid ingredients in a cocktail shaker with cracked ice and shake well. Strain into a chilled cocktail glass and garnish with lemon twist.

Eat My Martini

6 parts honey vodka
1 part amontillado sherry
Almond-stuffed olive

Combine liquid ingredients in a cocktail shaker with cracked ice and shake well. Strain into a chilled cocktail glass and garnish with olive.

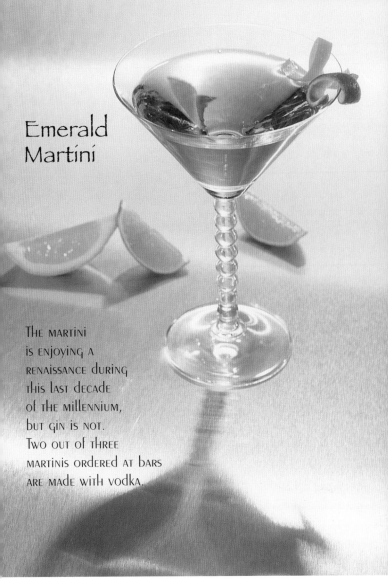

Emerald Martini

The martini is enjoying a renaissance during this last decade of the millennium, but gin is not. Two out of three martinis ordered at bars are made with vodka.

Emerald Martini

6 parts citrus-flavored vodka
2 parts chartreuse

Lemon twist
Lime twist

Combine liquid ingredients in a mixing glass with cracked ice and stir well. Strain into a chilled cocktail glass and garnish with lemon and lime twists.

Nick and Nora Charles,
the sophisticated sleuthing couple from
The Thin Man novels and movies,
were dyed-in-the-wool martini drinkers.
Nick used to measure out the vermouth
with an eye dropper.

Extra Dry Vodka Martini

4 parts vodka
3 to 5 drops dry vermouth

1/8 teaspoon lemon juice
Lemon twist

Combine liquid ingredients in a cocktail shaker with cracked ice and shake well. Strain into a chilled cocktail glass and garnish with lemon twist.

W. H. Auden often prepared for his lectures
with a few martinis. On one occasion in 1947,
he had a few too many before he spoke at Harvard.
The topic was supposed to have been
Miguel de Cervantes, but when Auden stood up
at the podium, he apologized for his new dentures,
and then told the eager crowd that he'd never been able
to read Don Quixote to the end, and
bet that no one in the audience had either.

Fare Thee Well Martini

6 parts gin
1 part dry vermouth
1 dash sweet vermouth
1 dash Cointreau

Combine all ingredients in a mixing glass with cracked ice and stir well. Strain into a chilled cocktail glass.

Farmer's Martini

6 parts gin
1 part dry vermouth

1 part sweet vermouth
3 to 5 dashes Angostura bitters

Combine all ingredients in a cocktail shaker with cracked ice and shake well. Strain into a chilled cocktail glass.

FDR was a serious martini drinker and carried a martini "kit" with him whenever he traveled. During the Teheran conference, he insisted on mixing one of his specialties for Joseph Stalin. Stalin found it "cold on the stomach," but liked it. FDR's martini was most likely the first "Dirty Martini."

FDR's Martini

2 parts gin
1 part vermouth

1 teaspoon olive brine
Lemon twist
Cocktail olive

Rub the lemon twist around the rim of a chilled cocktail glass and discard the peel. Combine gin, vermouth, and olive brine in a cocktail shaker with cracked ice and shake well. Strain into chilled glass and garnish with olive.

Fifty-Fifty Martini

4 parts gin
4 parts dry vermouth
Cocktail olive

Combine liquid ingredients in a mixing glass with cracked ice and stir well. Strain into a chilled cocktail glass and garnish with olive.

The martini reached
the height of popularity in the 1950s.
One Manhattan bar served martinis
"dry, extra dry, or very dry."
The drier the martini,
the more the drink cost.

Fifty-Fifty Vodka Martini

4 parts vodka
4 parts dry vermouth
Cocktail olive

Combine liquid ingredients in a mixing glass with cracked
ice and stir well. Strain into a chilled cocktail glass and
garnish with olive.

"I've got to get out of these wet clothes
and into a dry martini."
This immortal line has been attributed
to Robert Benchley, Billy Wilder, and
Alexander Woollcott. No one is sure who
actually said it. All three men were known for their
bon mots. My money's on Woollcott, drama critic for
the New York Times during the 1920s and 1930s.
He also appeared in several screwball comedies.
It is believed he uttered this line after shooting
a scene where he was tossed into a
swimming pool, fully clothed.

Fine and Dandy

4 parts gin   **2 parts fresh lemon juice**
2 parts triple sec   **1 dash orange bitters**

Combine all ingredients in a cocktail shaker with cracked
ice and shake well. Strain into a chilled cocktail glass.

The martini seems to lend itself to more jokes
and apocryphal stories than all other cocktails.
One of the more famous stories goes like this:
A man arrives at a restaurant several minutes
before his wife to instruct the head waiter,
"No matter what kind of soup I order,
fill the tureen with martinis.
My wife has a fit if I order even one drink."
His instructions were followed out,
and then the man called to the waiter:
"I'll have some more soup,
and this time, make it extra-dry."

Fino Martini

6 parts gin or vodka
1 teaspoon fino sherry
Lemon twist

Combine liquid ingredients in a mixing glass with ice cubes and stir well. Strain into a chilled cocktail glass and garnish with lemon twist.

Fretful Martini

6 parts gin
1 part blue curaçao
1 dash Angostura bitters
Cocktail olive

Combine liquid ingredients in a cocktail shaker with cracked ice and shake well. Strain into a chilled cocktail glass and garnish with olive.

Frozen Martini

5 parts gin
1 part dry vermouth
2 almond-stuffed cocktail olives

Place gin, vermouth, olives, cocktail glass, and cocktail shaker in freezer for at least 3 hours. When all components are thoroughly chilled, combine gin and vermouth in the chilled cocktail shaker and shake well. Place the two frozen olives in the chilled cocktail glass and pour the gin and vermouth mixture over it.

Fuzzy Martini

4 parts vanilla-flavored vodka
1 part coffee-flavored vodka
1 teaspoon peach schnapps
Fresh peach slice

Combine liquid ingredients in a cocktail glass and garnish with a fresh peach slice.

The Gibson is thought to be named
for the famed Gibson Girls, Charles Dana Gibson's
lovely pinups of the early twentieth century.
The two cocktail onions are believed
to represent breasts.

Gibson

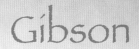

8 parts gin or vodka
3 to 5 dashes dry vermouth
2 cocktail onions

Combine liquid
ingredients in a mixing
glass with ice cubes
and stir well.
Strain into a chilled
cocktail glass and
garnish with onions.

The last shot
of the day on a movie
set is called the
"Martini Shot".

Gilroy Martini

6 parts buffalo grass vodka
2 parts dry vermouth
2 drops garlic juice
Garlic-stuffed olive

Combine liquid ingredients
in a cocktail shaker with cracked
ice and shake well. Strain into a
chilled cocktail glass and
garnish with olive.

Gimlet

8 parts gin or vodka
2 parts Rose's lime juice

Combine all ingredients in a
cocktail shaker with cracked ice
and shake well. Strain into a
chilled cocktail glass.

Gin and It

8 parts gin
2 parts sweet vermouth
Lemon twist

Combine liquid ingredients in a
cocktail shaker with cracked ice
and shake well. Strain into a
chilled cocktail glass and garnish
with lemon twist.

William Faulkner loved the
strong drink that eventually killed him.
In the years before he was completely
incapacitated by alcohol, he couldn't write
without having a few martinis beforehand.
He wrote, "When I have one martini,
I feel bigger, wiser, taller.
When I have a second, I feel superlative.
When I have more,
there's no holding me."

Gimlet

Golf Martini

The martini is a thoroughly modern cocktail.
Even though the drink was most likely
invented in the nineteenth century, it did
not gain popularity until well into the twentieth.
After Prohibition, the martini gained in popularity.
After World War II, martinis got drier,
and sweeter drinks lost their appeal.
By the mid-1950s, the true mark of a sophisticate
was a dry, icy gin martini, with only a trace of
vermouth. Here's a variation on the classic.

Golf Martini

8 parts gin
3 to 5 dashes Angostura bitters

2 parts dry vermouth
Cocktail olive

Combine liquid ingredients in a mixing glass with cracked ice and shake well. Strain into a chilled cocktail glass and garnish with olive.

Great Caesar's Martini

6 parts vodka
1 part dry vermouth
Anchovy-stuffed olive

Combine liquid ingredients in a cocktail shaker with cracked ice and shake well. Strain into a chilled cocktail glass and garnish with olive.

Green Martini

6 parts gin
1 part chartreuse
Almond-stuffed olive

Combine liquid ingredients in a cocktail shaker with cracked ice and shake well. Strain into a chilled cocktail glass and garnish with olive.

Gumdrop Martini

4 parts lemon-flavored rum
2 parts vodka
1 part Southern Comfort
1/2 teaspoon Dry vermouth

1 part fresh lemon juice
Bar sugar
Lemon slice
Gumdrops

Rim a chilled cocktail glass with bar sugar. Combine liquid ingredients in a cocktail shaker with cracked ice and shake well. Strain into the chilled cocktail glass and garnish with lemon slice and gumdrops.

How Much Vermouth?

The original recipe
for the dry martini
actually wasn't very dry
by today's standards.
The proportions were
two parts gin to
one part French or
dry vermouth.

77

Gypsy Martini

8 parts gin
2 parts sweet vermouth
Maraschino cherry

Combine liquid ingredients in a cocktail shaker with cracked ice and shake well. Strain into a chilled cocktail glass and garnish with cherry.

Hasty Martini

6 parts gin
1 part dry vermouth
3 to 5 dashes Pernod
1 teaspoon grenadine

Combine all ingredients in a cocktail shaker with cracked ice and shake well. Strain into a chilled cocktail glass.

Hep Cat

6 parts berry vodka
1 part dry vermouth
1 dash sweet vermouth
1 dash Cointreau

Combine all ingredients in a mixing glass with cracked ice and stir well. Strain into a chilled cocktail glass.

Hoffman House Martini

8 parts gin
1 part dry vermouth

3 to 5 dashes orange bitters
Cocktail olive

Combine liquid ingredients in a mixing glass with cracked ice and stir well. Strain into a chilled cocktail glass and garnish with olive.

William Randolph Hearst used to entertain Hollywood stars at his San Simeon estate in Cambria, California. But "W. R." was a teetotaler. Upon arrival, each guest's luggage was searched for offending bottles and flasks. Gin was confiscated and only returned to the guest when he or she left. Fortunately for the Hollywood crowd, Hearst's staff was not above being bribed, and a well-placed gratuity allowed gin to flow at San Simeon, albeit in secret.

Hollywood Martini

6 parts gin
1 part Goldwasser
1 part dry vermouth
1 blue cheese-stuffed olive

Combine liquid ingredients in a cocktail shaker with cracked ice and shake well. Strain into a chilled cocktail glass and garnish with olive.

Homestead Martini

6 parts gin
2 parts sweet vermouth
Orange twist

Combine liquid ingredients in a mixing glass with ice and stir well. Strain into a chilled cocktail glass and garnish with orange twist.

Homestead
Martini

Honeydew Martini

6 parts vodka
1 part Midori

1 part triple sec
Lemon twist

Combine liquid ingredients in a cocktail shaker with
cracked ice and shake well. Strain into a chilled cocktail
glass and garnish with lemon twist.

Hoosier Cocktail

4 parts buffalo grass vodka
2 parts light rum
1 part dry vermouth

Combine all ingredients in a mixing glass with cracked
ice and stir well. Strain into a chilled cocktail glass.

Hot & Dirty Martini

6 parts pepper vodka
1 part dry vermouth
1 teaspoon olive brine
Olive stuffed with pickled jalapeño pepper

Combine liquid ingredients in a cocktail shaker with
cracked ice and shake well. Strain into a chilled cocktail
glass and garnish with olive.

Hotel Plaza Cocktail

2 parts gin
2 parts dry vermouth

2 parts sweet vermouth
Maraschino cherry

Combine liquid ingredients in a mixing glass with ice
cubes and stir well. Strain into a chilled cocktail glass
and garnish with cherry.

In the never-ending quest for the coldest and the driest martini, one has to make this inevitable choice: Straight up or on the rocks? Each has its advantages and drawbacks. Ideally, all liquid ingredients should be stored in the freezer, and glasses should be chilled, thus making ice superfluous. But there is much to be said for the bell-like tones of ice cubes tinkling in a crystal highball glass. Are you willing to risk diluting your martini with melting ice? Or are you a purist, the thought of a martini on the rocks simply not part of your world? This variation will work either way.

Ideal Martini

6 parts gin
2 parts dry vermouth

1/2 teaspoon maraschino liqueur
1 teaspoon fresh lemon juice
Lemon twist

Combine liquid ingredients in a cocktail shaker with cracked ice and shake well. Strain into a chilled cocktail glass and garnish with lemon twist.

Imperial Martini

6 parts gin
2 parts dry vermouth

1/2 teaspoon maraschino liqueur
3 to 5 dashes Angostura bitters

Combine all ingredients in a mixing glass with ice and stir well. Strain into a chilled cocktail glass.

"In and out"
refers to the method of mixing this martini.

In and Out Martini

7 parts vodka
Dry vermouth

2 blue cheese-stuffed olives
Lemon twist

Pour vermouth into a well-chilled martini glass. Swish it around and then discard. Pour vodka into the glass and garnish with olives and lemon twist.

Irish Martini

6 parts buffalo grass vodka
1 part dry vermouth
Irish whiskey
Lemon twist

Rinse a chilled cocktail glass with Irish whiskey. Combine vodka and vermouth in a cocktail shaker with cracked ice and shake well. Strain into cocktail glass and garnish with lemon twist.

Imperial Martini

In Havana, Ernest Hemingway had a many-martini lunch with famous prizefighter Gene Tunney. As the two men got drunker, Hemingway got belligerent and tried to goad Tunney into a fight. (Hemingway considered himself quite the authority on boxing.) He kept punching at Tunney. Tunney, ever the gentleman, asked Hemingway to stop. But he would not. Finally, Tunney decided to give him a little "liver punch," just to get him to stop, and he let him have it. Hemingway buckled, his face went gray, and Tunney thought he was going to go out. But he didn't, and after that, Hemingway was the perfect gentleman for the rest of the afternoon.

Island Martini

6 parts gold rum
1 part dry vermouth
1 part sweet vermouth
Lemon twist

Combine liquid ingredients in a cocktail shaker with cracked ice and shake well. Strain into a chilled cocktail glass and garnish with lemon twist.

Jack London Martini

6 parts currant vodka
2 parts Dubonnet blanc
1 part maraschino liqueur
Lemon twist

Combine liquid ingredients in a cocktail shaker with cracked ice and shake well. Strain into a chilled cocktail glass and garnish with lemon twist.

Jamaican Martini

6 parts gin
1 part red wine
1 tablespoon dark rum
3 to 5 dashes orange bitters
Cherry peppers

Combine liquid ingredients in a cocktail shaker with cracked ice and shake well. Strain into a chilled cocktail glass and garnish with cherry peppers.

James Bond Martini

6 parts gin
2 parts vodka
1 part Lillet blanc
Lemon twist

Combine liquid
ingredients in a
cocktail shaker with
cracked ice and shake
well. Strain into a
chilled cocktail glass
and garnish with
lemon twist.

Jamie's Martini

6 parts vodka
1 part triple sec
2 parts fresh orange juice
1/4 teaspoon bar sugar

Combine all ingredients in a mixing glass with cracked ice and stir well. Strain into a chilled cocktail glass.

H. L. Mencken usually drank beer,
but made an exception when he spent
an evening with Philip Goodman.
When Mencken came up to New York from Baltimore,
he and Goodman would go to a speakeasy
in Union City, New Jersey, and
eat a dinner of knockwurst, boiled beef, sauerkraut,
mashed potatoes, and cheesecake.
They would wash this down with
several beers and coffees.
They would then return to Manhattan,
stop at a restaurant on West Forty-Fourth Street,
have more cheesecake and some strudel,
and more coffee and more beer.
They would always end the evening
by having double martinis.
Goodman believed that the gin aided digestion—
that it "oxidized" the food.

Journalist Martini

6 parts gin
1 teaspoon dry vermouth
1 teaspoon sweet vermouth
1 teaspoon triple sec
1 teaspoon fresh lime juice
1 dash Angostura bitters

Combine all ingredients in a cocktail shaker with cracked ice and shake well. Strain into a chilled cocktail glass.

One of the many martini legends credits the bartender at the Knickerbocker Hotel, a Manhattan hotel popular at the turn of the century, as the martini's creator.

Knickerbocker

6 parts gin
2 parts dry vermouth
1/2 teaspoon sweet vermouth
Lemon twist

Combine liquid ingredients in a mixing glass with cracked ice and stir well. Strain into a chilled cocktail glass and garnish with lemon twist.

Kup's Indispensable Martini

6 parts gin
1 1/2 parts dry vermouth
1 1/2 parts sweet vermouth
Orange twist

Combine liquid ingredients in a cocktail shaker with cracked ice and shake well. Strain into a chilled cocktail glass and garnish with orange twist.

Kyoto

6 parts gin　　　　　**1 part dry vermouth**
2 parts melon liqueur　**1/4 teaspoon fresh lemon juice**
Melon ball

Combine liquid ingredients in a mixing glass with ice cubes and stir well. Strain into a chilled cocktail glass and garnish with melon ball.

Leap Year Martini

6 parts citrus-flavored vodka
1 part sweet vermouth
1 part Grand Marnier
1/2 teaspoon fresh lemon juice

Combine all ingredients in a cocktail shaker with cracked ice and shake well. Strain into a chilled cocktail glass.

Sylvia Plath, Anne Sexton, and George Starbuck all took Robert Lowell's creative writing course at the Boston Center for Adult Education. After each class, they would pile into Sexton's old Ford, drive to the Ritz Hotel, and park illegally in a loading zone— Sexton explaining, "It's OK, we're only going to get loaded." They then proceeded into the Ritz to have three or four martinis each.

Lemon Drop Martini

6 parts lemon-flavored vodka
1 part dry vermouth

Granulated sugar
Lemon twist

Rim a chilled cocktail glass with granulated sugar. Combine liquid ingredients in a cocktail shaker with cracked ice and shake well. Strain into cocktail glass and garnish with lemon twist.

Another martini joke:
A slightly tipsy guest at a party approaches the host and asks, "Do lemons have legs?"
"Lemons with legs!
You must be completely gone!," replies the host.
"Oh dear," sighs the guest,
"I'm afraid I've just squeezed your canary into my martini."

Lemon Twist

6 parts lemon-flavored rum
1 part dry vermouth
Lemon twist

Combine liquid ingredients in a cocktail shaker with cracked ice and shake well. Strain into a chilled cocktail glass and garnish with lemon twist.

London Martini

6 parts gin
1/2 teaspoon maraschino liqueur
3 to 5 dashes orange bitters
1/2 teaspoon bar sugar
Lemon twist

Combine liquid ingredients in a mixing glass and stir well. Pour mixture into a cocktail shaker with cracked ice and shake well. Strain into a chilled cocktail glass and garnish with lemon twist.

James Bond's vodka martini—
"shaken not stirred"—
was a radical concept when Ian Fleming
introduced it as a "Vesper" in Casino Royale. A martini
was never shaken, and it had to be made with gin.
But who would argue with James Bond? His
"Vesper" started a martini revolution. Today, much
to purists' chagrin, vodka martinis are more popular
than the original gin cocktail.

Low Tide Martini

6 parts vodka
1 part dry vermouth
Lime twist

1 teaspoon clam juice
Olive stuffed with smoked clam

Combine liquid ingredients in a cocktail shaker with
cracked ice and shake well. Strain into a chilled cocktail
glass and garnish with olive and lime twist.

Macaroon

6 parts vodka
1 part chocolate liqueur
1 part Amarretto
Orange twist

Combine liquid ingredients in a mixing glass with cracked
ice and stir well. Strain into a chilled cocktail glass and
garnish with orange twist.

Mama's Martini

6 parts vanilla vodka
1 part apricot brandy
3 to 5 dashes Angostura bitters
3 to 5 dashes lemon juice

Combine all ingredients in a cocktail shaker with cracked
ice and shake well. Strain into a chilled cocktail glass.

Manhasset

6 parts rye whiskey
1/2 part dry vermouth
1/2 part sweet vermouth
1 tablespoon fresh lemon juice
Lemon twist

Combine liquid ingredients in a cocktail shaker with cracked ice and shake well. Strain into a chilled cocktail glass and garnish with lemon twist.

Manhasset

A Manhattan is thought to be the "opposite" of a martini.
While a martini is made with clear liquor, gin or vodka, and dry vermouth,
a Manhattan is made with amber whiskey and sweet vermouth
(and don't forget the bitters)!

Is a cherry really the opposite of an olive?

Manhattan

6 parts rye whiskey
2 parts sweet vermouth

1 dash Angostura bitters
Maraschino cherry

Combine liquid ingredients in a mixing glass with ice and stir well. Strain into a chilled cocktail glass and garnish with cherry.

Maritime Martini

6 parts gin
2 parts dry vermouth
Anchovy-stuffed olive

Combine liquid ingredients in a cocktail shaker with cracked ice and shake well. Strain into a chilled cocktail glass and garnish with olive.

Some say the martini was developed in Europe, others in New York. But I believe that this elegant drink had its not so elegant beginnings in the 1860s, in California, after the Gold Rush. Apparently, the martini was invented by a man about to hop on the ferry from Martinez, California, to San Francisco. He needed some fortification for the journey across the Bay. All there was at hand was some rot-gut gin. To take the burn off the gin, he mixed it with an equal part of vermouth, and sweetened it with a few drops of maraschino and orange bitters. And the martini, or "Martinez Cocktail," was born— a California native.

Martinez Cocktail

4 parts gin
2 parts sweet vermouth
1 part maraschino liqueur

1 teaspoon sugar syrup (optional)
1-3 dashes Angostura bitters

Combine all ingredients in a mixing glass with cracked ice and stir well. Strain into a chilled old-fashioned glass.

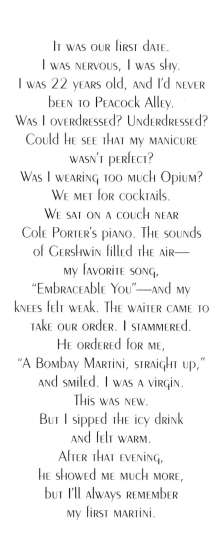

It was our first date.
I was nervous, I was shy.
I was 22 years old, and I'd never
been to Peacock Alley.
Was I overdressed? Underdressed?
Could he see that my manicure
wasn't perfect?
Was I wearing too much Opium?
We met for cocktails.
We sat on a couch near
Cole Porter's piano. The sounds
of Gershwin filled the air—
my favorite song,
"Embraceable You"—and my
knees felt weak. The waiter came to
take our order. I stammered.
He ordered for me,
"A Bombay Martini, straight up,"
and smiled. I was a virgin.
This was new.
But I sipped the icy drink
and felt warm.
After that evening,
he showed me much more,
but I'll always remember
my first martini.

Martini

6 parts gin
1 part dry vermouth
Cocktail olive

Combine liquid ingredients in a
mixing glass with ice cubes and stir
well. Strain into a chilled cocktail
glass and garnish with olive.

Martini Milano

4 parts gin
1 part dry vermouth
1 part dry white wine
1 teaspoon Campari
Lime twist

Combine liquid ingredients in a cocktail shaker with cracked ice and shake well. Strain into a chilled cocktail glass and garnish with lime twist.

Martini Navratilova

6 parts vodka
2 parts dry vermouth
3 to 5 dashes orange bitters

Combine all ingredients in a cocktail shaker with cracked ice and shake well. Strain into a chilled cocktail glass.

Martinis for Four

1 cup gin
1 tablespoon dry vermouth
4 large pimento-stuffed green olives

Fill a 4-cup glass measuring cup 1/3 full with ice. Add gin and vermouth and stir gently. Immediately strain mixture into chilled martini glasses. Add an olive to each glass and serve immediately.

Martunia

6 parts gin   **1 part sweet vermouth**
1 part dry vermouth   **Edible flowers**

Combine liquid ingredients in a cocktail shaker with
cracked ice and shake well. Strain into a chilled cocktail
glass and garnish with edible flower petals.

The Ritz bar in Paris was and is a favorite haunt of many literary figures. James Jones and William Styron once spent all night getting drunk and continued into the next day. They ended up at the Ritz at noon, drinking straight-up martinis. At about three in the afternoon, they decided to call it a night.

Metropolitan

6 parts currant vodka
1 part Lillet blanc
1/2 teaspoon fresh lime juice
Lemon twist

Combine liquid ingredients in a cocktail shaker with cracked ice and shake well. Strain into a chilled cocktail glass and garnish with lemon twist.

Mocha Blanca Martini

6 parts coffee-flavored vodka
2 parts white chocolate liqueur
White chocolate curl

Combine liquid ingredients in a mixing glass and stir well. Strain into a chilled cocktail glass and garnish with chocolate curl.

Moll Flanders

4 parts gin
2 parts sloe gin
2 parts dry vermouth
3 to 5 dashes Angostura bitters

Combine all ingredients in a mixing glass with cracked ice and stir well. Strain into a chilled cocktail glass.

John Lardner posits
that the drinks of primitive people
are apt to be sweet and thick.
The martini, then, represents the most advanced
and sophisticated civilization,
since it is clear, cold, thin, and dry.
This is the ultimate martini—
the "Naked" Martini—
the zenith of a civilized people.

Naked Martini

6 parts gin
Cocktail olive

Chill gin in freezer for at least 2 hours. Pour gin into a chilled cocktail glass and garnish with olive.

Luis Buñuel, the great film director,
had his own recipe for a very dry martini:
"Connoisseurs who like their martinis very dry
suggest simply allowing a ray of sunlight
to shine through the bottle of Noilly Prat
before it hits the gin."

Negroni

4 parts gin
2 parts Campari
1 part sweet vermouth
Orange twist

Combine liquid ingredients in a cocktail shaker with
cracked ice and shake well. Strain into a chilled cocktail
glass and garnish with orange twist.

Newbury

6 parts gin
2 parts sweet vermouth
1 part triple sec
Lemon twist

Combine liquid ingredients in a cocktail shaker with
cracked ice and shake well. Strain into a chilled cocktail
glass and garnish with lemon twist.

New Orleans Martini

6 parts vanilla vodka
1 parts dry vermouth
1 part Pernod
1 dash Angostura bitters
Fresh mint sprig

Combine liquid ingredients in a cocktail shaker with
cracked ice and shake well. Strain into a chilled cocktail
glass and garnish with mint sprig.

Negroni

Nightmare

6 parts gin
2 parts Madeira wine
2 parts cherry brandy
Orange twist

Combine liquid ingredients in a
mixing glass with cracked ice and
stir well. Strain into a chilled
cocktail glass and garnish with
orange twist.

Ninotchka

6 parts vanilla-flavored vodka
2 parts white chocolate liqueur
1 part fresh lemon juice

Combine all ingredients in a cocktail shaker with cracked ice and
shake well. Strain into a chilled
cocktail glass.

Northern Exposure Moose Martini

6 parts currant-flavored vodka
1 teaspoon Chambord liqueur
Juniper berries soaked in vermouth

Combine liquid ingredients in a cocktail shaker with cracked ice and shake well. Strain into a chilled cocktail glass and garnish with juniper berries.

In the early 1940s, a martini at Pete's Tavern would run you fifty cents. This may explain why so many starving writers and artists made it their home away from home. The more successful ones were drinking at the Algonquin.

Nutty Martini

6 parts vodka
1 part Frangelico
Lemon twist

Combine liquid ingredients in a cocktail shaker with cracked ice and shake well. Strain into a chilled cocktail glass and garnish with lemon twist.

Oakland Cocktail

4 parts vodka
2 parts dry vermouth
2 parts fresh orange juice

Combine all ingredients in a cocktail shaker with cracked ice and shake well. Strain into a chilled cocktail glass.

Octopus's Garden

6 parts gin
2 parts dry vermouth
Smoked baby octopus
Black olive

Combine liquid ingredients in a cocktail shaker with cracked ice and shake well. Strain into a chilled cocktail glass and garnish with olive and octopus.

My grandmother swore
this recipe came straight from the old country
and that it was my duty to pass it on.

Old Country Martini

6 parts vodka
2 parts Madeira wine
2 parts cherry brandy
Orange twist

Combine liquid ingredients in a mixing glass with cracked ice and stir well. Strain into a chilled cocktail glass and garnish with orange twist.

The writers of the
famed Algonquin Roundtable
loved their martinis.
But when they gathered in the Rose Room,
Prohibition was law,
and the Algonquin Hotel was legally dry.
To alleviate this problem,
after a meal, the denizens of the Roundtable
would visit their friend, Neysa McMein,
who lived in the hotel.
She had a still in her bathroom.

Opal Martini

6 parts gin
1 part triple sec
2 parts fresh orange juice
1/4 teaspoon bar sugar

Combine all ingredients
in a mixing glass with
cracked ice and shake
well. Strain into a
chilled cocktail glass.

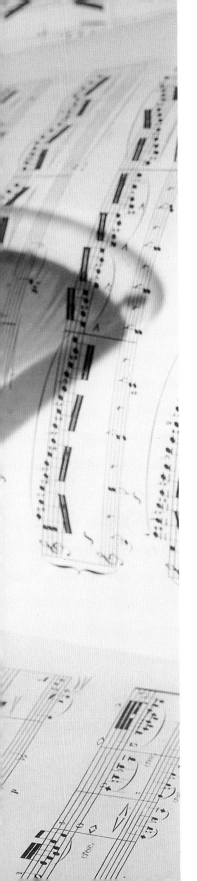

When Oscar Wilde
toured the United States
on a lecture tour
in the 1880s,
he impressed Leadville,
Colorado miners
with his ability to
out-drink them.
Their drink of choice?
Gin, with dry vermouth.

Opera Martini

6 parts gin
2 parts Dubonnet blanc
1 part maraschino liqueur
Lemon twist

Combine liquid ingredients
in a cocktail shaker with
cracked ice and shake
well. Strain into a chilled
cocktail glass and garnish
with lemon twist.

Orange Martini

6 parts vodka
1 part triple sec
1 dash orange bitters
Orange twist

Combine liquid ingredients in a
cocktail shaker with cracked ice
and shake well. Strain into a chilled
cocktail glass and garnish with
orange twist.

Osaka Dry

6 parts vodka
1 part sake
Pickled plum

Combine liquid ingredients in a
cocktail shaker with cracked ice
and shake well. Strain into a chilled
cocktail glass and garnish with
plum.

Oyster Martini

6 parts vodka
1 part dry vermouth
Smoked oyster

Combine liquid ingredients in a
cocktail shaker with cracked ice
and shake well. Strain into a chilled
cocktail glass and garnish with a
smoked oyster on a toothpick.

Paisley Martini

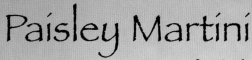

6 parts gin
1/2 teaspoon dry vermouth
1/2 teaspoon Scotch
Cocktail olive

Combine liquid ingredients
in a cocktail shaker with
cracked ice and shake well.
Strain into a chilled
cocktail glass and
garnish with olive.

Palm Beach
Martini

Pall Mall Martini

4 parts gin
1 part dry vermouth
1 part sweet vermouth
1 teaspoon white crème de menthe
1 dash orange bitters

Combine all ingredients in a mixing glass with ice cubes and stir well. Strain into a chilled cocktail glass.

Palm Beach Martini

6 parts gin
1 teaspoon sweet vermouth
4 parts grapefruit juice

Combine all ingredients in a cocktail shaker with cracked ice and shake well. Strain into a chilled cocktail glass.

Parrothead Martini

Pat the Parrothead claims that all Jimmy Buffett fans celebrate with the Parrothead Martini.

6 parts silver tequila
1 part triple sec
1 teaspoon fresh lime juice
Lime twist

Combine liquid ingredients in a cocktail shaker with cracked ice and shake well. Strain into a chilled cocktail glass and garnish with lime twist.

Parisian Martini

6 parts gin
2 parts dry vermouth
1 part crème de cassis

Combine all ingredients in a cocktail shaker with cracked ice and shake well. Strain into a chilled cocktail glass.

"New York is
the greatest city in the world for lunch,"
said William Emerson, Jr.
"And when that first martini hits the liver
like a silver bullet,
there is a sigh of contentment
that can be heard in Dubuque."

Park Avenue Martini

6 parts gin
1 part sweet vermouth
1 part pineapple juice

Combine all ingredients in a cocktail shaker with cracked ice and shake well. Strain into a chilled cocktail glass.

Peach Blossom Martini

6 parts peach vodka
1 part Dubonnet rouge
1 part maraschino liqueur
Fresh peach slice

Combine liquid ingredients in a cocktail shaker with cracked ice and shake well. Strain into a chilled cocktail glass and garnish with peach slice.

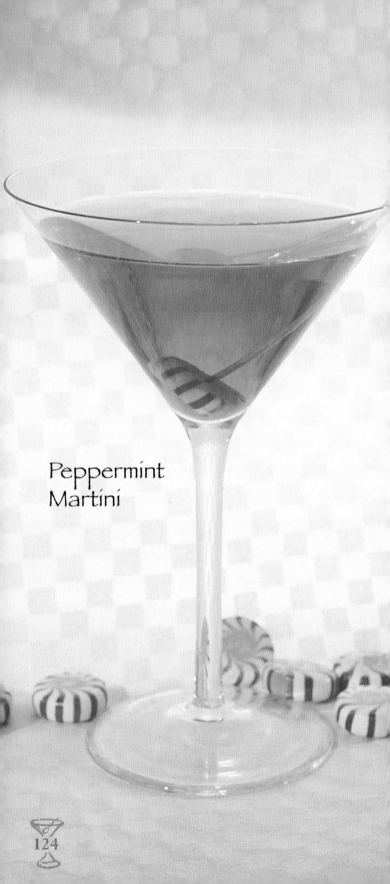

Peppermint
Martini

124

Peachy Martini

6 parts strawberry-flavored vodka
2 parts peach brandy
Lemon twist

Combine liquid ingredients in a cocktail shaker with cracked ice and shake well. Strain into a chilled cocktail glass and garnish with lemon twist.

Peggy's Martini

6 parts gin
1 part sweet vermouth
1/2 teaspoon Dubonnet rouge
1/2 teaspoon Pernod

Combine all ingredients in a mixing glass with cracked ice and stir well. Strain into a chilled cocktail glass.

Peppermint Martini

6 parts pepper vodka
2 parts white crème de menthe
Fresh mint sprig

Combine liquid ingredients in a cocktail shaker with cracked ice and shake well. Strain into a chilled cocktail glass and garnish with mint sprig.

Here's another classic cocktail joke.
A visitor to a midtown bar orders a Manhattan.
When it's placed before him, he notices that there's a
sprig of parsley floating on top.
"What is that THING in my Manhattan?"
he asks the bartender. The bartender replies,
without blinking,
"That, sir, is Central Park."

Perfect Manhattan

6 parts rye whiskey
1 part dry vermouth
1 part sweet vermouth
Maraschino cherry

Combine liquid ingredients in a cocktail shaker with cracked ice and shake well. Strain into a chilled cocktail glass and garnish with cherry.

The first martini?
Anecdotal history tells us
that in 1608
Henry Hudson served gin
to the Lenape Indians
on an unnamed island.
The Lenapes became very drunk,
and when they recovered,
named the island "Manhachtanienk" or
"the island where we became intoxicated."
Over the years, this name evolved into
"Manhattan."

Perfect Martini

6 parts gin
1 part dry vermouth
1 part sweet vermouth
Cocktail olive

Combine liquid ingredients in a cocktail shaker with cracked ice and shake well. Strain into chilled cocktail glass and garnish with olive.

Picadilly Martini

6 parts gin
2 parts dry vermouth
1/2 teaspoon Pernod
1 dash grenadine

Combine all ingredients in a mixing glass with ice and stir well. Strain into a chilled cocktail glass.

If you order a martini in England,
you'll probably be served a glass of sweet vermouth.
Be on the safe side,
and order the British version of the martini—
"Pink Gin."

Pink Gin Martini

8 parts gin
1 teaspoon Angostura bitters

Pour bitters into a cocktail glass and swirl around until the inside of the glass is completely coated with the bitters. Pour gin into the glass. This drink should be served at room temperature.

Plaza Martini

2 parts gin
2 parts dry vermouth
2 parts sweet vermouth

Combine all ingredients in a cocktail shaker with cracked ice and shake well. Strain into a chilled cocktail glass.

Pompano Martini

5 parts gin   **2 parts fresh grapefruit juice**
1 part dry vermouth   **1 dash orange bitters**

Combine all ingredients in a cocktail shaker with cracked ice and shake well. Strain into a chilled cocktail glass.

Pretty Martini

4 parts vodka   **1 part Amaretto**
1 part Grand Marnier   **1 part dry vermouth**
Orange twist

Combine liquid ingredients in a cocktail shaker with cracked ice and shake well. Strain into a chilled cocktail glass and garnish with orange twist.

Prince Edward Martini

6 parts gin
1 part Drambuie
Lemon twist

Combine liquid ingredients in a cocktail shaker with cracked ice and shake well. Strain into a chilled cocktail glass and garnish with lemon twist.

Princess Elizabeth Martini

6 parts sweet vermouth
1 part dry vermouth
2 teaspoons Benedictine

Combine all ingredients in a cocktail shaker with cracked ice and shake well. Strain into a chilled cocktail glass.

Quarterdeck Martini

6 parts berry vodka
1 part maraschino liqueur
1 part grapefruit juice
Fresh mint sprig

Combine liquid ingredients in a mixing glass with cracked ice and stir well. Strain into a chilled cocktail glass and garnish with mint sprig.

Queen Elizabeth Martini

6 parts gin
1 part dry vermouth
2 teaspoon Benedictine

Combine all ingredients in a cocktail shaker with cracked ice and shake well. Strain into a chilled cocktail glass.

Racquet Club

6 parts gin
2 parts dry vermouth
3 to 5 dashes orange bitters

Combine all ingredients in a cocktail shaker with cracked ice and shake well. Strain into a chilled cocktail glass.

Red Dog Martini

6 parts vodka
1 part ruby port
2 teaspoons fresh lime juice
1 teaspoon grenadine
Lime twist

Combine liquid ingredients in a cocktail shaker with cracked ice and shake well. Strain into a chilled cocktail glass and garnish with lime twist.

Renaissance Martini

6 parts gin
1 part fino sherry
Grated nutmeg

Combine liquid ingredients in a cocktail shaker with cracked ice and shake well. Strain into a chilled cocktail glass and garnish with nutmeg.

Rendezvous

6 parts gin
2 parts cherry brandy
1 part Campari
Fresh cherries

Combine liquid ingredients in a cocktail
shaker with cracked ice and shake well.
Strain into a chilled cocktail glass and
garnish with fresh cherry.

Although most agree
that the martini was invented in the 1860s
in Northern California,
the drink did not achieve
widespread recognition in the United States
until after Prohibition.
It might have become more popular earlier,
but the Volstead Act put an end to its ascension.
During Prohibition, gin was the easiest
of the hard liquors to bootleg, and rot-gut—
bathtub gin—became ubiquitous.
It's no coincidence that sweet mixed drinks
also became prevalent then.
Drinkers wanted to mask the taste
of the harsh homemade stuff.
When Prohibition ended, people could at last get fine,
imported gin, and there was no need to dilute it.
The martini, once again,
was on its way to immortality.

Resolution Martini

6 parts gin
2 parts apricot brandy
1 part fresh lemon juice

Combine ingredients in a cocktail shaker with cracked ice
and shake well. Strain into a chilled cocktail glass.

Road Runner Martini

6 parts pepper vodka   **1 part gold tequila**
1 part dry vermouth   **Jalapeño stuffed olive**

Combine liquid ingredients in a cocktail shaker with
cracked ice and shake well. Strain into a chilled cocktail
glass and garnish with olive.

Rum Martini

Rolls Royce

6 parts gin
2 parts dry vermouth
2 parts sweet vermouth
1/4 teaspoon Benedictine

Combine ingredients in a cocktail shaker with cracked ice and shake well. Strain into a chilled cocktail glass.

Rum Martini

6 parts light rum
1 part dry vermouth
1 dash orange bitters
Almond-stuffed olive

Combine liquid ingredients in a cocktail shaker with cracked ice and shake well. Strain into a chilled cocktail glass and garnish with olive.

Russian Martini

4 parts vodka
4 parts gin
1 part white chocolate liqueur

Combine liquid ingredients in a cocktail shaker with cracked ice and shake well. Strain into a chilled cocktail glass.

Russian Rose

6 parts strawberry-flavored vodka
1 part dry vermouth
1 part grenadine
1 dash orange bitters

Combine all ingredients in a mixing glass with cracked ice and stir well. Strain into a chilled cocktail glass.

Saketini

6 parts gin
1 part sake
Lemon twist wrapped with
Pickled ginger

Combine liquid ingredients in a cocktail shaker with cracked ice and shake well. Strain into a chilled cocktail glass and garnish with lemon twist.

Secret Martini

6 parts gin
2 parts Lillet blanc
2 dashes Angostura bitters
Cocktail olive

Combine liquid ingredients in a mixing glass with cracked ice and stir well. Strain into a chilled cocktail glass and garnish with olive.

Saketini

Seventh Heaven

6 parts gin
1 part maraschino liqueur
1 part grapefruit juice
Fresh mint sprig

Combine liquid ingredients in a mixing glass with cracked ice and stir well. Strain into a chilled cocktail glass and garnish with mint sprig.

Sexy Devil

4 parts vodka
2 parts cranberry vodka
1 part dry vermouth
Fresh strawberry
Lemon peel

Combine liquid ingredients in a cocktail shaker with cracked ice and shake well. Strain into a chilled cocktail glass and garnish with lemon peel and strawberry.

Shrimptini

6 parts gin or vodka
2 parts dry vermouth
Dash of Tabasco®
Large cooked shrimp

Combine liquid ingredients in a cocktail shaker with cracked ice and shake well. Strain into a chilled cocktail glass and garnish with and cooked shrimp.

Silver Streak

"Silver bullet"
is one the martini's nickname.
Sleek and elegant, powerful and cold,
a Silver Bullet always hits its mark.
The Silver Streak is another variation
on a theme.

Silver Streak

6 parts gin
3 parts Jagermeister
Lemon twist

Combine liquid ingredients in a mixing glass with cracked ice and stir well. Strain into a chilled cocktail glass and garnish with lemon twist.

Sloe Gin Martini

6 parts sloe gin
2 parts dry vermouth
3 to 5 dashes Angostura bitters
Lemon twist

Combine liquid ingredients in a cocktail shaker with cracked ice and shake well. Strain into a chilled cocktail glass and garnish with lemon twist.

Smoky Martini

6 parts gin
1 part dry vermouth
1 teaspoon scotch
Lemon twist

Combine liquid ingredients in a mixing glass with cracked ice and stir well. Strain into a chilled cocktail glass and garnish with lemon twist.

Southern Martini

6 parts gin
1 part triple sec
3 to 5 dashes orange bitters
Lemon twist

Combine liquid ingredients in a mixing glass with cracked ice and stir well. Strain into a chilled cocktail glass and garnish with lemon twist.

THE relationship
between a Russian and a bottle of vodka
is almost mystical.

—Richard Owen

Soviet Martini

6 parts ashberry-flavored or currant vodka
1 part dry vermouth
1 part fino sherry
Lemon twist

Combine liquid ingredients in a mixing glass with cracked ice and stir well. Strain into a chilled cocktail glass and garnish with lemon twist.

Spiced Treat Martini

6 parts cinnamon vodka
1 part chocolate liqueur
1 part coffee liqueur
Chocolate cocktail straw

Combine liquid ingredients in a mixing glass with cracked ice and stir well. Strain into a chilled cocktail glass and garnish with chocolate straw.

Springtime Martini

6 parts buffalo grass vodka
2 parts Lillet blanc
Miniature pickled asparagus spear

Combine liquid ingredients in a
cocktail shaker with cracked ice and
shake well. Strain into a chilled
cocktail glass and garnish with
asparagus spear.

Staten Island Cocktail

6 parts coffee vodka
1 part dry vermouth
2 parts fresh lime juice
Maraschino cherry

Combine liquid ingredients in a cocktail shaker with cracked ice and shake well. Strain into a chilled cocktail glass and garnish with cherry.

Sweet and Spicy Martini

6 parts cinnamon vodka
1 part sweet vermouth
1 part orange liqueur
Cinnamon stick

Combine liquid ingredients in a cocktail shaker with cracked ice and shake well. Strain into a chilled cocktail glass and garnish with cinnamon stick.

In one musical number
of the 1949 Broadway production of
"Gentlemen Prefer Blondes,"
Miles White's award-winning costumes
featured two martinis per showgirl—
one over each breast—
with nipples doing double duty
as olives.

Strawberry Blonde

6 parts strawberry vodka
2 parts Lillet blanc
Fresh strawberry

Combine liquid ingredients in a cocktail shaker with cracked ice and shake well. Strain into a chilled cocktail glass and garnish with fresh strawberry.

St.Petersburg

6 parts vodka
3 to 5 dashes orange bitters
Orange peel

Combine liquid ingredients in a cocktail
shaker with cracked ice and shake well.
Strain into a chilled cocktail glass and
garnish with orange peel.

Summer Breeze

6 parts citrus vodka
2 parts melon liqueur
1 part dry vermouth
1/4 teaspoon fresh lemon juice
Melon ball

Combine liquid ingredients in a mixing glass with ice cubes and stir well. Strain into a chilled cocktail glass and garnish with melon ball.

Sweet Martini

6 parts gin
2 parts sweet vermouth
1 dash orange bitters
Orange twist

Combine liquid ingredients in a mixing glass with cracked ice and stir well. Strain into a chilled cocktail glass and garnish with orange twist.

Sweetie Martini

6 parts gin
1 part dry vermouth
1 part sweet vermouth
Lemon twist

Combine liquid ingredients in a cocktail shaker with cracked ice and shake well. Strain into a chilled cocktail glass and garnish with lemon twist.

"The three-martini lunch
is the epitome of American efficiency.
Where else can
you get an earful, a bellyful, and a snootful
at the same time?"

—Gerald Ford

Tequini

6 parts silver tequila
1 part dry vermouth
1 dash orange bitters
Lemon twist

Combine liquid ingredients in a cocktail shaker with
cracked ice and shake well. Strain into a chilled cocktail
glass and garnish with lemon twist. Note: Enhance this
drink by rubbing the lemon twist over the rim of the glass.

Raymond Chandler,
the great American mystery novelist,
really didn't want to write the screenplay
for the film of "The Blue Dahlia," so he struck a deal
with his producer, John Houseman.
He agreed to write the script only
if it was written into his contract that he could
write it while drunk. The contract
also had to include the following:
Paramount would provide limousines, secretaries,
and nurses for Chandler 24 hours a day,
a doctor would be on call to administer vitamin shots
since Chandler never ate when he was drinking,
and there would be a direct phone line
from his house to the studio.
The studio would also take the Chandlers' maid shopping.
Houseman agreed to this over lunch with Chandler,
at which time Chandler had three double martinis
and three stingers.
He went straight to work after lunch
and finished the screenplay
in about two weeks.

Third Degree Martini

6 parts gin
2 parts dry vermouth
1 part Pernod
Star anise

Combine liquid ingredients in a cocktail shaker with cracked ice and shake well. Strain into a chilled cocktail glass and garnish with star anise.

Three Stripes

4 parts gin
2 parts dry vermouth
2 parts fresh orange juice

Combine all ingredients in a cocktail shaker with cracked ice and shake well. Strain into a chilled cocktail glass.

Tootsie Roll Martini

6 parts vodka
1 part chocolate liqueur
1 part Grand Marnier
Orange twist

Combine liquid ingredients in a cocktail shaker with cracked ice and shake well. Strain into a chilled cocktail glass and garnish with orange twist.

Tovarisch

6 parts vodka
2 parts kümmel
2 parts fresh lime juice
Black olive

Combine liquid ingredients in a cocktail shaker with cracked ice and shake well. Strain into a chilled cocktail glass and garnish with black olive.

Tovarisch

Truffle Martini

6 parts strawberry vodka　　**1 part chocolate liqueur**
1 part Grand Marnier　　　　**Orange twist**

Combine liquid ingredients in a cocktail shaker with
cracked ice and shake well. Strain into a chilled cocktail
glass and garnish with orange twist.

Turf Martini

4 parts gin
2 parts dry vermouth
1 part Pernod
1 part fresh lemon juice
3 to 5 dashes Angostura bitters
Almond-stuffed olive

Combine liquid ingredients in a cocktail shaker with
cracked ice and shake well. Strain into a chilled cocktail
glass and garnish with olive.

Tuxedo

4 parts vodka
3 parts dry vermouth
1/2 teaspoon maraschino liqueur
3 to 5 dashes orange bitters
Lemon twist

Combine liquid ingredients in a cocktail shaker with
cracked ice and shake well. Strain into a chilled cocktail
glass and garnish with lemon twist.

Ulanda

4 parts gin
2 parts triple sec
1 tablespoon Pernod

Combine all ingredients in a mixing glass with cracked ice
and stir well. Strain into a chilled cocktail glass.

Valencia
Martini

Valencia Martini

6 parts gin
2 parts amontillado sherry
Olive

Combine liquid ingredients in a mixing glass with cracked ice and stir well. Strain into a chilled cocktail glass and garnish with olive.

Vanilla Twist

6 parts vanilla vodka
1 part Cointreau
1 part dry vermouth
Vanilla bean

Combine liquid ingredients in a cocktail shaker with cracked ice and shake well. Strain into a chilled cocktail glass and garnish with vanilla bean.

Ian Fleming's James Bond
not only drank vodka martinis,
he also drank champagne, sherry, scotch—
whatever the occasion called for.
But the cinematic James Bond was a hard-core
vodka martini drinker, largely because Smirnoff bought
the product placement rights.
The popularity of the movies helped make the vodka martini
the most popular drink of the 60s.
oday, two out of three martinis
are made with vodka.

Vodka Martini

6 parts vodka
2 parts dry vermouth (or to taste)
Olive

Combine liquid ingredients in a cocktail shaker with cracked ice and shake well. Strain into a chilled cocktail glass and garnish with olive.

Vanilla Twist

6 parts pineapple vodka
1 part dry vermouth
1 part Lillet blanc
Pineapple wedge

Combine liquid ingredients in a cocktail shaker
with cracked ice and shake well. Strain into a chilled
cocktail glass and garnish with pineapple wedge.

Warsaw Martini

4 parts potato vodka
1 part dry vermouth
1 part blackberry brandy
1 tablespoon fresh lemon juice

Combine all ingredients in a cocktail shaker with cracked ice and shake well. Strain into a chilled cocktail glass.

Wembly Martini

6 parts gin
1 part dry vermouth
1 teaspoon apricot brandy
1 teaspoon Calvados
Lemon twist

Combine liquid ingredients in a cocktail shaker with cracked ice and shake well. Strain into a chilled cocktail glass and garnish with lemon twist.

What Is That Martini?

6 parts vodka
1 part Sambuca
Licorice twist
3 coffee beans

Combine liquid ingredients in a mixing glass with cracked ice and stir well. Strain into a chilled cocktail glass and garnish with licorice twist and coffee beans.

168

Woo Woo Martini

6 parts cranberry vodka
1 part peach schnapps
Lemon twist

Combine liquid ingredients in a cocktail shaker with cracked ice and shake well. Strain into a chilled cocktail glass and garnish with lemon twist.

Xena Martini

5 parts honey-flavored vodka
1 part buffalo grass vodka
1 teaspoon Lillet blanc
Pickled asparagus spear

Combine liquid ingredients in a cocktail shaker with cracked ice and shake well. Strain into a chilled cocktail glass and garnish with asparagus spear.

Zippy Martini

6 parts vodka
1 part dry vermouth
3 to 4 dashes Tabasco® sauce
Pickled jalapeño pepper slice

Combine liquid ingredients in a cocktail shaker with cracked ice and shake well. Strain into a chilled cocktail glass and garnish with pepper.

Recipe Index

174

My Own
Martini Recipes

Send us your martini recipes if they are not included in <u>The</u> <u>Martini</u> <u>Book.</u> We'd love to hear about them and with your permission use in future editions.

Send recipes to: Black Dog & Leventhal
              151 W. 19th Street
              New York, NY 10011

My Own Martini Recipes

Send us your martini recipes if they are not included in <u>The</u> <u>Martini</u> <u>Book.</u> We'd love to hear about them and with your permission use in future editions.
Send recipes to: Black Dog & Leventhal
        151 W. 19ʰ Street
        New York, NY 10011

My Own
Martini Recipes

Send us your martini recipes if they are not included in _The_ _Martini_ _Book._ We'd love to hear about them and with your permission use in future editions.
Send recipes to: Black Dog & Leventhal
151 W. 19th Street
New York, NY 10011

187